BLACK BEAUTY

Black Beauty

ANNA SEWELL

EXCLUSIVE COLLECTION

For my husband
ANTHONY JOHN RANSON
with love from your wife, the publisher.
Eternally grateful for your
unconditional love.

Readers who are interested in other titles from
Wordsworth Editions are invited to visit our website at
www.wordsworth-editions.com

This edition published 2021 by
Wordsworth Editions Limited
8B East Street, Ware,
Hertfordshire SG12 9HJ

ISBN   978 1 84022 817 5

© Wordsworth Editions Limited 2021

Text © Wordsworth Editions Limited 1993

Wordsworth® is a registered trade mark of
Wordsworth Editions Limited

Wordsworth Editions
is the company founded in 1987 by
MICHAEL TRAYLER

Typeset in Great Britain by Antony Gray
Printed and bound by Clays Ltd, Elcograf S.p.A

CONTENTS

An Appreciation and Life of the Author

He liveth best who loveth best
All creatures great and small,
For the good God who loveth us
He made them first of all.

COLERIDGE

The year of Grace one thousand eight hundred and twenty was a year fraught with many important events, but little did those who passed beneath the shadows of the old church in Yarmouth know that the faint sun of a wind-swept March day was ushering into the world a girl-child whose pen was one day to be used to her own fame and to the generous service of promoting kindness to that noble animal, the horse.

In that little house beneath trees that were already dreaming towards the spring, within hearing of the bells of the Church of St Nicholas, on this thirtieth day of March, Anna Sewell, the author of *Black Beauty*, was born.

There was no silver spoon in the tiny Anna's mouth, for things were not going too well with her father, Isaac Sewell. Whilst he rejoiced in this acquisition to his family, financial clouds were crowding upon his business horizon.

A few days after Anna was born her father made the discovery that he had been overreached and swindled in a business venture that he had entered into a short time before, and the husband with so young a wife, and now further domestic responsibilities, had to look about him for new business openings.

But Isaac Sewell came from a hardy stock that had, through many decades, been accustomed to a harsher persecution than the lack of money, so he took heart in memory of the Friends who were both his wife's and his own ancestors, and took a little house just off Bishopsgate Street, London, and opposite a gin palace. In this he had been badly advised, for the same fate that had met his other business at the birth of Anna came upon this new enterprise with the birth of his only son, Philip.

This bad fortune must have been very trying for his wife, Mary Sewell (*née* Wright), for Mrs Sewell was a woman of a very sensitive and artistic nature as is shown by her well-known works, *Mother's Last Words*, *Our Father's Care*, *Thy Poor Brother*, and many a homely ballad.

Trying as these troubles were her staunchness of spirit is shown by the remark in her diary when, in writing of Anna's birth, she says, 'to be an unclouded blessing for fifty-eight years, the perennial joy of my life'.

Isaac Sewell, on his second stroke of bad fortune, had to begin his business life all over again. He chose Dalston, and there the little family lived for nine or ten years that were full of happiness despite the strictest economy and hard work. Happiness had come because the fret and harass of both debt and care were absent, and in this bright atmosphere Anna and Philip thrived.

The two children had been their mother's playfellows and helpmates from the moment they were old enough to be so, and they spared no pains, as they grew older, to help her in every possible way. Mary Sewell had trained her children to find glory, not degradation, in work. Work was the finest outlet for Anna's high-spirited nature, for she was very highly strung and courageous.

Anna soon developed a great love for Nature and art as well, and as quite a child made pen and ink and pencil drawings of the beauties of nature which were most admirably done.

Had the authoress of *Black Beauty* been stronger it is

highly likely that the world would have acclaimed her as an artist, but she was not fated to maintain the healthy vigour of those days at Dalston.

It was at Dalston that Mary Sewell's first little book was written, and there was the spirit of sacrifice in Mrs Sewell's desire to give expression to her thoughts.

She wrote to earn money with which to buy books to educate her two children.

Mrs Sewell must have been a splendid teacher as well as a devoted mother, for she instilled not only knowledge into her children's minds, but she taught them to be fearless. Neither Anna nor Philip were in the least afraid of animals or insects of any kind, and darkness held no terrors for them.

One of the happiest recollections of the two children was a visit to their grandparents who lived at Buxton, just outside Norwich.

It was the first of many visits; and here they found the unfettered freedom of the country and a grandfather who knew the heart of a child, and fostered their affection for all the wonders of the countryside.

It was at Dalston that Anna sprained her elbow, and, when spoken to of this painful accident, Anna said simply, 'I bored it well.' It was typical of the patient courage and cheerfulness under suffering that she showed throughout the whole of her tranquil life.

Anna could not have had a better example to follow than her mother, for Mrs Sewell was never happy unless she was ameliorating the conditions of those who suffered, and in those days there were many crying evils that flourished under the mantle of justice.

The fortunes of Isaac Sewell were slightly on the mend and, in order to make more room for his growing family, he purchased an old stable building lying near his home, and this he remodelled.

Anna's grandfather suggested a scheme whereby their income might be supplemented by the keeping of cows, but the new interest met with misfortune owing to the dishonesty of the man who delivered the milk to the various customers that the Sewell family had obtained.

There was now a new occupant of the home in the shape of Anna's uncle Richard and, as Mrs Sewell could find no time for her lessons with Anna, it was arranged that Anna should go as a day boarder to a school about a mile distant from her home.

The Sewell family was now in troubled waters, but the worst was yet to come.

Returning from school one day Anna, racing up the carriage drive to the garden gate, fell and sprained her ankle very severely. It was destined to result in Anna being something of a cripple for the rest of her life, but as Mrs Sewell says in her diary: 'Little [did we think] that henceforth her dear life was to be coloured by this event, *not* discoloured.'

Everything that could be done *was* done, but there were doctors who made mistakes and Anna Sewell became more and more crippled.

Mary Sewell never abandoned hope that one day that high-spirited child would run and walk and ramble as she had done during her nature trips, but alas . . .

All those who knew Anna Sewell in those days of affliction loved her, for she was an example of most persevering industry and cheerful patience. Her sufferings never made gloom or a cloud in the house. Anna never brooded over her loss of power, or loss of the changes or amusements which others enjoy. Her own mind was always a storehouse of refreshment to herself; it was a rich garden which circumstances never allowed to be fully cultivated, but it was full of thought and ready appreciation of the genius and talents of others. She was her mother's sunshine always. 'There never came the slightest cloud between us,' writes Mrs Sewell.

Mr Sewell removed to Brighton in 1836 to take up his position as manager of the London and County Bank's Brighton branch, and there a remedy to cure Anna was tried. It proved to be worse than her disease. A doctor bled her severely and to this draining away of life her mother attributed the many disablements which subsequently afflicted Anna. Her health was full of fluctuations, but as time went on she gradually grew worse and her loved employments had to be laid aside by tired hands. In Brighton days though, she must have possessed some walking power for in a journal written there in 1844 she tells of pleasant walks with her friends, trips to London to visit the picture-galleries, and other things which suggest some measure of activity.

It was in the year 1845 that the Sewell family removed to Lancing, and in order to get Mr Sewell to the station a pony chaise became part of the household staff, and it was Anna who was accustomed to drive her father to and from Shoreham Station. No doubt Anna Sewell learned to love horses more and more through this self-imposed pleasure and duty.

The following year Mrs Sewell took her children to Germany for a holiday, but Anna was left there for treatment which proved so satisfactory that she returned with the use of both legs – she walked!

Anna Sewell had the artist's instinct for form strongly developed. Her own drawings prove that; and it was this gift of form that made her so admirable a critic of manner and arrangements in word painting.

Nor was she a lenient judge. 'Oh, if only I can pass my Nannie, I don't fear the world after that,' said Mrs Sewell, accepting her own child's criticism with eagerness.

In the autumn of 1857 the family paid a visit to Santander

in Spain, and on their return they settled at Blue Lodge, Wick, near both Bath and Bristol, and at Wick Mrs Sewell's chief works were written. Mrs Bayly, the author of *Ragged Homes and How to Mend Them*, mentions a very pleasant visit paid to Mrs Sewell at Blue Lodge, Wick, in the summer of 1863: 'The mother was then writing the last chapters of *Thy Poor Brother* in which Anna was assisting her. I was once with mother and daughter when Mrs Sewell was reading aloud something she had prepared for the Press. It was beautiful to witness the intense love and admiration and pride which beamed in the daughter's eyes, but this in nowise prevented her being, as I could see, a severe critic.

'It was the future author of *Black Beauty* who drove me to the station, and she evidently believed in a horse having a moral nature if we may judge by her mode of remonstrance: "Now thee shouldn't walk up this hill – didn't thee see how it rains? Now thee must go a little faster – thou would be sorry for us to be late at the station."

'I think it was during this drive that I spoke to Anna about something Horace Bushnell had written about animals. It was never forgotten.'

Soon after the publication of *Black Beauty*, Mrs Bayly says: 'I had a little note written from her sofa in which she says: "The thoughts you gave me from Horace Bushnell years ago have followed me entirely through the writing of my book, and have more than anything else helped me to feel it was worth a great effort, to try at least to bring the thoughts of men more in harmony with the purposes of God in this subject." '

Poor Anna Sewell! The maladies from which she suffered were mainly of a very painful and depressing character, and had her face been marred with grief no one would have been a whit surprised. It was a wonderful evidence of the triumph of the spirit over the body that her face was not only sweet and peaceful but often radiant, and so evidently did this proceed from the power of the Spirit of God, that, in her presence one had the feeling of being on holy ground; her face shone with the far-off light of intense spirituality.

For the last seven years of Anna's life, the work which formed for her an unfailing interest was the writing of *Black Beauty*.

The first mention of the book occurs in the journal, under the date November 6th, 1871: 'I am writing the life of a horse, and getting dolls and boxes ready for Christmas.'

That is the only mention of it until December 1876, when she writes: 'I am getting on with my little book *Black Beauty*.'

The next entry comes against the date of August 21st, 1877: 'The first proofs of *Black Beauty* are come – very nice type.'

It is extremely touching to remember that this 'Beautiful Equine Drama', as it has been called, was thought out almost entirely from the sofa where so much weakness and pain were daily endured. When a time came during which she was capable of enduring the fatigue of writing, it was done in pencil – the mother sitting by received the paper and made a fair copy of it.

That a book accomplished in such a fragmentary way should 'show no joins', says much for the skill of the writer; but oh, what discipline must have been endured in having perpetually to 'leave off in the most interesting place'.

Among the very few papers left in Anna Sewell's handwriting is the following:

'I have for six years been confined to the house and to my sofa, and have from time to time, when I am able, been writing what I think will turn out a little book, its special aim being to induce kindness, sympathy, and an understanding treatment of horses.

'In thinking of cab horses I have been led to think of cabmen, and am anxious if I can, to present their true condition, and their great difficulties, in a correct and telling manner.

'Some weeks ago I had a conversation at my open window with an intelligent cabman, who was waiting at our door, which has deeply impressed me.

'He led the conversation on to the Sunday question, after telling me he never plied on the Sabbath. I found there was a sore, even a bitter, feeling against religious people who, by their use of cabs on Sunday, practically deny the Sabbath to the drivers. "Even ministers do it, ma'am," he said. "And I say it's a shame on religion."

'Then he told me of one of the London drivers who had driven a lady to church. As she stepped from the cab she handed the driver a tract on the observation of the Sabbath. This naturally disgusted the man. "Now, ma'am," said my friend, "I call that hypocrisy, don't you?" I suppose most of us agree with him, and yet it might not have been done hypocritically. So few Christians apparently realise the responsibility of taking a cab on Sunday.'

This, to my mind, shows how deeply incensed Anna Sewell was at the fact that horses were used when they could be resting, and that religious people, or so-styled religious people, should offend in this respect.

Black Beauty was published near the end of the year 1877, and Anna Sewell lived just long enough to hear of its success. Poor wasted and patient writer! She knew enough to lighten a supreme moment, but she did not live long enough to know what lasting good her 'little book' achieved, or of those who read it and saw to it that patient horses should be cared for and befriended.

Black Beauty is read by the squire, his lady, their stablemen and boys; and it has taught them to love and care for horses more than any other book ever published.

Our national papers, foremost among them *The Times*, have borne the strongest witness to the remarkable improvement which has taken place in the treatment and care of horses. Perhaps few who notice these changes and improvements know how much is due to the genius and prayers of one fragile woman who so loved horses.

> She never went forth to sow
> But there rose from her lowly couch of pain
> The fervent pleading prayer –

the prayer for happier men, happier horses, and happier homes, and that we might know how to use, and not abuse, God's munificent gifts to us.

God heard the prayers of Anna Sewell and permitted her to be a fellow-worker with Himself in bringing about these beneficent changes.

In May 1878, Anna Sewell was laid to rest in the quiet little burying-ground in the village next to Lammas, near Norwich, where her ancestors for many generations sleep. It is a high sequestered spot surrounded by trees and a high hawthorn hedge where the birds are never disturbed. But her life remains to us as an ideal and as an inspiration as long as *Black Beauty* is read. Her life-work for dumb creatures who cannot speak for themselves will remain and spread her influence far and wide throughout the world. She indeed opened her mouth for the dumb.

BLACK BEAUTY

CHAPTER ONE

My Early Home

The first place that I can well remember, was a large pleasant meadow with a pond of clear water in it. Some trees overshadowed the pond, and rushes and water-lilies grew at the deep end. Over the hedge on one side we looked into a ploughed field; and on the other, we looked over a gate at our master's house which stood by the roadside. At the top of the meadow was a plantation of fir trees; and at the bottom, a running brook overhung by a steep bank.

Whilst I was young I lived upon my mother's milk, as I could not eat grass. In the daytime I ran by her side, and at night I lay down close by her. When it was hot, we used to stand by the pond in the shade of the trees; and when it was cold, we had a nice warm shed near the plantation.

As soon as I was old enough to eat grass, my mother used to go out to work in the daytime, and to come back in the evening.

There were six young colts in the meadow besides me. They were older than I was; some were nearly as large as grown-up horses. I used to run with them, and have great fun. We used to gallop all together round and round the field, as hard as we could go. Sometimes we had rather rough play, for they would frequently bite and kick as well as gallop.

One day, when there was a good deal of kicking, my

mother whinnied to me to come to her; and then she said: 'I wish you to pay attention to what I am going to say to you. The colts who live here are very good colts, but they are carthorse colts, and, of course, they have not learned good manners.

'You have been well bred and well born; your father has a great name in these parts, and your grandfather twice won the Cup at the Newmarket races; your grandmother had the sweetest temper of any horse I ever knew, and I think you have never seen me kick or bite.

'I hope you will grow up gentle and good, and never learn bad ways. Do your work with a good will; lift up your feet well when you trot, and never bite or kick even in play.'

I have never forgotten my mother's advice; I knew she was a wise old horse, and our master thought a great deal of her. Her name was Duchess, but he often called her Pet.

Our master was a good, kind man. He gave us good food, good lodging, and kind words; and he spoke as kindly to us as he did to his little children. We were all fond of him, and my mother loved him very much. When she saw him at the gate, she would neigh with joy, and trot up to him. He would pat and stroke her and say, 'Well, old Pet! How is your little Darkie?' I was a dull black, so he called me Darkie.

Then he would give me a piece of bread, which was very good, and sometimes he brought a carrot for my mother. All the horses would come to him, but I think we were his favourites. My mother always took him to the town on a market day in a light gig.

There was a ploughboy, Dick, who sometimes came into our field to pluck blackberries from the hedge. When he had eaten all he wanted, he would have, what he called, fun with the colts, throwing sticks and stones at them to make them gallop. We did not much mind him, for we could gallop off; but sometimes a stone would hit and hurt us.

One day he was at this game, and did not know that the master was in the next field; but he was there, watching what was going on. Over the hedge he jumped in a moment, and catching Dick by the arm, gave him such a box on the ear as made him roar with pain. As soon as we saw the master, we trotted up nearer to see what was going on.

'Bad boy!' he said, 'bad boy! to chase the colts. This is not the first time nor the second, but it shall be the last. There, take your money and go home; I shall not want you on my farm again.' So we never saw Dick again.

Old Daniel, the man who looked after the horses, was just as gentle as our master, so we were well off.

CHAPTER TWO

The Hunt

Before I was two years old, a circumstance happened which I have never forgotten.

It was early in the spring; there had been a little frost in the night, and a light mist still hung over the plantations and meadows.

The other colts and I were feeding in the lower part of the field when we heard, quite in the distance, what sounded like the cry of dogs.

The oldest of the colts raised his head, pricked up his ears, and said, 'There are the hounds!' and immediately cantered off, followed by the rest of us, to the upper part of the field, where we could look over the hedge and see several fields beyond. My mother and an old riding horse of our master were also standing near, and seemed to know all about it.

'They have found a hare,' said my mother; 'and if they come this way, we shall see the hunt.'

Soon the dogs were all tearing down the field of young wheat next to our meadow. I never heard such a noise as they made. They did not bark, nor howl, nor whine, but kept up a 'Yo! yo, o, o! Yo! yo, o, o!' at the top of their voices. After them came a number of men on horseback, some of them in green coats, all galloping as fast as they could.

The old horse snorted and looked eagerly after them; and we young colts wanted to be galloping with them, but they were soon away into the fields lower down. Here it seemed as if they had come to a stand; the dogs left off barking, and ran about in every direction with their noses to the ground.

'They have lost the scent,' said the old horse; 'perhaps the hare will get off.'

'What hare?' I said.

'Oh! I don't know *what* hare; possibly it may be one of our own hares out of the plantation. Any hare they can find will do for the dogs and men to run after.'

Before long the dogs began their 'Yo! yo, o, o!' again; and back they came all together at full speed, making straight for our meadow at the part where the high bank and hedge overhung the brook.

'Now we shall see the hare,' said my mother; and just then a hare, wild with fright, rushed by, and made for the plantation. On came the dogs, followed by the huntsmen. The dogs burst through the bank, leaped the stream, and came dashing across the field. Six or eight men leaped their horses clean over the hedge and stream, following close upon the dogs. The hare tried to get through the fence; but it was too thick, and she turned sharp round to make for the road.

Alas! it was too late; the dogs were upon her with their wild cries. We heard one shriek, and that was the end of her. One of the huntsmen rode up and whipped off the dogs, who would soon have torn her to pieces. He held her up by the leg, torn and bleeding; and all the gentlemen seemed well pleased.

As for me, I was so astonished that I did not at first see what was going on by the brook; but when I did look, there was a sad sight. Two fine horses were down, one was struggling in the stream, and the other was groaning on the grass. One of the riders, covered with mud, was getting out of the water; the other lay quite still.

'His neck is broken,' said my mother.

'And serve him right, too,' said one of the colts.

I thought the same, but my mother did not join with us.

'Well, no,' she said, 'you must not say that. But though I am an old horse, and have seen and heard a great deal, I never yet could make out why men are so fond of this sport. They often hurt themselves, spoil good horses, and tear up the fields; and all this for a hare, a fox, or a stag, that they could get more easily some other way. But we are only horses, and don't understand.'

Whilst my mother was saying this, we stood and looked on. Many of the riders had gone to the young man; but my master, who had been watching what was going on, was the first to raise him. His head fell back and his arms hung down, and everyone looked very serious.

There was no noise now; even the dogs were quiet, and seemed to know that something was wrong. They carried him to our master's house. I heard afterwards that the young fellow was George Gordon, the Squire's only son, a fine, tall young man, and the pride of his family.

People were now riding off in all directions, to the doctor's, to the farrier's, and no doubt to Squire Gordon, to let him know about his son.

When Mr Bond, the farrier, came to look at the black horse that lay groaning on the grass, he felt him all over and shook his head; one of the horse's legs was broken. Then someone ran to our master's house and came back with a gun. Presently there was a loud bang and a dreadful shriek, and then all was still; the black horse moved no more.

My mother seemed much troubled. She said she had known that horse for years. His name was Rob Roy; a good bold horse with no vice in him. Afterwards she never would go to that part of the field.

Not many days after, we heard the church bell tolling for a long time; and looking over the gate we saw a long, strange, black coach covered with black cloth and drawn by black horses. After that came another, and another, and another; and all were black. Meanwhile the bell kept tolling, tolling. They were carrying young Gordon to the churchyard to bury him. He would never ride again. What they did with Rob Roy I never knew; but 'twas all for one little hare.

CHAPTER THREE

My Breaking In

I was now beginning to grow handsome; my coat had grown fine and soft, and was glossy black. I had one white foot, and a pretty white star on my forehead. People thought me very handsome. My master would not sell me till I was four years old; he said lads ought not to work like men, and colts ought not to work like horses till they were quite grown up.

When I was four years old, Squire Gordon came to look at me. He examined my eyes and my mouth, and felt my legs all down. Then I had to walk, trot, and gallop before him. He seemed to like me, and said, 'When he has been well broken in, he will do very well.' My master promised to break me in himself as he would not like me to be frightened or hurt; and he lost no time about it, for the next day the breaking in began.

Everyone may not know what breaking in is, so I will describe it. To break in a horse is to teach it to wear a saddle and bridle, and to carry on its back a man, woman, or child; to go just the way the rider wishes, and to do so quietly. Besides this, the horse has to learn to wear a collar, a crupper, and a breeching; and he must learn to stand still whilst these are put on. Then he must be taught to have a cart or a chaise fixed behind him, so that he cannot walk or trot without dragging it after him; and he must learn to go quickly or slowly, just as his driver wishes.

He must never start at what he sees, speak to other horses, bite, kick, or have any will of his own; but must always do his master's will, even though he may be very tired or hungry.

But the worst of all is that when his harness is once on, he may neither jump for joy nor lie down for weariness. So you see this breaking in is a great thing.

Of course I had long been used to a halter and a headstall, and to be led about in the fields and lanes quietly, but now I was to have a bit and a bridle.

My master gave me some oats as usual, and after a good deal of coaxing, he got the bit into my mouth and fixed the bridle. What a nasty thing the bit was! Those who have never had one in their mouth cannot think how bad it feels. A great piece of cold, hard steel as thick as a man's finger is pushed between your teeth and over your tongue, with the ends coming out at the corners of your mouth, and is held fast there by straps over your head, under your throat, round your nose, and under your chin; so that no way in the world can you get rid of the nasty hard thing. Bad! bad! Yes, very bad! At least, I thought so; but I knew my mother always wore one when she went out, and that all horses did when they were grown up. And so, what with the nice oats, and what with my master's pats, kind words, and gentle ways, I got to wear my bit and bridle.

Next came the saddle, but that was not half so bad. My master put it on my back very gently, whilst old Daniel held my head. Then, patting and talking to me all the time, he made the girths fast under my body. I had a few oats, then I was led about for a little while; and this went on every day till I began to look for the oats and the saddle.

At length, one morning my master got on my back and rode me round the meadow on the soft grass. It certainly did feel queer; but I must say I felt rather proud to carry my master; and, as he continued to ride me a little every day, I soon became accustomed to it.

The next unpleasant business was putting on the iron shoes; that too was very hard at first. My master went with me to the smith's forge to see that I was not hurt or frightened. The blacksmith took my feet in his hand, one after the other, and cut away some of the hoof. It did not pain me, so I stood still on three legs till he had done them all. Then he took a piece of iron the shape of my foot, clapped it on, and drove some nails through the shoe quite into my hoof, so that the shoe was firmly held. My feet were very stiff and heavy, but in time I got used to it.

And now having got so far, my master went on to break me to harness; for this there were more new things to wear. First, they placed a stiff, heavy collar just on my neck, and a bridle with great side-pieces, called blinkers, against my eyes. And blinkers indeed they were, for I could not see on either side, but only straight in front of me. Next there was a small saddle with a nasty stiff strap that went right under my tail; that was the crupper. I hated the crupper – to have my long tail doubled up and poked through that strap was almost as bad as the bit. I never felt more like kicking, but of course I could not kick such a good master; and so in time I got used to everything, and could do my work as well as my mother.

I must not forget to mention one part of my training which I have always considered a very great advantage. My master sent me for a fortnight to a neighbouring farmer who had a meadow which was skirted on one side by the railway. Here were some sheep and cows, and I was turned in amongst them.

I shall never forget the first train that ran by. I was feeding quietly near the pales which separated the meadow from the railway, when I heard a strange sound at a distance; and before I knew whence it came – with a rush and a clatter, and a puffing out of smoke – a long black train of something flew by, and was gone almost before I could draw my breath. I turned, and galloped to the further side of the meadow as fast as I could go; and there I stood snorting with astonishment and fear.

In the course of the day many other trains went by, some more slowly; these drew up at the station close by, and sometimes made an awful shriek and groan before they stopped. I thought it very dreadful, but the cows went on eating very quietly, and hardly raised their heads as the black, frightful thing came puffing and grinding past.

For the first few days I could not feed at peace; but as I found that this terrible creature never came into the field nor did me any harm, I began to disregard it; and very soon I cared as little about the passing of a train as the cows and sheep did.

Since then I have seen many horses much alarmed and restive at the sight or sound of a steam-engine; but thanks to my good master's care, I am as fearless at railway stations as in my own stable.

Now if anyone wants to break in a young horse well, that is the way to do it.

My master often drove me in double harness with my mother because she was steady, and could teach me how to go better than a strange horse. She told me the better I behaved, the better I should be treated, and that it was wisest always to do my best to please my master. 'But,' said she, 'there are a great many kinds of men: there are good, thoughtful men like our master, that any horse may be proud to serve; but there are bad, cruel men, who never ought to have a horse or a dog to call their own. Besides these, there are a great many men foolish, vain, ignorant, and careless, who never trouble themselves to think; these spoil more horses than anyone, just for want of sense. They don't mean it, but they do it for all that. I hope you will fall into good hands; but a horse never knows who may buy him, or who may drive him. It is all a chance; but still I say, "Do your best wherever you are, and keep up your good name." '

CHAPTER FOUR

Birtwick Park

At this time I used to stand in the stable, and my coat was brushed every day till it shone like a rook's wing. Early in May there came a man from Squire Gordon's, who took me away to the Hall. My master said, 'Goodbye, Darkie; be a good horse, and always do your best.' I could not say 'Goodbye,' so I put my nose into his hand; he patted me kindly, and then I left my first home. As I lived some years with Squire Gordon, I may as well tell you something about the place.

Squire Gordon's park skirted the village of Birtwick. It was entered by a large iron gate, at which stood the first lodge; and then you trotted along on a smooth road between clumps of large, old trees. Soon you passed another lodge and another gate, which brought you to the house and the gardens. Beyond this lay the home paddock, the old orchard, and the stables. There was accommodation for many horses and carriages; but I need only describe the stable into which I was taken. This was very roomy, with four good stalls. A large swinging window opened into the yard; this made it pleasant and airy.

The first stall was a large, square one, shut in behind with a wooden gate; the others were common stalls – good stalls, but not nearly so large. My stall had a low rack for hay and a low manger for corn; it was called a loose box, because the horse that was put into it was not tied up, but left loose to do as he liked. It is a great thing to have a loose box.

Into this fine box, clean, sweet, and airy, the groom put me. I never in my life was in a better box, and the sides were not so high but that I could see through the iron rails at the top all that went on.

The man gave me some very nice oats, patted me, spoke kindly, and then went away.

When I had eaten my corn, I looked round. In the stall next to mine stood a little fat grey pony, with a thick mane and tail, a very pretty head, and a pert little nose.

Putting my head up to the iron rails at the top of my box, I said, 'How do you do? What is your name?'

He turned round as far as his halter would allow, held up his head, and said: 'My name is Merrylegs. I am very handsome. I carry the young ladies on my back, and sometimes I take our mistress out in the low chair. They think a great deal of me, and so does James. Are you going to live next door to me in the box?'

'Yes,' I replied.

'Well, then,' he said, 'I hope you are good-tempered; next door to me I do not like anyone who bites.'

Just then a horse's head looked over from the stall beyond. The ears were laid back, and the eye looked rather ill-tempered. This tall chestnut mare, with a long, handsome neck, looked across to me and said, 'So it is you who have turned me out of my box. Is it not a very strange thing for a colt like you to come and turn a lady out of her own home?'

'I beg your pardon,' I said, 'I have turned no one out. The man who brought me put me here, and I had nothing to do with it. And as to my being a colt, I am turned four years old, and am a grown-up horse. I never yet had words with horse or mare, and it is my wish to live at peace.'

'Well,' she said, 'we shall see. Of course I do not want to have words with a young thing like you.'

I said no more.

In the afternoon, when she went out, Merrylegs told me all about the mare.

'The thing is this,' said Merrylegs. 'Ginger has a bad habit of biting and snapping: that is why she is called Ginger. When she was in the loose box, she used to snap very much. One day she bit James in the arm and made it bleed, and so Miss Flora and Miss Jessie, who are very fond of me, were afraid to come into the stable. They used to bring me nice things to eat – an apple, or a carrot, or a piece of bread; but after Ginger stood in that box, they dare not come, and I miss them very much. I hope, if you do not bite or snap, that they will now come again.'

I told him I never bit anything but grass, hay, and corn, and could not think what pleasure Ginger found in it.

'Well, I don't think she does find pleasure in it,' said Merrylegs; 'it is just a bad habit. She says no one was ever kind to her, and so why should she not bite? Of course it is a very bad habit; but I am sure, if all she says be true, she must have been very ill-used before she came here. John and James do all they can to please her, and our master never uses a whip if a horse behaves himself; so I think she might be good-tempered here.

'You see,' he said with a wise look, 'I am twelve years old; I know a great deal, and I can tell you there is not a better place for a horse all round the country than this. John is the best groom that ever was; he has been here fourteen years; and you never saw such a kind boy as James is. So it is all Ginger's own fault that she did not stay in that box.'

CHAPTER FIVE

A Fair Start

The name of the coachman was John Manly. He had a wife and one little child, and they lived in the coachman's cottage very near the stables.

The next morning he took me into the yard and gave me a good grooming. Just as I was going into my box with my coat soft and bright, the Squire came in to look at me, and seemed pleased.

'John,' he said, 'I meant to have tried the new horse this morning, but I have other business. You may as well take him for a round after breakfast. Go by the common and the Highwood, and come back by the water-mill and the river; that will show his paces.'

'I will, sir,' said John.

After breakfast he came and fitted me with a bridle. He was very particular in letting out and taking in the straps, to fit my head comfortably. Then he brought the saddle, but it was not broad enough for my back; he saw this in a moment, and went for another, which fitted nicely. He rode me at first slowly, then at a trot, and afterwards at a canter; and when we were on the common he gave me a light touch with his whip, and we had a splendid gallop.

'Ho, ho! my boy,' he said, as he pulled me up, 'you would like to follow the hounds, I think.'

As we came back through the park, we met the Squire and Mrs Gordon walking. They stopped, and John jumped off.

'Well, John, how does he go?'

'First-rate, sir,' answered John. 'He is as fleet as a deer, and has a fine spirit, too; but the lightest touch of the rein will guide him. Down at the end of the common we met one of those travelling carts hung all over with baskets, rugs, and suchlike. You know, sir, many horses will not pass these carts quietly; but he just took a good look at it, and then went on as quietly and pleasantly as could be.

'Some men were shooting rabbits near the Highwood, and a gun went off close by: he pulled up a little and looked, but did not stir a step to right or left. I just held the rein steady and did not hurry him; it's my opinion he has not been frightened or ill-used while he was young.'

'That's well,' said the Squire. 'I will try him myself tomorrow.'

The next day I was brought up for my master. I remembered my mother's counsel and my good old master's, and I tried to do exactly what the Squire wanted me to do. I found he was a very good rider, and thoughtful for his horse, too. When we came home, the lady was at the hall door as he rode up.

'Well, my dear,' she said, 'how do you like him?'

'He is exactly what John said, my dear. A pleasanter creature I never wish to mount. What shall we call him?'

'Would you like Ebony?' said she; 'he is as black as ebony.'

'No; not Ebony.'

'Will you call him Blackbird, like your uncle's old horse?'

'No; he is far handsomer than old Blackbird ever was.'

'Yes,' she said, 'he is really quite a beauty, and he has such a sweet, good-tempered face and such a fine, intelligent eye – what do you say to calling him Black Beauty?'

'Black Beauty – why, yes, I think that is a very good name. If you like, it shall be so'; and that is how I got my name.

When John went into the stable, he told James that master and mistress had chosen a good sensible English name for me that meant something; not like Marengo, or Pegasus, or Abdallah. They both laughed, and James said: 'If it were not for bringing back the past, I should have named him Rob Roy, for I never saw two horses more alike.'

'That's no wonder,' said John. 'Didn't you know that Farmer Grey's old Duchess was the mother of them both?'

I had never heard that before. So poor Rob Roy who was killed at that hunt was my brother! I do not wonder that my mother was so troubled. It seems that horses have no relations; at least, they never know each other after they are sold.

John seemed very proud of me: he used to make my mane and tail almost as smooth as a lady's hair, and he would talk to me a great deal. Of course I did not understand all he said, but I learned more and more to know what he *meant*, and what he wanted me to do. I grew very fond of him, because he was so gentle and kind, and seemed to know just how a horse feels; and when he cleaned me, he knew the tender places and the ticklish places; and when he brushed my head, he went as carefully over my eyes as if they were his own, and never stirred up any ill-temper.

James Howard, the stable boy, was just as gentle and pleasant in his way; so I thought myself well off. There was another man who helped in the yard, but he had very little to do with Ginger and me.

A few days after this I had to go in the carriage with Ginger. I wondered how we should get on together; but except laying her ears back when I was led up to her, she behaved very well. She did her work honestly, and did her full share; and I never wish to have a better partner in double harness.

When we came to a hill, instead of slackening her pace, she would throw her weight right into the collar, and pull away straight up. We had both the same sort of courage at our work; and John had more often to hold us in than to urge us forward. He never had to use the whip with either of us. Then our paces were much the same, and I found it very easy to keep step with her when trotting. This made it pleasant, and master always liked us to keep step well, and so did John. After we had been out two or three times together, we grew quite friendly and sociable; this made me feel very much at home.

As for Merrylegs, he and I soon became great friends. He was such a cheerful, plucky, good-tempered little fellow that he was a favourite with every one, and especially with Miss Jessie and Flora, who used to ride him about in the orchard and have fine games with him and their little dog Frisky.

Our master had two other horses that stood in another stable. One was Justice, a roan cob, used for riding, or for the luggage cart; the other was an old brown hunter, named Sir Oliver; he was past work now, but was a great favourite with the master, who gave him the run of the park; he sometimes did a little light carting on the estate, or carried one of the young ladies when they rode out with their father; for he was very gentle, and could be trusted with a child as well as Merrylegs. The cob was a strong, well-made, good-tempered horse, and we sometimes had a little chat in the paddock, but of course I could not be so intimate with him as with Ginger, who stood in the same stable.

CHAPTER SIX

Liberty

I was quite happy in my new place, and if there was one thing that I missed, it must not be thought I was discontented. All who had to do with me were good, and I had a light, airy stable and the best of food.

What more could I want? Why, liberty! For three years and a half of my life I had had all the liberty I could wish for; but now, week after week, month after month, and no doubt year after year, I must stand up in a stable night and day except when I am wanted; and then I must be just as steady and quiet as any old horse who has worked twenty years. I must wear straps here and straps there, a bit in my mouth, and blinkers over my eyes.

Now, I am not complaining, for I know it must be so. I mean only to say that for a young horse, full of strength and spirits, who has been used to some large field or plain where he can fling up his head, toss up his tail, gallop away at full speed, and then go round and back again with a snort to his companions – I say it is hard never now to have a bit more liberty to do as he likes.

Sometimes, when I have had less exercise than usual, I have felt so full of life and spring that when John has taken me out to exercise, I really could not keep quiet. Do what I would, it seemed as if I must jump, dance, or prance; and many a good shake I know I must have given him, especially at the first, but he was always good and patient.

'Steady, steady, my boy,' he would say; 'wait a while, and we'll have a good swing, and soon get the tickle out of your feet.' Then as soon as we were out of the village, he would give me a few miles at a spanking trot, and bring me back as fresh as before, only clear of the fidgets, as he called them.

Spirited horses, when not enough exercised, are often called skittish, when in fact it is only play; and some grooms will punish them, but our John did not; he knew it was only high spirits. Still, he had his own ways of making me understand by the tone of his voice or the touch of the rein. If he was very serious and quite determined, I always knew it by his voice, and that had more power over me than anything else, for I was very fond of him.

I ought to say that sometimes we had our liberty for a few hours; this used to be on fine Sundays in the summer-time. The carriage never went out on Sundays, because the church was not far off.

It was a great treat to us to be turned out into the Home Paddock or the old orchard: the grass was so cool and soft to our feet; the air was so sweet, and the freedom to do as we liked – to gallop, lie down, roll over on our backs, or nibble the sweet grass – was so pleasant. Then, as we stood together under the shade of the large chestnut tree, was a very good time for talking.

CHAPTER SEVEN

Ginger

One day, when Ginger and I were standing alone in the shade, we had a long talk. She wanted to know all about my bringing up and breaking in; so I told her.

'Well,' said she, 'if I had had your bringing up I might have as good a temper as you; but now I don't believe I ever shall.'

'Why not?' I said.

'Because it has been all so different with me,' she replied. 'I never had anyone, horse or man, that was kind to me, or that I cared to please; for in the first place I was taken from my mother as soon as I was weaned, and put with a lot of other young colts; none of them cared for me, and I cared for none of them. There was no kind master like yours to look after me, talk to me, and bring me nice things to eat.

'The man that had the care of us never gave me a kind word in my life. I do not mean that he ill-used me, but he did not care for us more than to see that we had plenty to eat and were sheltered in the winter.

'A footpath ran through our field, and very often the big boys passing through would fling stones to make us gallop. I was never hit, but one fine young colt was badly cut in the face, and I should think it would leave a scar for life. We did not mind the boys, but of course it made us more wild, and we settled it in our minds that boys were our enemies. We had very good fun in the meadows, either galloping up and down and chasing each other round and round the field, or standing still under the shade of the trees.

'But when it came to breaking in, that was a bad time for
me. Several men came to catch me; and when at last they
closed me in at one corner of the field, one caught me by
the forelock, another took me by the nose, holding it so
tight I could hardly draw my breath, and a third, grasping
my under jaw in his hard hand, wrenched my mouth open;
and so by force they got on the halter and put the bar into
my mouth.

'Then one dragged me along by the halter, and another
flogged me behind. This was the first experience I had of
man's kindness: it was all force. They did not give me a
chance to know what they wanted. I was high bred, with a
great deal of spirit, and no doubt was very wild, and gave
them plenty of trouble; but then it was dreadful to be shut
up in a stall, day after day, instead of having my liberty. I
fretted and pined and wanted to get loose. You know
yourself, it's bad enough when you have a kind master and
plenty of coaxing; but there was nothing of that sort for
me.

'There was one – the old master, Mr Ryder – who, I
think, could soon have brought me round, and have done
anything with me; but he had given up all the hard part of
the trade to his son and to another experienced man. My
master came only at times to oversee.

'His son was a strong, tall, bold man called Samson; and
he used to boast that he had never found a horse that could
throw him. There was no gentleness in him as there was in
his father, but only hardness: a hard voice, a hard eye, and a
hard hand. I felt from the first that what he wanted was to
wear all the spirit out of me, and just make me into a quiet,
humble, obedient piece of horse-flesh. "Horse-flesh!" Yes,
that is all that he thought about'; and Ginger stamped her
foot as if the very thought of him made her angry.

Then she went on: 'If I did not do exactly what he
wanted, he would get put out, and make me run round with

that long rein in the training field till he had tired me out. I think he drank a good deal, and I am quite sure that the oftener he drank the worse it was for me.

'One day he had worked me hard in every way he could, and when I lay down I was tired, miserable, and angry; it all seemed so hard. The next morning he came for me early, and ran me round again for a long time. I had scarcely had an hour's rest when he came again for me with a saddle and bridle and a new kind of bit.

'I could never quite tell how it came about. He had only just mounted me on the training ground, when something I did put him out of temper, and he jerked me hard with the rein. The new bit was very painful, and I reared up suddenly; this angered him still more, and he began to flog me.

'I felt my whole spirit set against him, and I began to kick, and plunge, and rear as I had never done before; we had a regular fight. For a long time he stuck to the saddle and punished me cruelly with his whip and spurs; but my blood was thoroughly up, and I cared for nothing he could do if only I could get him off.

'At last, after a terrible struggle, I threw him off backwards. I heard him fall heavily upon the turf, and without looking behind me, galloped off to the other end of the field; there I turned round and saw my persecutor slowly rise from the ground and go into the stable. I stood under an oak tree and watched, but no one came to catch me.

'Time passed; the sun was very hot, the flies swarmed round me and settled on my bleeding flanks where the spurs had dug in. I felt hungry, for I had not eaten since the early morning; but there was not enough grass in that meadow for a goose to live on. I wanted to lie down and rest, but with the saddle strapped tightly on my back there was no comfort, nor was there a drop of water to drink. The afternoon wore on, and the sun got low. I saw the other colts led in, and I knew they were having a good feed.

'At last, just as the sun went down, I saw the old master come out with a sieve in his hand. He was a very fine old gentleman with quite white hair, but I should know him by his voice amongst a thousand. It was not high, nor yet low, but full, clear, and kind; and when he gave orders it was so steady and decided that everyone, both horses and men, knew that he expected to be obeyed.

'He came quietly along, now and then shaking about the oats that he had in the sieve, speaking cheerfully and gently to me: "Come along, lassie, come along, lassie; come along, come along." I stood still and let him come up.

'He held the oats towards me and I began to eat without fear; his voice took all my fear away. He stood by, patting and stroking me whilst I was eating, and seeing the clots of blood on my side he seemed very vexed. "Poor lassie! it was a bad business, a bad business!" Then he quietly took the rein and led me to the stable.

'Just at the door stood Samson. I laid my ears back and snapped at him. "Stand back," said the master, "and keep out of her way; you've done a bad day's work for this filly." He growled out something about a vicious brute. "Hark ye," said his father, "a bad-tempered man will never make a good-tempered horse. You've not learned your trade yet, Samson."

'Then he led me into my box, took off the saddle and bridle with his own hands, and tied me up. Calling for a pail of warm water and a sponge, he took off his coat, and while the stable man held the pail, he sponged my sides for some time so tenderly that I was sure he knew how sore and bruised they were. "Whoa! my pretty one," he said; "stand still, stand still." His very voice did me good, and the bathing was very comforting.

'The skin was so broken at the corners of my mouth that I could not eat the hay, for the stalks hurt me. He looked closely at my mouth, shook his head, and told the man to fetch me a good bran mash and put some meal into it. How good that mash was! so soft and healing to my mouth. He stood by, stroking me and talking to the man all the time I was eating. "If a high-mettled creature like this," said he, "can't be broken in by fair means, she never will be good for anything."

'After that he often came to see me, and when my mouth was healed, the other breaker, Job, went on training me. As he was steady and thoughtful, I soon learned what he wanted.'

CHAPTER EIGHT

Ginger's Story Continued

The next time that Ginger and I were together in the paddock, she told me about her first place.

'After my breaking in,' she said, 'I was bought by a dealer to match another chestnut horse. For some weeks he drove us together, and then we were sold to a fashionable gentleman, and were sent up to London. I had been driven with a bearing rein by the dealer, and I hated it worse than anything else; but in this place we were reined far tighter, the coachman and his master thinking in this way we looked more stylish. We were often driven about in the Park and other fashionable places. You, who never had a bearing rein on, don't know what it is; but I can tell you it is dreadful.

'I like to toss my head about, and hold it as high as any horse; but you can fancy how it would feel if you tossed your head up high and were obliged to hold it there for hours together, not able to move it at all, except with a jerk still higher; and all this time your neck was aching till you did not know how to bear it.

'Besides this, you have two bits instead of one; and mine was a sharp one. It hurt my tongue and my jaw, and the blood from my tongue coloured the froth that kept flying from my lips, as I chafed and fretted at the bits and rein. It was worse when we had to stand by the hour waiting for our mistress at some grand party or entertainment; and if I fretted or stamped with impatience, the whip was laid on. It was enough to drive one mad.'

'Did not your master take any thought for you?' I said.

'No,' said she, 'he cared only to have a stylish turn-out, as they call it. I think he knew very little about horses; he left that to his coachman, who told him that I was of an irritable temper, and that I had not been well broken to the bearing rein, but that I should soon get used to it.

'However, *he* was not the man to do it; for when I was in the stable, miserable and angry, instead of being soothed and quieted by kindness, I only got a surly word or a blow. If he had been civil, I would have tried to bear it. I was willing to work, and ready to work hard too; but to be tormented for nothing but their fancies angered me. What right had they to make me suffer like that? Besides the soreness in my mouth and the pain in my neck, the bearing rein always made my windpipe feel bad; and if I had stopped there long, I know it would have spoiled my breathing.

'I grew more and more restless and irritable; I could not help it. Then I began to snap and kick when anyone came to harness me, and for this the groom beat me. One day, as they had just buckled us into the carriage and were straining my head up with that rein, I began to plunge and kick with all my might. I soon broke a lot of harness, and kicked myself clear; so my stay there was ended.

'Soon I was sent to Tattersall's to be sold. Of course I could not be warranted free from vice; so nothing was said about that. My handsome appearance and good paces soon brought a gentleman to bid for me, and I was bought by another dealer. He tried me in all kinds of ways and with different bits, and soon found out what I could bear. At last he drove me quite without a bearing rein, and then sold me as a perfectly quiet horse to a gentleman in the country.

'He was a good master, and I was getting on very well, but his old groom left him and a new one came. This man was as hard-tempered and hard-handed as Samson; he always spoke in a rough, impatient voice, and if I did not move in the stall the moment he wanted me, he would hit me above the hocks with the stable broom or the fork, whichever he might have in his hand. Everything he did was rough, and I began to hate him; he wanted to make me afraid of him, but I was too high-mettled for that.

'One day when he had aggravated me more than usual, I bit him; this of course put him in a great rage, and he began to hit me about the head with a riding whip. After that, he never dared to come into my stall again, either my heels or my teeth were ready for him, and he knew it. I was quite quiet with my master, but of course he listened to what the man said, and so I was sold again.

'The same dealer heard of me, and said he thought he knew of a place where I should do well. " 'Twas a pity," he said, "that such a fine horse should go to the bad, for want of a real good chance"; and the end of it was that I came here not long before you did. I had now made up my mind that men were my natural enemies, and that I must defend myself. Of course it is very different here; but who knows how long it will last? I wish I could think about things as you do; but I can't after all I have gone through.'

'Well,' I said, 'I think it would be a real shame if you were to bite or kick John or James.'

'I don't mean to,' she said, 'while they are good to me. I did once bite James pretty sharp, but John said, "Try her with kindness," and instead of punishing me as I expected, James came to me with his arm bound up, and brought me a bran mash and stroked me; and I have never snapped at him since; and I won't again.'

I was sorry for Ginger, but of course I knew very little then, and I thought most likely she made the worst of it. However, I found that as the weeks went on, she grew much more gentle and cheerful, and lost the watchful, defiant look that she used to turn on any strange person who came near her. And one day James said, 'I do believe that mare is getting fond of me, she quite whinnied after me this morning when I had been rubbing her forehead.'

'Aye, aye, Jim, 'tis the Birtwick balls,' said John: 'she'll be as good as Black Beauty by and by; kindness is all the physic she wants, poor thing!' Master noticed the change too, and one day when he got out of the carriage and came to speak to us as he often did, he stroked her beautiful neck. 'Well, my pretty one, well, how do things go with you now? You are a good bit happier than when you came to us, I think.'

She put her nose up to him in a friendly, trustful way, while he rubbed it gently.

'We shall make a cure of her, John,' he said.

'Yes, sir, she's wonderfully improved; she's not the same creature that she was. It's the Birtwick balls, sir,' said John, laughing.

This was a little joke of John's; he used to say that a regular course of the Birtwick horse-balls would cure almost any vicious horse. These balls, he said, were made up of patience and gentleness, firmness and petting: one pound of each to be mixed with half a pint of common-sense, and given to the horse every day.

CHAPTER NINE

Merrylegs

Mr Blomefield, the Vicar, had a large family of boys and girls, who sometimes came to play with Miss Jessie and Flora. One of the girls was as old as Miss Jessie; two of the boys were older, and there were several little ones. When they came, there was plenty of work for Merrylegs, for nothing pleased them so much as getting on him in turn, and riding him all about the orchard and the home paddock by the hour together.

One afternoon he had been out with them a long time, and when James brought him in and put on his halter, he said:

'There, you rogue, mind how you behave yourself, or we shall get into trouble.'

'What have you been doing, Merrylegs?' I asked.

'Oh!' said he, tossing his little head, 'I have only been giving these young people a lesson. They did not know when they had had enough, nor when I had had enough; so I just pitched them off backwards: that was the only thing they could understand.'

'What?' said I, 'you threw the children off? I thought you knew better than that! Did you throw Miss Jessie or Miss Flora?'

He looked very much offended, and said:

'Of course not; I would not do such a thing for the best oats that ever came into the stable. Why, I am as careful of our young ladies as the master could be; and as for the little ones, it is I who teach them to ride. When they seem frightened or a little unsteady on my back, I go as smoothly and as quietly as old pussy when she is after a bird; and when they are all right, I go on again faster, just to use them to it. So don't you trouble yourself preaching to me; I am the best friend and riding master those children have.

'It is not they; it is the boys. Boys,' said he, shaking his mane, 'are quite different; they must be broken in, as we were broken in when we were colts, and must just be taught what's what.'

'The other children had ridden me about for nearly two hours, and then the boys thought it was their turn; and so it was, and I was quite agreeable. They rode me in turn, and I galloped them about, up and down the fields and all about the orchard for a good hour.

'They had each cut a great hazel stick for a riding whip, and laid it on a little too hard; but I took it in good part, till at last I thought we had had enough; so I stopped two or three times by way of a hint. Boys, you see, think a horse or pony is like a steam engine or threshing machine, that can go on as long and as fast as they please. They never think that a pony can get tired, or have any feelings; so as the one whipping me could not understand, I just rose up on my hind legs and let him slip off behind – that was all. He mounted me again, and I did the same. Then the other boy got up; and as soon as he began to use his stick, I laid him on the grass; and so on, till they were able to understand: that was all.

'They are not bad boys; they don't wish to be cruel. I like them very well; but you see I had to give them a lesson. When they brought me to James and told him, I think he was very angry to see such big sticks. He said they were only fit for drovers or gypsies, and not for young gentlemen.'

'If I had been you,' said Ginger, 'I would have given those boys a good kick, and that would have given them a lesson.'

'No doubt you would,' said Merrylegs; 'but then I am not quite such a fool (begging your pardon) as to anger our master or make James ashamed of me. Besides, those children are under my charge when they are riding; I tell you they are entrusted to me. Why, only the other day I heard our master say to Mrs Blomefield, "My dear madam, you need not be anxious about the children; my old Merrylegs will take as much care of them as you or I could: I assure you I would not sell that pony for any money, he is so perfectly good-tempered and trustworthy." Do you think I am such an ungrateful brute as to forget all the kind treatment I have had here for five years, and all the trust they place in me, and turn vicious because a couple of ignorant boys used me badly?

'No! no! you never had a good place where they were kind to you, and so you don't know. I'm sorry for you, but I can tell you good places make good horses. I wouldn't vex our people for anything; I love them, I do,' said Merrylegs; and he gave a low 'Ho, ho, ho', through his nose, as he used to do in the morning when he heard James's footstep at the door.

'Besides,' he went on, 'if I took to kicking, where should I be? Why, sold off in a jiffy with no character; and I might find myself slaved about under a butcher's boy; or worked to death at some seaside place where no one cared for me, except to find out how fast I could go; or flogged along in some cart with three or four great men in it going out for a Sunday spree, as I have often seen in the place I lived in before I came here. No,' said he, shaking his head, 'I hope I shall never come to that.'

CHAPTER TEN

A Talk in the Orchard

Ginger and I were not of the regular tall, carriage-horse breed; we had more of the racing blood in us. We stood about fifteen and a half hands high, and were therefore just as good for riding as for driving. Our master used to say that he disliked either horse or man that could do but one thing; and as he did not want to show off in London parks, he preferred a more active and usual kind of horse.

As for us, our greatest pleasure was when we were saddled for a riding party – the master on Ginger, the mistress on me, and the young ladies on Sir Oliver and Merrylegs. It was so cheerful to be trotting and cantering all together that it always put us in high spirits. I had the best of it, for I always carried the mistress. Her weight was little, her voice sweet, and her hand so light on the rein that I was guided almost without feeling it.

Oh! if people knew what a comfort to horses a light hand is, and how it keeps a good mouth and a good temper, they surely would not chuck, and drag, and pull at the rein as they often do. Our mouths are so tender, that where they have not been spoiled or hardened with bad or ignorant treatment, they feel the slightest movement of the driver's hand, and we know in an instant what is required of us. My mouth had never been spoiled, and I believe that was why the mistress preferred me to Ginger, although her paces were certainly quite as good. She used often to envy me, and said it was all the fault of breaking in, and the gag bit in London, that her mouth was not so perfect as mine; and then old Sir Oliver would say, 'There, there! don't vex yourself; you have the greatest honour; a mare that can carry a tall man of our master's weight, with all your spring and sprightly action, does not need to hold her head down because she does not carry the lady; we horses must take things as they come, and always be contented and willing so long as we are kindly used.'

I had often wondered how it was that Sir Oliver had such a very short tail; it really was only six or seven inches long, with a tassel of hair hanging from it; and on one of our holidays in the orchard, I ventured to ask him by what accident he had lost his tail.

'Accident!' he snorted, with a fierce look, 'it was no accident! It was a cruel, shameful, cold-blooded act! When I was young I was taken to a place where these cruel things were done. I was tied up, and made fast so that I could not stir; and then they came and cut my long, beautiful tail through the flesh and through the bone, and took it away.'

'How dreadful!' I exclaimed.

'Dreadful! Ah, it was dreadful! but it was not only the pain, though that was terrible and lasted a long time; it was not only the indignity of having my best ornament taken from me, though that was bad; but it was this – how could I ever again brush the flies off my sides and off my hind legs? You who have tails just whisk the flies off without thinking about it; and you can't tell what a torment it is to have them settle upon you, and sting and sting, and yet have nothing in the world with which to lash them off. I tell you it is a lifelong wrong, and a lifelong loss. But, thank Heaven! men don't do it now.'

'What did they do it for then?' said Ginger.

'For fashion!' said the old horse, with a stamp of his foot. 'For fashion! if you know what that means. There was not a well-bred young horse in my time that had not his tail docked in that shameful way, just as if the good God that made us did not know what we wanted and what looked best.'

'I suppose it is fashion that makes them strap our heads up with those horrid bits that I was tortured with in London,' said Ginger.

'Of course it is,' said he. 'To my mind, fashion is one of the most wicked things in the world. Now look, for instance, at the way they serve dogs, cutting off their tails to make them look plucky, and shearing up their pretty little ears to a point, to make them look sharp, forsooth.

'I had a dear friend once, a brown terrier – Skye,' they called her. She was so fond of me that she would never sleep out of my stall. She made her bed under the manger, and there she had a litter of five as pretty little puppies as need be. None were drowned, for they were a valuable kind; and how pleased she was with them! And when they got their eyes open and crawled about, it was a real pretty sight.

'But one day the man came and took them all away. I thought he might be afraid I should tread upon them: but it was not so. In the evening poor Skye brought them back again, one by one, in her mouth; not the happy little things that they were, but bleeding and crying pitifully. They had all had a piece of their tails cut off, and the soft flap of their pretty little ears was cut quite off. How their mother licked them, and how troubled she was, poor thing! I never forgot it. The wounds healed in time, and they forgot the pain; but the nice, soft flap, that of course was intended to protect the delicate part of their ears from dust and injury, was gone for ever.

'Why don't they cut their own children's ears into points to make them look sharp? Why don't they cut the end off their noses to make them look plucky? One would be just as sensible as the other. What right have they to torment and disfigure God's creatures?'

Sir Oliver, though he was so gentle, was a fiery old fellow; and what he said was all so new to me and so dreadful, that I found a bitter feeling toward men that I had never had before rise up in my mind. Of course, Ginger was much excited. With flashing eyes and distended nostrils, she flung up her head, declaring that men were both brutes and blockheads.

'Who talks about blockheads?' said Merrylegs, who just came up from the old apple tree, where he had been rubbing himself against the low branch. 'Who talks about blockheads? I believe that is a bad word.'

'Bad words were made for bad things,' said Ginger; and she told him what Sir Oliver had said. 'It is all true,' said Merrylegs sadly, 'and I've seen that about the dogs over and over again where I lived first; but we won't talk about it here. You know that master, John, and James are always good to us; and talking against men in such a place as this doesn't seem fair or grateful. You know there are good masters and good grooms besides ours, though of course ours are the best.'

This wise speech of good little Merrylegs, which we knew was quite true, cooled us all down, specially Sir Oliver, who was dearly fond of his master; and to turn the subject I said, 'Can anyone tell me the use of blinkers?'

'No!' said Sir Oliver, shortly, 'because they are no use.'

'They are supposed,' said Justice in his calm way, 'to prevent horses from shying and starting, and getting so frightened as to cause accidents.'

'Then what is the reason they do not put them on riding horses, especially on ladies' horses?' said I.

'There is no reason at all,' said he quietly, 'except the fashion. They say that a horse would be so frightened to see the wheels of his own cart or carriage coming behind him that he would be sure to run away, although of course when he is ridden he sees them all about him if the streets are crowded. I admit they do sometimes come too close to be pleasant, but we don't run away; we are used to it, and understand it. If we never had blinkers put on, we should never want them; we should see what was there, and know what was what, and be much less frightened than by only seeing bits of things that we can't understand.'

Of course there may be some nervous horses which have been hurt or frightened when they were young; these may be the better for them: but as I never was nervous, I can't judge.

'I consider,' said Sir Oliver, 'that blinkers are dangerous things in the night. We horses can see much better in the dark than men can, and many an accident would never have happened if horses might have had the full use of their eyes.

'Some years ago, I remember, there was a hearse with two horses returning one dark night, and just by Farmer Sparrow's house where the pond is close to the road, the wheels went too near the edge, and the hearse was overturned into the water. Both the horses were drowned, and the driver hardly escaped. Of course after this accident a stout white rail was put up that might easily be seen; but if those horses had not been partly blinded, they would of themselves have kept farther from the edge, and no accident would have happened.

'When our master's carriage was overturned, before you came here, it was said that if the lamp on the left side had not gone out, John would have seen the great hole that the road-makers had left; and so he might. But if oh! Colin had not had blinkers on, he would have seen it, lamp or no lamp, for he was far too knowing an old horse to run into danger. As it was, he was very much hurt, the carriage was broken, and how John escaped nobody knew.'

'I should say,' said Ginger, curling her nostril, 'that these men who are so wise had better give orders that in future all foals should be born with their eyes set just in the middle of their foreheads, instead of on the side. Men always think they can improve upon Nature and mend what God has made.'

Things were getting rather sore again, when Merrylegs held up his knowing little face and said:

'I'll tell you a secret – I believe John does not approve of blinkers; I heard him talking to master about it one day. The master said that if horses had been used to them, it might be dangerous in some cases to leave them off; and John said he thought it would be a good thing if all colts were broken in without blinkers, as was done in some foreign countries; so let us cheer up and have a run to the other end of the orchard. I believe the wind has blown down some apples, and we may just as well eat them as for the slugs to have them.'

Merrylegs' suggestions could not be resisted; so we broke off our long conversation and got up our spirits by munching some very sweet apples which lay scattered on the grass.

CHAPTER ELEVEN

Plain Speaking

The longer I lived at Birtwick, the more proud and happy I felt at having such a place. Our master and mistress were respected and beloved by all who knew them; they were good and kind to everybody and everything: not only to men and women, but to horses and donkeys, to dogs and cats, and to cattle and birds. There was no oppressed or ill-used creature that had not a friend in them, and their servants took the same tone. If any of the village children were known to treat any creature cruelly, they soon heard about it from the Hall.

The Squire and Farmer Grey had worked together, as they said, for more than twenty years to get bearing reins on the cart horses done away with, and in our parts you seldom saw them: but sometimes if mistress met a heavily-laden horse, with his head strained up, she would stop the carriage and get out, and reason with the driver in her sweet, serious voice, and try to show him how foolish and cruel it was.

I don't think any man could withstand our mistress. I wish all ladies were like her.

Our master sometimes used to speak his mind very freely. I remember he was riding me towards home one morning, when he saw a powerful man driving towards us in a light pony chaise, with a beautiful little bay pony with slender legs and a high-bred, sensitive head and face. Just as he came to the park gates the little thing turned towards them.

The man, without word or warning, wrenched the creature's head round with such force and suddenness that he nearly threw it on its haunches. Recovering itself, it was going on when he began to lash it furiously. The pony plunged forward, but the strong, heavy hand held the pretty creature back with force almost enough to break its jaw, whilst the whip still cut into him. It was a dreadful sight to me, for I knew what fearful pain it gave that delicate little mouth; but master gave me the word, and we were up with him in a second.

'Sawyer,' he cried in a stern voice, 'is that pony made of flesh and blood?'

'Flesh and blood and temper,' he said. 'He's too fond of his own will, and that won't suit me.'

The man spoke as if he was in a strong passion. He was a builder who had often been to the park on business.

'And do you think,' said master sternly, 'that treatment like this will make him fond of your will?'

'He had no business to take that turn; his road was straight on!' said the man roughly.

'You have often driven that pony up to my place,' said master; 'it only shows the creature's memory and intelligence. How did he know that you were not going there again? But that has little to do with it. I must say, Mr Sawyer, that more unmanly, brutal treatment of a little pony it was never my painful lot to witness; and by giving way to such passion, you injure your own character as much, nay more than you injure your horse. And remember, we shall all have to be judged according to our works, whether they be towards man or towards beast.'

Master rode me home slowly, and I could tell by his voice how the thing had grieved him.

He was just as free in speaking to gentlemen of his own rank as to those below him; for another day, when we were out, we met a Captain Langley, a friend of our master. He was driving a splendid pair of greys in a kind of brake. After a little conversation the Captain said, 'What do you think of my new team, Mr Douglas? You know you are the judge of horses in these parts, and I should like your opinion.'

The master backed me a little so as to get a good view of them. 'They are an uncommonly handsome pair,' he said, 'and if they are as good as they look, I am sure you need not wish for anything better; but I see you yet hold to that pet scheme of yours for worrying your horses and lessening their power.'

'What do you mean,' said the other – 'the bearing reins? Oh, ah! I know that's a hobby of yours. Well, the fact is, I like to see my horses hold their heads up.'

'So do I,' said master, 'as well as any man, but I don't like to see them *held up*; that takes all the shine out of it. Now you are a military man, Langley, and no doubt like to see your regiment look well on parade, "Heads up", and all that kind of thing. But you would not take much credit for your drill if all your men had their heads tied to a backboard!

'It might not do much harm on parade, except to worry and fatigue them, but how would it be in a bayonet charge against the enemy, when they want the free use of every muscle, and all their strength thrown forward? I would not give much for their chance of victory; and it is just the same with horses; you fret and worry their temper and decrease their power; you will not let them throw their weight against their work, and so they have to do too much with their joints and muscles, and of course it wears them up faster. You may depend upon it horses were intended to have their heads free, as free as men's are, and if we could act a little more according to common sense, and a good deal less according to fashion, we should find many things work easier; besides, you know as well as I that if a horse makes a false step he has much less chance of recovering himself if his head and neck are fastened back.

'And now,' said the master laughing, 'I have given my hobby a good trot out, can't you make up your mind to mount him too, Captain? Your example would go a long way.'

'I believe you are right in theory,' said the other, 'and that's rather a hard hit about the soldiers; but – well, I'll think about it,' and so they parted.

CHAPTER TWELVE

A Stormy Day

One day, late in the autumn, my master had a long journey to go on business. I was put into the dog-cart, and John went with his master. I always liked to go in the dog-cart, it was so light, and the high wheels ran along so pleasantly. There had been a great deal of rain, and now the wind was very high and blew the dry leaves across the road in a shower. We went merrily along till we came to the toll-bar and the low wooden bridge. The river banks were rather high, and the bridge, instead of rising, went across just level, so that in the middle, if the river was full, the water would be nearly up to the woodwork and planks; but as there were good substantial rails on each side, people did not mind it.

The man at the gate said the river was rising fast, and he feared it would be a bad night. Many of the meadows were under water, and in one low part of the road the water was half-way up to my knees; the bottom was good, and master drove gently, so it was no matter.

When we got to the town, of course I had a good bait; but as the master's business engaged him a long time, we did not start for home till rather late in the afternoon. The wind was then much higher, and I heard the master say to John he had never been out in such a storm; and so I thought, as we went along the skirts of a wood, where the great branches were swaying about like twigs, and the rushing sound of the wind through the trees was terrible.

'I wish we were well out of this wood,' said my master.

'Yes, sir,' said John, 'it would be rather awkward if one of these branches came down upon us.'

The words were scarcely out of his mouth, when there was a groan, a crack, and a splitting sound, and tearing, crashing down amongst the other trees, came an oak, torn up by the roots, which fell right across the road just before us. I will never say I was not frightened, for I was. I stopped still, and I believe I trembled. Of course I did not turn round or run away; I was not brought up to do that. John jumped out and in a moment was at my head.

'That was a very near touch,' said my master. 'What's to be done now?'

'Well, sir, we can't drive over that tree nor yet get round it; there will be nothing for it but to go back to the four crossways, and that will be a good six miles before we get round to the wooden bridge again. It will make us late, but the horse is fresh.'

So back we went, and round by the crossroads; but by the time we got to the bridge, it was very nearly dark, and we could just see that the water was over the middle of it; but as that happened sometimes when the floods were out, master did not stop.

We were going along at a good pace, but the moment my feet touched the first part of the bridge, I felt sure there was something wrong. I dare not go forward, and so I made a dead stop. 'Go on, Beauty,' said my master, giving me a touch with the whip; but I dare not stir. He gave me a sharp cut; I jumped, but I dared not go forward.

'There's something wrong, sir,' said John; and he sprang out of the dog-cart and came to my head and looked all about. He tried to lead me forward. 'Come on, Beauty, what's the matter?' Of course I could not tell him, but I knew very well that the bridge was not safe.

Just then the man at the toll-gate on the other side ran out of the house, tossing a torch about like one mad.

'Hoy, hoy, hoy, halloo, stop!' he cried.

'What's the matter?' shouted my master.

'The bridge is broken in the middle, and part of it is carried away; if you come on you'll be into the river.'

'Thank God!' said my master. 'You Beauty!' said John; and taking the bridle, he gently turned me round to the right-hand road by the river side. The sun had set some time, the wind seemed to have lulled off after that furious blast which tore up the tree. It grew darker and darker, and more and more still. I trotted quietly along, the wheels hardly making a sound on the soft road.

For a good while neither master nor John spoke; and then the master began to speak in a serious voice. I could not understand much of what they said, but I found they thought that if I had gone on as the master wanted me, most likely the bridge would have given way under us, and horse, chaise, master, and man would have fallen into the river; and as the current was flowing very strongly, and there was no light and no help at hand, it was more than likely we should all have been drowned. Master said, God had given men reason by which they could find out things for themselves; but He had given animals knowledge which did not depend on reason, much more prompt and perfect in its way, by which they had often saved the lives of men.

John had many stories to tell of dogs and horses, and the wonderful things they had done. He thought people did not value their animals half enough, nor make friends of them as they ought to do. I am sure he makes friends of them if ever a man does.

At last we came to the park gates, and found the gardener looking out for us. He said that mistress had been in a dreadful way ever since dark, fearing some accident had happened; and that she had sent James off on Justice, the roan cob, towards the wooden bridge to make enquiry after us.

We saw a light at the hall door and at the upper windows, and as we came up mistress ran out saying, 'Are you really safe, my dear? Oh! I have been so anxious, fancying all sorts of things. Have you had no accident?'

'No, my dear; but if your Black Beauty had not been wiser then we were, we should all have been carried down the river at the wooden bridge.'

I heard no more, as they went into the house and John took me to the stable. Oh! what a good supper he gave me that night – a good bran mash and some crushed beans with my oats, and such a thick bed of straw. I was glad of it, for I was tired.

CHAPTER THIRTEEN

The Devil's Trademark

One day, when John and I had been out on some business for our master, and were returning gently on a long straight road, at some distance we saw a boy trying to leap a pony over a gate. The pony would not take the leap, and the boy cut him with the whip, but he only turned off on one side; he whipped him again, but the pony turned off on the other side. Then the boy got off and gave him a hard thrashing, knocking him about the head; then he got up again and tried to make him leap the gate, kicking him all the time shamefully; but still the pony refused.

When we were nearly at the spot, the pony put down his head, threw up his heels, and sent the boy neatly over into a broad quickset hedge; and with the rein dangling from his head, he set off home at a full gallop. John laughed out quite loudly. 'Serve him right!' he said.

'Oh! oh! oh!' cried the boy, as he struggled about amongst the thorns; 'I say, come and help me out.'

'Thank ye,' said John, 'I think you are quite in the right place; and maybe a little scratching will teach you not to leap a pony over a gate that is too high for him'; and so with that John rode off.

'It may be,' said he to himself, 'that young fellow is a liar as well as cruel; we'll just go home by Farmer Bushby's, Beauty, and then if anybody wants to know, you and I can tell 'em, ye see.' So we turned off to the right, and soon came up to the stack-yard within sight of the house. The farmer was hurrying out into the road, and his wife was standing at the gate looking very frightened.

'Have you seen my boy?' said Mr Bushby, as we came up; 'he went out an hour ago on my black pony, and the creature is just come back without a rider.'

'I should think, sir,' said John, 'he had better be without a rider, unless he can be ridden properly.'

'What do you mean?' said the farmer.

'Well, sir, I saw your son whipping, kicking, and knocking that good little pony about shamefully, because he would not leap a gate that was too high for him. The pony behaved well, sir, and showed no vice; but at last he just threw up his heels and tipped the young gentleman into the thorn hedge. He wanted me to help him out; but – I hope you will excuse me, sir – I did not feel inclined to do so. There are no bones broken, sir; he'll only get a few scratches. I love horses, and it roiles me to see them badly used. It is a bad plan to aggravate an animal till he uses his heels; the first time is not always the last.'

During this time the mother began to cry, 'Oh! my poor Bill, I must go and meet him; he must be hurt.'

'You had better go into the house, wife,' said the farmer; 'Bill wants a lesson about this, and I must see that he gets it. This is not the first time nor the second that he has ill-used that pony, and I shall stop it. I am much obliged to you, Manly. Good-evening.'

So we went on, John chuckling all the way home. He told James about it, who laughed and said, 'Serve him right. I knew that boy at school; he took great airs on himself because he was a farmer's son; he used to swagger about and bully the little boys. Of course we elder ones would not have any of that nonsense, and let him know that in the school and playground farmers' sons and labourers' sons were all alike.

'I well remember one day, just before afternoon school, I found him at the large window catching flies and pulling off their wings. He did not see me, and I gave him a box on the ears that laid him sprawling on the floor. Well, angry as I was, I was almost frightened; he roared and bellowed in such a style. The boys rushed in from the playground, and the master ran in from the road to see who was being murdered.

'Of course I said fair and square at once what I had done, and why; then I showed the master the poor flies, some crushed and some crawling about helpless, and I showed him the wings on the window-sill. I never saw him so angry before; but as Bill was still howling and whining, like the coward that he was, he did not give him any more punishment of that kind, but set him up on a stool for the rest of the afternoon, and said that he should not go out to play for that week.

'Then he talked to all the boys very seriously about cruelty, and said how hard-hearted and cowardly it was to hurt the weak and the helpless. But what stuck in my mind was this – he said that cruelty was the devil's own trademark, and if we saw anyone who took pleasure in cruelty, we might know to whom he belonged, for the devil was a murderer from the beginning and a tormentor to the end. On the other hand, where we saw people who loved their neighbours and were kind to man and beast, we might know that was God's mark; for "God is Love".'

'Your master never taught you a truer thing,' said John; 'there is no religion without love. People may talk as much as they like about their religion, but if it does not teach them to be good and kind to man and beast, it is all a sham – all a sham, James; and it won't stand when things come to be turned inside out and put down for what they are.'

CHAPTER FOURTEEN

James Howard

One morning, early in December, John had just led me into my box after my daily exercise, and was strapping my cloth on. James was coming in from the corn-chamber with some oats, when the master came into the stable. He looked rather serious, and held an open letter in his hand. John fastened the door of my box, touched his cap, and waited for orders.

'Good-morning, John,' said the master; 'I want to know if you have any complaint to make of James?'

'Complaint, sir? No, sir.'

'Is he industrious at his work and respectful to you?'

'Yes, sir, always.'

'You never find he slights his work when your back is turned?'

'Never, sir.'

'That's well; but I must put another question: have you any reason to suspect that when he goes out with the horses to exercise them, or takes a message, he stops about talking to his acquaintances, or goes into houses where he has no business, leaving the horses outside?'

'No, sir, certainly not, and if anybody has been saying that about James, I don't believe it; and I don't mean to believe it unless I have it fairly proved before witnesses. It's not for me to say who has been trying to take away James's character; but I will say this, sir, that a steadier, smarter, more pleasant, honest young fellow I never had in this stable. I can trust his word and I can trust his work.

'He is gentle and clever with the horses, and I would rather have them in his charge than in that of half the young fellows I know in laced hats and liveries; and whoever wants a character of James Howard,' said John, with a decided jerk of his head, 'let them come to John Manly.'

The master stood all this time grave and attentive; but as John finished his speech, a broad smile spread over his face, and looking kindly across at James, who all this time had stood still at the door, he said: 'James, my lad, set down the oats and come here. I am very glad to find that John's opinion of your character agrees so exactly with my own. John is a cautious man,' he said, with a droll smile, 'and it is not always easy to get his opinion about people; so I thought if I beat the bush on this side, the birds would fly out, and I should learn what I wanted to know quickly; so now we will come to business.

'I have a letter from my brother-in-law, Sir Clifford Williams, of Clifford Hall. He wants me to find him a trustworthy young groom, about twenty or twenty-one, who knows his business. His old coachman, who has lived with him twenty years, is getting feeble, and he wants a man to work with him and get into his ways, so that he would be able, when the old man was pensioned off, to step into his place. He would have eighteen shillings a week at first, a stable suit, a driving suit, a bedroom over the coach-house, and a boy under him. Sir Clifford is a good master, and if you could get the place, it would be a good start for you. I don't want to part with you, and if you left us I know John would lose his right hand.'

'That I should, sir,' said John, 'but I would not stand in his light for the world.'

'How old are you, James?' said master.

'Nineteen next May, sir.'

'That's young. What do you think, John?'

'Well, sir, it is young; but he is as steady as a man, strong, and well grown; and though he has not had much experience in driving, he has a light, firm hand, a quick eye, and is very careful. I am quite sure no horse of his will be ruined for want of having his feet and shoes looked after.'

'Your word will go the farthest, John,' said the master, 'for Sir Clifford adds in a postscript, "If I could find a man trained by your John, I should like him better than any other." So James, lad, think it over; talk to your mother at dinner-time, and then let me know what you wish.'

In a few days after this conversation, it was fully settled that James should go to Clifford Hall in a month or six weeks as it best suited his master, and in the meantime he was to get all the practice in driving that could be given him.

I never knew the carriage go out so often before. When the mistress did not go out, the master usually drove himself in the two-wheeled chaise; but now, whether it was master or the young ladies who wanted to go out, or whether it was only an errand had to be done, Ginger and I were put into the carriage and James drove us. At first, John rode with him on the box, telling him this and that, and afterwards James drove alone.

Then it was wonderful what a number of places the master would go to in the city on Saturday, and what queer streets we were driven through. He was sure to go to the railway-station just as the train was coming in, when cabs and carriages, carts and omnibuses were all trying to get over the bridge together. That bridge wanted good horses and good drivers when the railway bell was ringing, for it was narrow, and there was a very sharp turn up to the station where it would not have been at all difficult for people to run into each other if they did not look sharp and keep their wits about them.

CHAPTER FIFTEEN

The Old Ostler

After this, my master and mistress decided to pay a visit to some friends who lived about forty-six miles from our home, and James was to drive them. The first day we travelled thirty-two miles; there were some long, heavy hills, but James drove so carefully and thoughtfully that we were not at all harassed. He never forgot to put on the drag as we went downhill, nor to take it off at the right place. He kept our feet on the smoothest part of the road; and if the uphill was very long, he set the wheels a little across the road so that the carriage should not run back, and gave us breathing time. All these little things help a horse very much, particularly if he gets kind words into the bargain.

We stopped once or twice on the road; and just as the sun was going down, we reached the town where we were to spend the night. We stopped at the principal hotel, a very large one in the Market Place. We drove under an archway into a long yard, at the further end of which were the stables and coach-houses. Two ostlers came to take us out. The head ostler was a pleasant, active little man, with a crooked leg and a yellow striped waistcoat. I never saw a man unbuckle harness so quickly as he did; and then with a pat and a good word he led me to a long stable with six or eight stalls in it and two or three horses. The other man brought Ginger – James stood by whilst we were rubbed down and cleaned.

I never was cleaned so lightly and quickly as by that little old man. When he had done, James stepped up and felt me over, as if he thought I could not be thoroughly done; but he found my coat as clean and smooth as silk.

'Well,' he said, 'I thought I was pretty quick, and our John quicker still, but you do beat all I ever saw for being quick and thorough at the same time.'

'Practice makes perfect,' said the crooked little ostler, 'and 'twould be a pity if it didn't. Forty years' practice, and not perfect! Ha! ha! that would be a pity. As to being quick, why, bless you! that is only a matter of habit. If you get into the habit of being quick, it is just as easy as being slow – easier, I should say. In fact, it does not agree with my health to be hulking about over a job twice as long as it need take. Bless you! I couldn't whistle if I crawled over my work as some folks do.

'You see, I have been about horses ever since I was twelve years old, in hunting stables and racing stables. Being small, you see, I was a jockey for several years; but at the Goodwood the turf was very slippery and my poor Lark-spur got a fall, and I broke my knee; and so of course I was of no more use there.

'But I could not live without horses, of course I couldn't, so I took to the hotels; and I can tell you it is a downright pleasure to handle an animal like this: well-bred, well-mannered, well-cared-for. Bless you! I can tell how a horse is treated. Give me the handling of a horse for twenty minutes, and I'll tell you what sort of a groom he has had.

'Look at this one, pleasant, quiet, turns about just as you

want him to do, holds up his feet to be cleaned out, or anything else you please to wish. Then you'll find another fidgety, fretful, won't move the right way, or starts across the stall, tosses up his head as soon as you come near him, lays back his ears, and seems afraid of you, or else squares about at you with his heels.

'Poor things! I know what sort of treatment they have had. If they are timid, the treatment makes them start or shy; if they are high-mettled, it makes them vicious or dangerous; their tempers are mostly made when they are young. Bless you! they are like children; train 'em up in the way they should go, as the good Book says, and when they are old they will not depart from it – if they have a chance, that is.'

'I like to hear you talk,' said James; 'that's the way we lay it down at home, at our master's.'

'Who is your master, young man? if it be a proper question. I should judge he is a good one, from what I see.'

'He is Squire Gordon, of Birtwick Park, on the other side of the Beacon Hills,' said James.

'Ah! so, so, I have heard tell of him; fine judge of horses, ain't he? the best rider in the country?'

'I believe he is,' said James, 'but he rides very little now, since the poor young master was killed.'

'Ah! poor gentleman; I read all about it in the paper at the time; a fine horse killed too, wasn't there?'

'Yes,' said James, 'he was a splendid creature, brother to this one, and just like him.'

'Pity! pity!' said the old man. ' 'Twas a bad place to leap, if I remember – a thin fence at top, a steep bank down to the stream, wasn't it? No chance for a horse to see where he is going. Now, I am for bold riding as much as any man, but still there are some leaps that only a very knowing huntsman has any right to take. A man's life and a horse's life are worth more than a fox's tail; at least, I should say they ought to be.'

During this time the other man had finished Ginger, and had brought our corn; so James and the old man left the stable together.

CHAPTER SIXTEEN

The Fire

Later on in the evening, a traveller's horse was brought in by the second ostler, and whilst he was cleaning him, a young man with a pipe in his mouth lounged into the stable to gossip.

'I say, Towler,' said the ostler, 'just run up the ladder into the loft and bring down some hay into this horse's rack, will you? Only first lay down your pipe.'

'All right,' said the other, and went up through the trap door; and I heard him step across the floor overhead and put down the hay. James came in to look at us the last thing, and then the door was locked.

I cannot say how long I had slept, nor what time in the night it was, but I woke up feeling very uncomfortable, though I hardly knew why. I got up: the air seemed all thick and choking. I heard Ginger coughing, and one of the other horses moved about restlessly. It was quite dark, and I could see nothing; but the stable was full of smoke, and I hardly knew how to breathe.

The trap door had been left open, and I thought that was the place from which the smoke came. I listened and heard a soft, rushing sort of noise, and a low crackling and snapping. I did not know what it was, but there was something in the sound so strange that it made me tremble all over. The other horses were now all awake; some were pulling at their halters, others were stamping.

At last I heard steps outside, and the ostler who had put up the traveller's horse burst into the stable with a lantern, and began to untie the horses, and try to lead them out; but he seemed in such a hurry, and was so frightened himself, that he frightened me still more. The first horse would not go with him; he tried the second and third, but they too would not stir. He came to me next and tried to drag me out of the stall by force; of course that was no use. He tried us all by turns and then left the stable.

No doubt we were very foolish, but danger seemed to be all round; there was nobody whom we knew to trust in, and all was strange and uncertain. The fresh air that had come in through the open door made it easier to breathe, but the rushing sound overhead grew louder, and as I looked upward, through the bars of my empty rack, I saw a red light flickering on the wall. Then I heard a cry of 'Fire!' outside, and the old ostler came quietly and quickly in. He got one horse out, and went to another; but the flames were playing round the trap door, and the roaring overhead was dreadful.

The next thing I heard was James's voice, quiet and cheery, as it always was.

'Come, my beauties, it is time for us to be off, so wake up and come along.' I stood nearest the door, so he came to me first, patting me as he came in.

'Come, Beauty, on with your bridle, my boy, we'll soon be out of this smother.' It was on in no time; then he took the scarf off his neck, and tied it lightly over my eyes, and, patting and coaxing, he led me out of the stable. Safe in the yard, he slipped the scarf off my eyes, and shouted, 'Here, somebody! take this horse while I go back for the other.'

A tall, broad man stepped forward and took me, and James darted back into the stable. I set up a shrill whinny as

I saw him go. Ginger told me afterwards that whinny was the best thing I could have done for her, for had she not heard me outside, she would never have had courage to come out.

There was much confusion in the yard; the horses were being got out of other stables, and the carriages and gigs were being pulled out of houses and sheds, lest the flames should spread farther. On the other side of the yard windows were thrown up, and people were shouting all sorts of things; but I kept my eye fixed on the stable door, where the smoke poured out thicker than ever, and I could see flashes of red light.

Presently I heard above all the stir and din a loud, clear voice, which I knew was master's:

'James Howard! James Howard! are you there?' There was no answer, but I heard a crash of something falling in the stable, and the next moment I gave a loud, joyful neigh, for I saw James coming through the smoke, leading Ginger with him; she was coughing violently and he was not able to speak.

'My brave lad!' said master, laying his hand on his shoulder, 'are you hurt?'

James shook his head, for he could not yet speak.

'Ay,' said the big man who held me, 'he is a brave lad, and no mistake.'

'And now,' said master, 'when you have got your breath, James, we'll get out of this place as quickly as we can.'

We were moving towards the entry when from the Market Place there came a sound of galloping feet and loud rumbling wheels.

' 'Tis the fire engine! the fire engine!' shouted two or three voices. 'Stand back, make way!' and clattering and thundering over the stones two horses dashed into the yard with the heavy engine behind them. The firemen leaped to the ground; there was no need to ask where the fire was – it was torching up in a great blaze from the roof.

We got out as fast as we could into the broad, quiet Market Place. The stars were shining, and except for the noise behind us, all was still. Master led the way to a large hotel on the other side, and as soon as the ostler came, he said, 'James, I must now hasten to your mistress; I trust the horses entirely to you; order whatever you think is needed'; and with that he was gone. The master did not run, but I never saw mortal man walk so fast as he did that night.

There was a dreadful sound before we got into our stalls – the shrieks of those poor horses that were left burning to death in the stable were very terrible! They made both Ginger and me feel very ill. We, however, were taken in and well done by.

The next morning the master came to see how we were and to speak to James. I did not hear much, for the ostler was rubbing me down; but I could see that James looked very happy, and I thought the master was proud of him.

Our mistress had been so much alarmed in the night, that the journey was put off till the afternoon; so James had the morning on hand, and went first to the inn to see about our harness and the carriage, and then to hear more about the fire. When he came back, we heard him tell the ostler about it.

At first no one could guess how the fire had been caused; but at last a man said he saw Dick Towler go into the stable with a pipe in his mouth, and when he came out he had not one, and went to the tap for another. Then the under ostler said he had asked Dick to go up the ladder to get down some hay, but told him to lay down his pipe first. Dick denied taking the pipe with him, but no one believed him.

I remember our John Manly's rule, never to allow a pipe in the stable, and thought it ought to be the rule everywhere.

James said the roof and floor had all fallen in, and that

only the black walls were standing. The two poor horses that could not be got out were buried under the burnt rafters and tiles.

CHAPTER SEVENTEEN

John Manly's Talk

The rest of our journey was very easy, and a little after sunset we reached the house of my master's friend. We were taken into a clean, snug stable, where was a kind coachman, who made us very comfortable. He seemed to think a great deal of James when he heard about the fire.

'There is one thing quite clear, young man,' he said. 'Your horses know whom they can trust. It is one of the hardest things in the world to get horses out of a stable when there is either fire or flood. I don't know why they won't come out, but they won't – not one in twenty.'

We stopped two or three days at this place and then returned home. All went well on the journey: we were glad to be in our own stable again, and John was equally glad to see us.

Before James and he left us for the night, James said, 'I wonder who is coming in my place.'

'Little Joe Green at the Lodge,' said John.

'Little Joe Green! Why, he's a child!'

'He is fourteen and a half,' said John.

'But he is such a little chap!'

'Yes, he is small, but he is quick, willing and kind-hearted too, and wishes very much to come, and his father would like it; and I know the master would like to give him the chance. He said, if I thought he would not do, he would look out for a bigger boy; but I said I was quite agreeable to try him for six weeks.'

'Six weeks!' said James, 'why, it will be six months before he can be of much use! It will make you a deal of work, John.'

'Well,' said John with a laugh, 'work and I are very good friends; I never was afraid of work yet.'

'You are a very good man,' said James; 'I wish I may ever be like you.'

'I don't often speak of myself,' said John, 'but as you are going away from us out into the world to shift for yourself, I'll just tell you how I look on these things. I was just as old as Joseph when my father and mother died of the fever, within ten days of each other, and left me and my crippled sister, Nelly, alone in the world, without a relation to whom we could look for help.

'I was a farmer's boy, not earning enough to keep myself, much less both of us, and she must have gone to the workhouse but for our mistress (Nelly calls her her angel, and she has good right to do so). The mistress went and hired a room for her with old Widow Mallet, and she gave her knitting and needlework, when she was able to do it; and when she was ill, she sent her dinners and many nice comfortable things, and was like a mother to her. Then the master took me into the stable under old Norman, the coachman that then was. I had my food at the house and my bed in the loft, and a suit of clothes and three shillings a week, so that I could help Nelly.

'Norman might have turned round and said that at his age he could not be troubled with a raw boy from the plough-tail; but he was like a father to me, and took no end of pains with me. When the old man died some years after, I stepped into his place; and now of course I have top wages, and can lay by for a rainy day or a sunny day as it may happen; and Nelly is as happy as a bird.

'So you see, James, I am not the man that should turn up his nose at a little boy, and vex a good, kind master. No! no! I shall miss you very much, James, but we shall pull through. There's nothing like doing a kindness when 'tis put in your way, and I am glad I can do it.'

'Then,' said James, 'you don't hold with that saying "Everybody look after himself, and take care of number one"?'

'No, indeed,' said John. 'Where would Nelly and I have been if master and mistress and old Norman had only taken care of number one? Why, she in the workhouse and I hoeing turnips! Where would Black Beauty and Ginger have been if you had only thought of number one? Why, roasted to death! No, Jim, no! that is a selfish, heathenish saying, whoever may use it, and any man who thinks he has nothing to do but take care of number one, why, it's a pity but what he had been drowned like a puppy or a kitten before he got his eyes open; that's what I think,' said John, with a very decided jerk of his head.

James laughed at this; but there was a thickness in his voice when he said, 'You have been my best friend except my mother; I hope you won't forget me.'

'No, lad, no!' said John, 'and if ever I can do you a good turn, I hope you won't forget me.'

The next day Joe came to the stables to learn all he could before James left. He learned to sweep the stable, to bring in the straw and hay, and began to clean the harness, and help to wash the carriage. As he was quite too short to do anything in the way of grooming Ginger and me, James taught him upon Merrylegs, for, under John, he was to have full charge of the pony. He was a nice little bright fellow, and always came whistling to his work.

Merrylegs was a good deal put out at being 'mauled about', as he said, 'by a boy who knew nothing'; but towards the end of the second week he told me confidentially that he thought the boy would turn out well.

At last the day came when James had to leave us; cheerful as he always was, he looked quite down-hearted that morning.

'You see,' he said to John, 'I am leaving a great deal behind – my mother and Betsy, you, a good master and mistress, and the horses and my old Merrylegs. At the new place there will not be a soul I shall know. If it were not that I shall get a higher place, and be able to help my mother better, I don't think I should have made up my mind to it; it is a real pinch, John.'

'Ay, James, lad, so it is, but I should not think much of you if you could leave your home for the first time and not feel it. Cheer up! you'll make friends there, and if you get on well – as I am sure you will – it will be a fine thing for your mother, and she will be proud enough that you have got into such a good place as that.'

So John cheered him up, but everyone was sorry to lose James. As for Merrylegs, he pined after him for several days, and went quite off his appetite. So when he exercised me, John took him out several mornings with a leading rein, and trotting and galloping by my side he got up the little fellow's spirits again, and Merrylegs was soon all right.

Joe's father would often come in and give a little help, as he understood the work, and Joe took a great deal of pains to learn, and John was quite encouraged about him.

CHAPTER EIGHTEEN

Going for the Doctor

One night, a few days after James had left, I had eaten my hay and was lying down in my straw fast asleep, when I was suddenly awakened by the stable bell ringing very loudly. I heard the door of John's house opened and his feet running up to the Hall. He was back again in no time. He unlocked the stable door and came in, calling out, 'Wake up, Beauty, you must go well now, if ever you did!' and almost before I could think, he had placed the saddle on my back and the bridle on my head. He just ran round for his coat, and then took me at a quick trot up to the Hall door. The Squire stood there with the lamp in his hand.

'Now, John,' he said, 'ride for your life – that is, for your mistress's life; there is not a moment to lose. Give this note to Doctor White. Give your horse a rest at the inn, and be back as soon as you can.'

John said, 'Yes, sir,' and was on my back in a minute. The gardener who lived at the lodge had heard the bell ring, and was ready with the gate open. Away we went through the park, through the village, and down the hill till we came to the toll-gate. John called very loudly and thumped upon the door: the man was soon out and flung open the gate.

'Now,' said John, 'do you keep the gate open for the Doctor; here's the money,' and off we went again.

There was before us a long piece of level road by the riverside. John said to me, 'Now, Beauty, do your best,' and so I did; I wanted neither whip nor spur, and for two miles

I galloped as fast as I could lay my feet to the ground. I don't believe that my old grandfather, who won the race at Newmarket, could have gone faster. When we came to the bridge John pulled me up a little and patted my neck. 'Well done, Beauty! good old fellow,' he said. He would have let me go more slowly, but my spirit was up, and I was off again as fast as before.

The air was frosty, the moon bright, and it was very pleasant. We went through a village, through a dark wood, then uphill, then downhill, till after an eight miles' run we came to the town. On through the streets we went and into the Market Place. All was quite still except for the clatter of my feet on the stones – everybody was asleep. The church clock struck three as we drew up at Doctor White's door.

John rang the bell twice, and then knocked at the door like thunder. A window was thrown up, and Doctor White, in his nightcap, put his head out and said, 'What do you want?'

'Mrs Gordon is very ill, sir; master wants you to come at once; he thinks she will die if you cannot get there – here is a note.'

'Wait,' he said, 'I will come.'

He shut the window and was soon at the door.

'The worst of it is,' he said, 'that my horse has been out all day and is quite done up; my son has just been sent for and he has taken the other. What is to be done? Can I have your horse?'

'He has come at a gallop nearly all the way, sir, and I was to give him a rest here, but I think my master would not be against it if you think fit, sir.'

'All right,' he said, 'I will soon be ready.'

John stood by me and stroked my neck. I was very hot. The Doctor came out with his riding whip.

'You need not take that, sir,' said John. 'Black Beauty will go till he drops. Take care of him, sir, if you can; I should not like any harm to come to him.'

'No! no! John,' said the Doctor, 'I hope not,' and in a minute we had left John far behind.

I will not describe our way back; the Doctor was a heavier man than John, and not so good a rider; however, I did my very best. The man at the toll-gate had it open. When we came to the hill, the Doctor drew me up. 'Now, my good fellow,' he said, 'take some breath.' I was glad he did, for I was nearly spent; but that breathing helped me on, and soon we were in the park. Joe was at the lodge gate, and my master was at the Hall door, for he had heard us coming. He spoke not a word; the Doctor went into the house with him, and Joe led me to the stable.

I was glad to get home; my legs shook under me, and I could only stand and pant. I had not a dry hair on my body, the water ran down my legs, and I steamed all over – Joe used to say, like a pot on the fire. Poor Joe! he was young and small, and as yet he knew very little, and his father, who would have helped him, had been sent to the next village; but I am sure he did the very best he knew.

He rubbed my legs and my chest, but he did not put my warm cloth on me; he thought I was so hot I should not like it. Then he gave me a pailful of water to drink. It was cold, and very good, and I drank it all; then he gave me some hay and some corn, and thinking he had done right, he went away.

Soon I began to shake and tremble, and turned deadly cold; my legs, loins, and chest ached, and I felt sore all over. Oh! how I wished for my warm, thick cloth as I stood and trembled. I wished for John, but he had eight miles to walk, so I lay down in my straw and tried to go to sleep.

After a long while I heard John at the door; I gave a low moan, for I was in great pain. He was at my side in a moment, stooping down by me. I could not tell him how ill I felt; but he seemed to know it all. He covered me up with two or three warm cloths, and then ran to the house for some hot water; then he made me some warm gruel, which I drank; then, I think, I went to sleep.

John seemed to be very much put out. I heard him say to himself, over and over again, 'Stupid boy! stupid boy! No cloth put on, and I dare say the water was cold too; boys are no good'; but Joe was a good boy after all.

I was now very ill; a strong inflammation had attacked my lungs, and I could not draw my breath without pain. John nursed me night and day. He would get up two or three times in the night to come to me; my master, too, often came to see me. 'My poor Beauty,' he said one day, 'my good horse, you saved your mistress's life, Beauty! Yes, you saved her life.'

I was very glad to hear that, for it seems the Doctor had said if we had been a little longer it would have been too late. John told my master he never saw a horse go so fast in his life; it seemed as if the horse knew what was the matter. Of course I did, though John thought I did not; at least, I knew as much as this, that John and I must go at the top of our speed, and that it was for the sake of the mistress.

CHAPTER NINETEEN

Only Ignorance

I do not know how long I was ill. Mr Bond, the horse doctor, came every day. One day he bled me, and John held a pail for the blood. I felt very faint after it, and thought I should die. I believe they all thought so too.

Ginger and Merrylegs had been moved into the other stable, so that I might be quiet, for the fever made me very quick of hearing; any little noise seemed quite loud, and I could tell everyone's footstep going to and from the house. I knew all that was going on. One night John had to give me a draught; Thomas Green came in to help him.

After I had taken it and John had made me as comfortable as he could, he said he should stay half an hour to see how the medicine settled. Thomas said he would stay with him, so they went and sat down on a bench that had been brought into Merrylegs' stall, and put down the lantern at their feet that I might not be disturbed with the light.

For a while both men sat silent, and then Tom Green said in a low voice:

'I wish, John, you'd say a bit of a kind word to Joe; the boy is quite broken-hearted; he can't eat his meals, and he can't smile. He says he knows it was all his fault, though he is sure he did the best he knew; and he says, if Beauty dies, no one will ever speak to him again. It goes to my heart to hear him; I think you might give him just a word, he is not a bad boy.'

After a short pause, John said slowly: 'You must not be too hard upon me, Tom. I know he meant no harm; I never said he did. I know he is not a bad boy, but you see I am sore myself. That horse is the pride of my heart, to say nothing of his being such a favourite with the master and mistress; and to think that his life may be flung away in this manner is more than I can bear. But if you think I am hard on the boy, I will try to give him a good word tomorrow – that is, I mean, if Beauty is better.'

'Well, John! thank you, I knew you did not wish to be too hard, and I am glad you see it was only ignorance.'

John's voice almost startled me as he answered, '*Only* ignorance! only *ignorance*! how can you talk about *only* ignorance? Don't you know that ignorance is the worst thing in the world, next to wickedness? – and which does the most mischief Heaven only knows. If people can say,

'Oh! I did not know, I did not mean any harm,' they think it is all right. I suppose Martha Mulwash did not mean to kill that baby when she dosed it with Dalby and soothing syrups; but she did kill it, and was tried for manslaughter.'

'And serve her right too,' said Tom. 'A woman should not undertake to nurse a tender little child without knowing what is good or what is bad for it.'

'Bill Starkey,' continued John, 'did not mean to frighten his brother into fits when he dressed up like a ghost, and ran after him in the moonlight; but he did; and that bright, handsome little fellow, that might have been the pride of any mother's heart, is just no better than an idiot, and never will be, if he lives to be eighty years old.

'You were a good deal cut up yourself, Tom, two weeks ago, when those young ladies left your hothouse door open, with a frosty east wind blowing right in, you said it killed a good many of your plants.'

'A good many!' said Tom. 'There was not one of the tender cuttings that was not nipped off. I shall have to strike all over again, and the worst of it is, that I don't know where to go to get fresh ones. I was nearly mad when I came in and saw what was done.'

'And yet,' said John, 'I am sure the young ladies did not mean it; it was only ignorance!'

I heard no more of this conversation, for the medicine took effect and sent me to sleep, and in the morning I felt much better; but I often thought of John's words when I came to know more of the world.

CHAPTER TWENTY

Joe Green

Joe Green went on very well; he learned quickly, and was so attentive and careful that John began to trust him in many things; but, as I have said, he was small for his age, and it was seldom that he was allowed to exercise either Ginger or me. But it so happened one morning that John was out with Justice in the luggage-cart, and the master wanted a note to be taken immediately to a gentleman's house about three miles distant, and sent his orders for Joe to saddle me and take it, adding the caution that he was to ride carefully.

The note was delivered, and we were quietly returning till we came to the brickfield. Here we saw a cart heavily laden with bricks. The wheels had stuck fast in the stiff mud of some deep ruts; and the carter was shouting and flogging the two horses unmercifully. Joe pulled up. It was a sad sight. There were the two horses straining and struggling with all their might to drag the cart out, but they could not move it; the sweat streamed from their legs and flanks, their sides heaved, and every muscle was strained, whilst the man, fiercely pulling at the head of the forehorse, swore and lashed most brutally.

'Hold hard,' said Joe, 'don't go on flogging the horses like that; the wheels are so stuck that they cannot move the cart.' The man took no heed, but went on lashing.

'Stop! pray stop,' said Joe; 'I'll help you to lighten the cart, they can't move it now.'

'Mind your own business, you impudent young rascal,

and I'll mind mine.' The man was in a towering passion and the worse for drink; and so he laid on the whip again. Joe turned my head, and the next moment we were going at a round gallop towards the house of the master brickmaker. I cannot say if John would have approved of our pace, but Joe and I were both of one mind, and so angry that we could not go slower.

The house stood close by the roadside. Joe knocked at the door and shouted, 'Hulloa! is Mr Clay at home?' The door was opened, and Mr Clay himself came out.

'Hulloa, young man! you seem in a hurry; any orders from the Squire this morning?'

'No, Mr Clay; but there's a fellow in your brickyard flogging two horses to death. I told him to stop and he wouldn't. I said I'd help him to lighten the cart, and he wouldn't; so I have come to tell you. Pray, sir, go.' Joe's voice shook with excitement.

'Thank ye, my lad,' said the man, running in for his hat. Then, pausing for a moment – 'Will you give evidence of what you saw if I should bring the fellow up before a magistrate?' he asked.

'That I will,' said Joe, 'and glad too.' The man was gone, and we were on our way home at a smart trot.

'Why, what's the matter with you, Joe? you look angry all over,' said John, as the boy flung himself from the saddle.

'I am angry all over, I can tell you,' said the boy, and then in hurried, excited words he told all that had happened. Joe was usually such a quiet, gentle little fellow that it was wonderful to see him so roused.

'Right, Joe! you did right, my boy, whether the fellow gets a summons or not. Many folks would have ridden by and said 'twas not their business to interfere. Now, I say, that with cruelty and oppression it is everybody's business to interfere when they see it; you did right, my boy.'

Joe was quite calm by this time, and proud that John approved of him. He cleaned out my feet, and rubbed me down with a firmer hand than usual.

They were just going home to dinner when the footman came down to the stable to say that Joe was wanted directly in master's private room; there was a man brought up for ill-using horses, and Joe's evidence was wanted. The boy flushed up to his forehead, and his eyes sparkled. 'They shall have it,' said he.

'Put yourself a bit straight,' said John. Joe gave a pull at his necktie and a twitch at his jacket, and was off in a moment. Our master being one of the county magistrates, cases were often brought to him to settle, or say what should be done.

In the stable we heard no more for some time, as it was the men's dinner-hour. But when Joe came next into the stable I saw he was in high spirits; he gave me a good-natured slap and said, 'We won't see such things done, will we, old fellow?' We heard afterwards that he had given his evidence so clearly, and the horses were in such an exhausted state, bearing marks of such brutal usage, that the carter was committed to take his trial, and might possibly be sentenced to two or three months in prison.

It was wonderful what a change had come over Joe. John laughed, and said he had grown an inch taller in that week; and I believe he had. He was just as kind and gentle as before, but there was more purpose and determination in all that he did – as if he had jumped at once from a boy into a man.

CHAPTER TWENTY-ONE

The Parting

I had now lived in this happy place three years, but sad changes were about to come over us. We heard from time to time that our mistress was ill. The Doctor was often at the house, and the master looked grave and anxious. Then we heard that she must leave her home at once and go to a warm country for two or three years. The news fell upon the household like the tolling of a death-bell. Everybody was sorry; but the master began directly to make arrangements for breaking up his establishment and leaving England. We used to hear it talked about in our stable; indeed, nothing else was talked about.

John went about his work silent and sad, and Joe scarcely whistled. There was a great deal of coming and going; Ginger and I had full work.

The first to go were Miss Jessie and Miss Flora with their governess. They came to bid us goodbye. They hugged poor Merrylegs like an old friend, and so indeed he was. Then we heard what had been arranged for us. Master had sold Ginger and me to his old friend the Earl of W—, for he thought we should have a good place there. Merrylegs he had given to the Vicar, who was wanting a pony for Mrs Blomefield; but it was on the condition that he should never be sold, and that when he was past work he should be shot and buried.

Joe was engaged to take care of him and to help in the house; so I thought that Merrylegs was well off. John had the offer of several good places, but he said he should wait a little and look round.

The evening before they left, the master came into the stable to give some directions and to give his horses the last pat. He seemed very low-spirited; I knew that by his voice. I believe we horses can tell more by the voice than many men can.

'Have you decided what to do, John?' he said. 'I find you have not accepted any of those offers.'

'No, sir, I have made up my mind that if I could get a situation with some first-rate colt-breaker and horse-trainer, it would be the right thing for me. Many young animals are frightened and spoiled by wrong treatment, which need not be if the right man took them in hand. I always get on well with horses, and if I could help some of them to a fair start, I should feel as if I was doing some good. What do you think of it, sir?'

'I don't know a man anywhere,' said master, 'that I should think so suitable for it as yourself. You understand horses, and somehow they understand you, and in time you might set up for yourself; I think you could not do better. If in any way I can help you, write to me; I shall speak to my agent in London, and leave your character with him.'

He asked John about his future, and then thanked him for his long and faithful service; but that was too much for John. 'Pray don't, sir, I can't bear it. You and my dear mistress have done so much for me that I could never repay it; but we shall never forget you, sir, and please God we may someday see mistress back again like herself; we must keep up hope, sir.' Master gave John his hand, but he did not speak; and they both left the stable.

The last sad day had come; the footman and the heavy luggage had gone off the day before, and there was only master and mistress and her maid left. Ginger and I brought the carriage up to the Hall door for the last time. The servants brought out cushions and rugs and many other things; and when all were arranged, master came down the steps carrying the mistress in his arms (I was on the side next the house and could see all that went on). He placed her carefully in the carriage, while the house servants stood round crying.

'Goodbye again,' he said as he got in; 'we shall not forget any of you – drive on, John.'

Joe jumped up, and we trotted slowly through the park and through the village, where the people were standing at their doors to have a last look and to say, 'God bless them.'

When we reached the railway station, I think mistress walked from the carriage to the waiting-room. I heard her say in her own sweet voice, 'Goodbye, John, God bless you.' I felt the rein twitch, but John made no answer, perhaps he could not speak. As soon as Joe had taken the things out of the carriage, John called him to stand by the horses while he went on the platform. Poor Joe! he stood close up to our heads to hide his tears.

Very soon the train came puffing up into the station. Two or three minutes after the doors were slammed to, the guard whistled, and the train glided away, leaving behind it only clouds of white steam and some very heavy hearts.

When it was quite out of sight, John came back.

'We shall never see her again,' he said – 'never.' He took the reins, mounted the box, and drove slowly home with Joe; but it was not our home now.

CHAPTER TWENTY-TWO

Earlshall

The next morning after breakfast, Joe put Merrylegs into the mistress's low chaise to take him to the vicarage. He came first and said goodbye to us, and Merrylegs neighed to us from the yard. Then John put the saddle on Ginger and the leading rein on me, and rode us across the country about fifteen miles to Earlshall Park, where the Earl of W— lived. Here was a very fine house and a great deal of stabling.

We went into the yard through a stone gateway, and John asked for Mr York. It was some time before he came. He was a fine-looking, middle-aged man, and his voice said at once that he expected to be obeyed. He was very friendly and polite to John; and after giving us a slight look, he called a groom to take us to our boxes, and invited John to take some refreshment.

We were taken to a light, airy stable and placed in boxes adjoining each other, where we were rubbed down and fed. In about half an hour John and Mr York, who was to be our new coachman, came in to see us.

'Now, Mr Manly,' he said, after carefully looking at us both, 'I can see no fault in these horses; but we all know that horses as well as men have their peculiarities, and that sometimes they need different treatment. I should like to know if there is anything particular in either of these that you would like to mention.'

'Well,' said John, 'I don't believe there is a better pair of horses in the country, and right grieved I am to part with them, but they are not alike. The black one has the most perfect temper I ever knew; I suppose he has never known a hard word or a blow since he was foaled, and all his pleasure seems to be what you wish to do.

'But the chestnut I fancy must have had bad treatment; we heard as much from the dealer. She came to us snappish and suspicious, but when she found what sort of a place ours was, it all went off by degrees. For three years I have never seen the smallest sign of temper, and if she is well treated there is not a better or more willing animal than she is; but she is naturally of a more irritable constitution than the black horse – flies tease her more; anything wrong in the harness frets her more; and if she were ill-used or unfairly treated, she would not be unlikely to give tit for tat. You know that many high-mettled horses will do so.'

'Of course,' said York, 'I quite understand; but you know it is not easy in stables like these to have all the grooms just what they should be; I do my best, and there I must leave it. I'll remember what you have said about the mare.'

They were going out of the stable, when John stopped and said: 'I had better mention that we have never used the bearing rein with either of them; the black horse never had one on, and the dealer said it was the gag-bit that spoiled the other's temper.'

'Well,' said York, 'if they come here, they must wear the bearing rein. I prefer a loose rein myself, and his lordship is always very reasonable about horses; but my lady – that's another matter. She will have style; and if her carriage horses were not reined up tight she wouldn't look at them. I always stand out against the gag-bit, and shall do so, but the rein must be tight up when my lady rides!'

'I am sorry for it, very sorry,' said John; 'but I must go now, or I shall lose the train.'

He came round to each of us to pat and speak to us for the last time; his voice sounded very sad.

I held my face close to him, as that was all I could do to say goodbye; and then he was gone, and I have never seen him since.

The next day Lord W— came to look at us; he seemed pleased with our appearance.

'I have great confidence in these horses,' he said, 'from the character my friend Mr Gordon has given me of them. Of course they are not a match in colour, but my idea is that they will do very well for the carriage whilst we are in the country. Before we go to London I must try to match Baron; the black horse, I believe, is perfect for riding.'

York then told him what John had said about us.

'Well,' said he, 'you must keep an eye to the mare, and put the bearing rein easy; I dare say they will do very well with a little humouring at first. I'll mention it to her ladyship.'

In the afternoon we were harnessed and put in the carriage, and as the stable clock struck three we were led round to the front of the house. It was all very grand, and the house three or four times as large as the old one at Birtwick, but not half so pleasant, if a horse may have an opinion. Two footmen, dressed in drab livery, with scarlet breeches and white stockings, were standing ready.

Presently we heard the rustling sound of silk as my lady came down the flight of stone steps. She stepped round to look at us. She was a tall, proud-looking woman, and did not seem pleased about something; but she said nothing, and got into the carriage. This was my first time of wearing a bearing rein, and I must say, though it certainly was a nuisance not to be able to get my head down now and then, it did not pull my head higher than I was accustomed to carry it. I felt anxious about Ginger, but she seemed to be quiet and content.

The next day at three o'clock we were again at the door, and the footmen were there as before. We heard the silk dress rustle as the lady came down the steps, and in an imperious voice she said: 'York, you must put those horses' heads higher; they are not fit to be seen.'

York got down and said very respectfully: 'I beg your pardon, my lady, but these horses have not been reined up for three years, and my lord said it would be safer to bring them to it by degrees; but if your ladyship pleases, I can take them up a little more.'

'Do so,' she said.

York came round to our heads and shortened the rein one hole, I think; every little makes a difference, be it for better or worse, and that day we had a steep hill to go up. Then I began to understand what I had heard. Of course I wanted to put my head forward and take the carriage up with a will, as we had been used to do; but no, I had now to pull with my head up, and that took all the spirit out of me, and brought the strain on my back and legs.

When he came in, Ginger said: 'Now you see what it is like; but this is not bad, and if it does not get much worse than this, I shall say nothing about it, for we are very well treated here. But if they strain me up tight, why, let 'em look out! I can't bear it and I won't.'

Day by day, hole by hole, our bearing reins were shortened, and instead of looking forward with pleasure to having my harness put on as I used to do, I began to dread it. Ginger, too, seemed restless, though she said very little. At last I thought the worst was over; for several days there had been no more shortening, and I determined to make the best of it and to do my duty, though now going out was a constant harass instead of a pleasure; but the worst was not come.

CHAPTER TWENTY-THREE

A Strike for Liberty

One day my lady came down later than usual, and the silk rustled more than ever.

'Drive to the Duchess of B—'s,' she said. Then, after a pause, she added: 'Are you never going to get those horses' heads up, York? Raise them at once, and let us have no more of this humouring nonsense.'

York came to me first, whilst the groom stood at Ginger's head. He drew my head back and fixed the rein so tight that it was almost intolerable; then he went to Ginger, who was impatiently jerking her head up and down against the bit, as was her way now. She had a good idea of what was coming, and the moment York took the rein off the terret in order to shorten it, she took her opportunity and reared up so suddenly that York had his nose roughly hit and his hat knocked off, and the groom was nearly thrown off his legs.

At once they both flew to her head, but she was a match for them, and went on plunging, rearing, and kicking in a most desperate manner. At last she kicked right over the carriage pole and fell down, after giving me a severe blow on my near quarter.

There is no knowing what further mischief she may have done had not York promptly sat himself down flat on her head to prevent her struggling, at the same time calling out, 'Unbuckle the black horse! Run for the winch and unscrew the carriage pole; and somebody cut the trace if you can't unhitch it.'

One of the footmen ran for the winch, and another brought a knife from the house. The groom set me free from Ginger and the carriage, and led me to my box. He just turned me in as I was, and ran back to York.

I was much excited by what had happened, and if I had ever been used to kick or rear, I am sure I should have done it then; but I never had, so there I stood, angry, sore in my leg, my head still strained up to the terret on the saddle, and with no power to get it down. I was very miserable, and felt much inclined to kick the first person who came near me.

Before long, however, Ginger was led in by two grooms, a good deal knocked about and bruised. York came with her and gave his orders, and then came to look at me. In a moment he let down my head.

'Confound these bearing reins!' he said to himself. 'I thought we should have some mischief soon – master will be sorely vexed; but there – if a woman's husband can't rule her, of course a servant can't; so I wash my hands of it, and if she can't get to the Duchess's garden party, I can't help it.'

York did not say this before the men; he always spoke respectfully when they were by. Now he felt me all over and soon found the place above my hock where I had been kicked. It was swollen and painful; so he ordered it to be sponged with hot water and then some lotion to be rubbed in.

Lord W— was much put out when he learned what had happened. He blamed York for giving way to his mistress, to which York replied that in future he would much prefer to receive his orders only from his lordship. But I think nothing came of it, for things went on the same as before. I thought York might have stood up better for his horses; but perhaps I am no judge.

Ginger was never put into the carriage again, but when her bruises were healed, one of Lord W—'s younger sons said he should like to have her; he was sure she would make a good hunter. As for me, I was obliged still to go in the carriage, and had a fresh partner, called Max, who had always been used to the tight rein. I asked him how it was he bore it.

'Well,' he said, 'I bear it because I must, but it is shortening my life, and it will shorten yours too if you have to stick to it.'

'Do you think,' I said, 'that our masters know how bad it is for us?'

'I can't say,' he replied, 'but the dealers and the horse doctors know it very well. I was at a dealer's once, who was training me and another horse to go as a pair; he was getting our heads up, as he said, a little higher and a little higher every day. A gentleman who was there asked him why he did so; "Because," said he, "people won't buy them unless we do. The London people always want their horses to carry their heads high, and to step high; of course it is very bad for the horses, but then it is good for trade. The horses soon wear up, or get diseased, and they come for another pair." That,' said Max, 'is what he said in my hearing, and you can judge for yourself.'

What I suffered for four long months with that rein it would be hard to describe; but I am quite sure that, had it lasted much longer, either my health or my temper would have given way. Before that, I never knew what it was to foam at the mouth; but now the action of the sharp bit on my tongue and jaw and the constrained position of my head and throat, always caused me to froth more or less at the mouth.

Some people think it very fine to see this, and say, 'What fine, spirited creatures!' But it is just as unnatural for horses as for men to foam at the mouth: it is a sure sign of some discomfort, and should be attended to. Besides this, there was a pressure on my windpipe, which often made my breathing very uncomfortable. When I returned from my work, my neck and chest were strained and painful, my mouth and tongue tender, and I felt worn and depressed.

In my old home I always knew that John and my master were my friends; but here, although in many ways I was well treated, I had no friend. York might have known, and very likely did know, how that rein harassed me; but I suppose he took it as a matter of course that could not be helped; at any rate, nothing was done to relieve me.

CHAPTER TWENTY-FOUR

Lady Anne, or a Runaway Horse

Early in the spring Lord W— and part of his family went up to London and took York with them. Ginger and I and some other horses were left at home for use, and the head groom was left in charge.

The Lady Harriet, who remained at the Hall, was a great invalid, and never went out in the carriage, and the Lady Anne preferred riding on horseback with her brother or cousins. She was a perfect horsewoman, and as gay and gentle as she was beautiful. She chose me for her horse, and named me Black Auster. I enjoyed very much these rides in the clear, cold air, sometimes with Ginger, sometimes with Lizzie. This Lizzie was a bright bay mare, almost thoroughbred, and a great favourite with the gentlemen on account of her fine action and lively spirit; but Ginger, who knew more of her than I did, told me she was rather nervous.

There was a gentleman of the name of Blantyre staying at the Hall; he always rode Lizzie, and praised her so much that one day Lady Anne ordered the side-saddle to be put on Lizzie and the other saddle on me. When we came to the door, the gentleman seemed very uneasy.

'How is this?' he said; 'are you tired of your good Black Auster?'

'Oh, no, not at all,' she replied, 'but I am amiable enough to let you ride him for once, and I will try your charming Lizzie. You must confess that in size and appearance she is far more like a lady's horse than my own favourite.'

'Do let me advise you not to mount her,' he said; 'she is a charming creature, but she is too nervous for a lady. I assure you she is not perfectly safe; let me beg you to have the saddles changed.'

'My dear cousin,' said Lady Anne, laughing, 'pray do not trouble your good, careful head about me. I have been a horsewoman ever since I was a baby, and I have followed the hounds a great many times, though I know you do not approve of ladies hunting; but still, that is the fact, and I intend to try this Lizzie that you gentlemen are all so fond of; so please help me to mount like the good friend you are.'

There was no more to be said. He placed her carefully on the saddle, looked to the bit and curb, gave the reins gently into her hand, and then mounted me. Just as we were moving off, a footman came out with a slip of paper and message from the Lady Harriet – 'Would Mr Blantyre ask this question for her at Dr Ashley's, and bring the answer?'

The village was about a mile off, and the Doctor's house was the last in it. We went along gaily enough till we came to his gate. There was a short drive up to the house between tall evergreens. Blantyre alighted at the gate and was going to open it for Lady Anne, but she said, 'I will wait for you here; you can hang Auster's rein on the gate.'

He looked at her doubtfully – 'I will not be five minutes,' he said.

'Oh, do not hurry yourself; Lizzie and I shall not run away from you.'

He hung my rein on one of the iron spikes, and was soon hidden amongst the trees. By the side of the road, a few paces off, Lizzie was standing quietly with her back to me. My young mistress was sitting easily with a loose rein, humming a little song. I listened to my rider's footsteps until they reached the house, and heard him knock at the door.

There was a meadow on the opposite side of the road, the gate of which stood open. Just then some cart horses and several young colts came trotting out in a very disorderly manner, whilst a boy behind was cracking a great whip. The colts were wild and frolicsome, and one of them bolted across the road and blundered up against Lizzie's hind legs. Whether it was the stupid colt, or the loud cracking of the whip, or both together I cannot say; but she gave a violent kick and dashed off into a headlong gallop. It was so sudden, that Lady Anne was nearly unseated, but she soon recovered herself.

I gave a loud, shrill neigh for help. Again and again I neighed, pawing the ground impatiently, and tossing my head to get the rein loose. I had not long to wait. Blantyre came running to the gate. He looked anxiously about, and just caught sight of the flying figure, now far away on the road. In an instant he sprang into the saddle. I needed no whip or spur, for I was as eager as my rider. He saw it, and giving me a free rein, and leaning a little forward, we dashed after them.

For about a mile and a half the road ran straight, then bent to the right, after which it divided into two roads. Long before we came to the bend Lady Anne was out of sight. Which way had she turned? A woman was standing at her garden gate, shading her eyes with her hand and looking eagerly up the road. Scarcely drawing the rein,

Blantyre shouted, 'Which way?' 'To the right,' cried the woman, pointing with her hand, and away we went up the right-hand road; then for a moment we caught sight of her; another bend and she was hidden again. Several times we caught glimpses, and then lost them. We scarcely seemed to gain ground upon them at all.

An old road-mender was standing near a heap of stones, with shovel dropped and hands raised. As we came near he made a sign to speak. Blantyre drew the rein a little. 'To the common, to the common, sir; she has turned off there.' I knew this common very well. It was for the most part very uneven ground, covered with heather and dark green furze bushes, with here and there a scrubby old thorn tree. There were also open spaces of fine, short grass, with ant-hills and mole-turns everywhere – the worst place I ever knew for a headlong gallop.

We had hardly turned on the common, when we caught sight again of the green habit flying on before us. My lady's hat was gone, and her long brown hair was streaming behind her. Her head and body were thrown back, as if she were pulling with all her remaining strength, and as if that strength were nearly exhausted. It was clear that the roughness of the ground had very much lessened Lizzie's speed, and there seemed a chance that we might overtake her.

Whilst we were on the high-road, Blantyre had given me my head; but now with a light hand and a practised eye, he guided me over the ground in such a masterly manner, that my pace was scarcely slackened, and we were decidedly gaining on them.

About half-way across the heath there had been a wide dyke recently cut, and the earth from the cutting was cast up roughly on the other side. Surely this would stop them! But no; with scarcely a pause Lizzie took the leap, stumbled among the rough clods, and fell. Blantyre groaned,

'Now, Auster, do your best!' He gave me a steady rein, I gathered myself well together, and with one determined leap cleared both dyke and bank.

Motionless among the heather, with her face to the earth, lay my poor young mistress. Blantyre kneeled down and called her name – there was no sound.

Gently he turned her face upward, it was ghastly white, and the eyes were closed. 'Annie, dear Annie, do speak!' but there was no answer. He unbuttoned her habit, loosened her collar, felt her hands and wrists, then started up and looked wildly round for help.

At no great distance were two men cutting turf, who, seeing Lizzie running wild without a rider, had left their work to catch her.

Blantyre's 'Halloo!' soon brought them to the spot. The foremost man seemed much troubled at the sight and asked what he could do.

'Can you ride?'

'Well, sir, I bean't much of a horseman, but I'd risk my neck for the Lady Anne; she was uncommon good to my wife in the winter.'

'Then mount this horse, my friend; your neck will be quite safe. Ride to the Doctor's and ask him to come instantly; then go on to the Hall; tell them all that you know, and bid them send me the carriage with Lady Anne's maid and other assistance. I shall stay here.'

'All right, sir, I'll do my best, and I pray God the dear young lady may open her eyes soon.' Then, seeing the other man, he called out: 'Here, Joe, run for some water, and tell my missis to come as quickly as she can to the Lady Anne.'

He then somehow scrambled into the saddle, and with a 'Gee up!' and a clap on my sides with both his legs, he started on his journey, making a little circuit to avoid the dyke. He had no whip, which seemed to trouble him, but my pace soon cured that difficulty, and he found the best thing he could do was to stick to the saddle, and hold me in, which he did manfully. I shook him as little as I could help, but once or twice on the rough ground he called out, 'Steady! Woah! Steady.' On the high-road we were all right; and at the Doctor's and at the Hall he did his errand like a good man and true. They asked him in to take a drop of something. 'No! no,' he said; 'I'll be back to 'em again by a short cut through the fields, and be there before the carriage.'

There was a great deal of hurry and excitement after the news became known. I was just turned into my box, the saddle and bridle were taken off, and a cloth thrown over me.

Ginger was saddled and sent off in great haste for Lord George, and I soon heard the carriage roll out of the yard.

It seemed a long time before Ginger came back and before we were left alone; and then she told me all that she had seen.

'I can't tell much,' she said; 'we went galloping nearly all the way, and got there just as the Doctor rode up. There was a woman sitting on the ground with the lady's head in her lap. The Doctor poured something into her mouth, but all that I heard was "She is not dead". Then I was led off by a man to a little distance. After a while the lady was taken to the carriage, and we came home together. I heard my master say to a gentleman who stopped him to enquire, that he hoped no bones were broken, but that she had not spoken yet.'

When Lord George took Ginger for hunting, York shook his head; he said it ought to be a steady hand to train a horse for the first season, and not a random rider like Lord George.

Ginger used to like it very much, but sometimes when she came back I could see that she had been very much strained, and now and then she gave a short cough. She had too much spirit to complain, but I could not help feeling anxious about her.

Two days after the accident Blantyre paid me a visit. He patted me and praised me very much, and told Lord George that he was sure the horse knew of Annie's danger as well as he did. 'I could not have held him in if I would,' said he; 'she ought never to ride any other horse.'

I found by their conversation that my young mistress was now out of danger and would soon be able to ride again. This was good news to me, and I looked forward to a happy life.

CHAPTER TWENTY-FIVE

Reuben Smith

I must now say a little about Reuben Smith, who was left in charge of the stables when York went to London. No one more thoroughly understood his business than he did, and when he was all right, there could not be a more faithful or valuable man. He was gentle and very clever in his management of horses, and could doctor them almost as well as a farrier, for he had lived two years with a veterinary surgeon. He was a first-rate driver, and could take a four-in-hand, or a tandem, as easily as a pair.

He was a handsome man, a good scholar, and had very pleasant manners. I believe everybody liked him; certainly the horses did. The only wonder was that he should be in an under situation, and not in the place of a head coachman like York: but he had one great fault – the love of drink. He was not like some men, always at it; he used to keep steady for weeks or months together; but then he would break out and have a 'bout' of it, as York called it, and be a disgrace to himself, a terror to his wife, and a nuisance to all that had to do with him. He was, however, so useful that two or three times York had hushed the matter up and kept it from the Earl's knowledge.

But one night, when Reuben had to drive a party home from a ball, he was so drunk that he could not hold the reins, and a gentleman of the party had to mount the box and drive the ladies home. Of course this could not be hidden. Reuben was at once dismissed, and his poor wife and little children had to turn out of the pretty cottage by the park gate and go where they could.

Old Max told me all this, for it happened a good while ago; but shortly before Ginger and I came Smith had been taken back again. York had interceded for him with the Earl, who is very kind-hearted, and the man had promised faithfully that he would never taste another drop as long as he lived there. Smith had kept his promise so well that York thought he might be safely trusted to fill his place whilst he was away; and he was so clever and honest that no one else seemed so well fitted for it.

It was now early in April, and the family was expected home some time in May. The light brougham was to be fresh done up, and as Colonel Blantyre was obliged to return to his regiment, it was arranged that Smith should drive him to the town in it, and then ride back; for this purpose he took the saddle with him, and I was chosen for the journey.

At the station the Colonel put some money into Smith's hand and bade him goodbye, saying: 'Take care of your young mistress, Reuben, and don't let Black Auster be hacked about by any random young prig that wants to ride him – keep him for the lady.'

We left the carriage at the maker's, and Smith drove me

to the 'White Lion', and ordered the ostler to feed me well and have me ready for him at four o'clock. A nail in one of my front shoes had started as I came along, but the ostler did not notice it till just about four o'clock. Smith did not come into the yard till five, and then he said he should not leave till six, as he had met with some old friends. The man then told him of the nail, and asked if he should have the shoe looked to.

'No,' said Smith, 'that will be all right till we get home.'

He spoke in a very loud, offhand way, and I thought it was very unlike him not to see about the shoe, as he was generally wonderfully particular about loose nails in our shoes. He came neither at six, seven, nor eight, and it was nearly nine o'clock before he called me; and then it was with a loud, rough voice. He seemed in a very bad temper and abused the ostler, though I could not tell what for.

The landlord stood at the door, and said, 'Have a care, Mr Smith!' but he answered angrily with an oath; and almost before he was out of the town he began to gallop, frequently giving me a sharp cut with his whip, though I was going at full speed. The moon had not yet risen, and it was very dark. Having been recently mended, the roads were stony, and going over them at this pace made my shoe looser, so that when we were near the turnpike gate it came off.

If Smith had been in his right senses, he would have been sensible of something wrong in my pace; but he was too madly drunk to notice anything.

Beyond the turnpike was a long piece of road, upon which some fresh stones had just been laid – large, sharp stones, over which no horse could be driven quickly without risk of danger. Over this road, with one shoe gone, I was forced to gallop at my utmost speed, my rider meanwhile cutting into me with his whip, and with wild curses urging me to go still faster. Of course my shoeless foot suffered dreadfully; the hoof was broken and split down to the quick, and the inside was terribly cut by the sharpness of the stones.

This could not go on; no horse could keep his footing under such circumstances as the pain was too great. I stumbled, and fell with violence on both my knees. Smith was flung off by my fall, and, owing to the speed at which I was going, he must have fallen with great force. I soon recovered my feet and limped to the side of the road, where it was free from stones.

The moon had just risen above the hedge, and by its light I could see Smith lying a few yards beyond me. After making one slight effort to rise, there was a heavy groan. He did not move. I could have groaned too, for I was suffering intense pain both from my foot and knees; but horses are used to bear their pain in silence. I uttered no sound, but stood there and listened.

One more heavy groan from Smith; but though he now lay in the full moonlight, I could see no motion. I could do nothing for him nor for myself. But, oh! how I listened for the sound of horse, or wheels, or footsteps. The road was not much frequented, and at this time of the night we might stay for hours before help came to us.

I stood watching and listening. It was a calm, sweet April night; there were no sounds except a few low notes of a nightingale; and nothing moved but the white clouds near the moon, and a brown owl that flitted over the hedge. It made me think of the summer nights long ago, when I used to lie beside my mother in the green, pleasant meadow at Farmer Grey's.

CHAPTER TWENTY-SIX

How it Ended

It must have been nearly midnight when I heard at a great distance the sound of a horse's feet. Sometimes the sound died away, then it grew clearer again and nearer. The road to Earlshall led through plantations that belonged to the Earl; the sound came in that direction, and I hoped it might be someone coming in search of us. As the sound came nearer and nearer, I was almost sure I could distinguish Ginger's step; a little nearer still, and I could tell she was in the dogcart. I neighed loudly, and was overjoyed to hear an answering neigh from Ginger and men's voices. They came slowly over the stones, and stopped at the dark figure that lay upon the ground.

One of the men jumped out, and stooped down over it. 'It is Reuben!' he said, 'and he does not stir.'

The other man followed and bent over him. 'He's dead,' he said; 'feel how cold his hands are.'

They raised him up, but there was no life, and his hair was soaked with blood. Laying him down again, they came and looked at me and saw my cut knees.

'Why, the horse has been down and has thrown him! Who would have thought the black horse would have done that? Nobody thought he could fall. Reuben must have been lying here for hours! Odd, too, that the horse has not moved from the place.'

Robert then attempted to lead me forward. I made a step, but almost fell again.

'Hallo! he's bad in his foot as well as his knees. Look

here – his hoof is cut all to pieces; he might well come down, poor fellow! I tell you what, Ned, I'm afraid it hasn't been all right with Reuben! Just think of him riding a horse over these stones without a shoe! Why, if he had been in his right senses, he would just as soon have tried to ride him over the moon. I'm afraid it has been the old thing over again.

'Poor Susan! she looked awfully pale when she came to my house to ask if he had come home. She made believe she was not a bit anxious, and talked of a lot of things that might have kept him. But for all that, she begged me to go and meet him. But what must we do? There's the horse to get home as well as the body – and that will be no easy matter.'

Then followed a conversation between them, till it was agreed that Robert, the groom, should lead me, and that Ned should take the body; it was a hard job to get it into the dog-cart, for there was no one to hold Ginger; but she knew as well as I did what was going on, and stood as still as a stone. I noticed that, because, if she had a fault, it was that she was impatient in standing.

Ned started off very slowly with his sad load, and Robert came and looked at my foot again; then he took his handkerchief and bound it closely round, and so led me home. I shall never forget that night walk; it was more than three miles. Robert led me on very slowly, and I limped and hobbled on as well as I could, suffering great pain. I am sure he was sorry for me, for he often patted and encouraged me, talking to me in a pleasant voice.

At last I reached my own box and had some corn; and after Robert had wrapped up my knees in wet cloths, he tied up my foot in a bran poultice to draw out the heat, and to cleanse it before the horse doctor saw it in the morning. Then I managed to get myself down on the straw and slept in spite of the pain.

The next day, after the farrier had examined my wounds, he said he hoped the joint was not injured, and if so, I should not be spoiled for work, but I should never lose the blemish. I believe they did the best to make a good cure, but it was a long and painful one. Proud flesh, as they called it, came up in my knees and was burnt out with caustic; and when at last my knees were healed, they put a blistering fluid over the front of both to bring off all the hair; they had some reason for this, and I suppose it was all right.

As Smith's death had been so sudden, and no one was there to see it, there was an inquest held. The landlord and ostler at the 'White Lion', with several other people, gave evidence that he was intoxicated when he started from the inn; the keeper of the toll-gate said he rode at a hard gallop through the gate; and my shoe was picked up amongst the stones; so the case was quite plain to them, and I was cleared of all blame.

Everybody pitied Susan; she was nearly out of her mind, and kept saying over and over again, 'Oh! he was so good – so good! It was all that cursed drink; why will they sell that cursed drink? Oh, Reuben, Reuben!' So she went on till after he was buried; and then, as she had no home or relations, she, with her six little children, were obliged once more to leave the pleasant home by the tall oak trees, and go into that great gloomy Union House.

CHAPTER TWENTY-SEVEN

Ruined, and Going Downhill

As soon as my knees were sufficiently healed, I was turned into a small meadow for a month or two. No other creature was there, and though I enjoyed the liberty and the sweet grass, yet I had been so long used to society that I felt very lonely. Ginger and I had become fast friends, and now I missed her company extremely.

I often neighed when I heard horses' feet passing in the road, but I seldom got an answer, till one morning the gate was opened, and who should come in but poor old Ginger! The man slipped off her halter and left her there. With a joyful whinny I trotted up to her; we were both glad to meet, but I soon found that it was not for our pleasure that she was brought to be with me. Her story would be too long to tell, but the end of it was that she had been ruined by hard riding, and was now turned off to see what rest would do.

Lord George was young and would take no warning. He was a hard rider, and would hurt whenever he could get a chance, quite careless of his horse. Soon after I left the stable there was a steeplechase, and he determined to ride. Though the groom told him the mare was a little strained, and was not fit for the race, he did not believe it, and on the day of the race he urged Ginger to keep up with the foremost riders. With her high spirit, she strained herself to the utmost and came in with the first three horses; but her wind was touched, beside which, he was too heavy for her, and her back was strained.

'And so,' she said, 'here we are, ruined in the prime of our youth and strength – you by a drunkard, and I by a fool; it is very hard.'

We both felt in ourselves that we were not what we had been. However, that did not spoil the pleasure we had in each other's company. We did not gallop about as we once did, but we used to feed and lie down together, and stand for hours under one of the shady lime trees with our heads close to each other; and so we passed our time till the family returned from town.

One day we saw the Earl come into the meadow, and York was with him. Seeing who it was, we stood still under our lime tree, and let them come up to us. They examined us carefully. The Earl seemed much annoyed.

'There is three hundred pounds flung away for no earthly use,' said he; 'but what I care most for is, that these horses of my old friend, who thought they would have had a good home with me, are ruined. The mare shall have a twelvemonth's run, and we shall see what that will do for her; but the black one must be sold; 'tis a great pity, but I could not have knees like these in my stables.'

'No, my lord, of course not,' said York, 'but he might get a place where appearance is not of much consequence, and still be well treated. I know a man in Bath, the master of some livery stables, who often wants a good horse at a low figure; I know he looks well after his horses. The inquest cleared the horse's character, and your lordship's recommendation or mine would be sufficient warrant for him.'

'You had better write to him, York. I should be more particular about the place than the money he would fetch.'

After this they left us.

'They'll soon take you away,' said Ginger, 'and I shall lose the only friend I have, and most likely we shall never see each other again. 'Tis a hard world!'

About a week after this, Robert came into the field with a

halter, which he slipped over my head and led me away. There was no leave-taking of Ginger; we neighed to each other as I was led off, and she trotted anxiously along by the hedge, calling to me as long as she could hear the sound of my feet.

Through the recommendation of York, I was bought by the master of the livery stables. I had to go by train, a new experience to me, requiring a good deal of courage the first time; but as I found the puffing, rushing, whistling, and more than all, the trembling of the horse-box in which I stood did me no real harm, I soon took it quietly.

When I reached the end of my journey, I found myself in a tolerably comfortable stable and well attended to. These stables were not so airy and pleasant as those I had been used to. The stalls were laid on a slope instead of being level, and as my head was kept tied to the manger, I was obliged always to stand on the slope, which was very fatiguing. Men do not seem to know yet that horses can do more work if they can stand comfortably and can turn about.

However, I was well fed and well cleaned, and, on the whole, I think our master took as much care of us as he could. He kept a good many horses and carriages of different kinds, for hire. Sometimes his own men drove them; at others the horse and chaise were let to gentlemen or ladies who drove themselves.

CHAPTER TWENTY-EIGHT

A Job Horse and his Drivers

Hitherto I had always been driven by people who at least knew how to drive; but in this place I was to get my experience of all the different kinds of bad and ignorant driving to which we horses are subjected; for I was a 'job-horse', and was let out to all sorts of people who wished to hire me; and as I was good-tempered and gentle, I think I was more often let out to the ignorant drivers than some of the other horses, because I could be depended upon. It would take a long time to tell of all the different styles in which I was driven, but I will mention a few of them.

First, there were the tight-rein drivers – men who seemed to think that all depended on holding the reins as hard as they could, never relaxing the pull on the horse's mouth or giving him the least liberty of movement. These are always talking about 'keeping the horse well in hand', and 'holding a horse up', just as if a horse was not made to hold himself up.

Some poor broken-down horses, whose mouths have been made hard and insensible by just such drivers as these, may, perhaps, find some support in it; but for a horse who can depend upon its own legs, has a tender mouth, and is easily guided, it is not only tormenting, but stupid.

Then there are the loose-rein drivers, who let the reins lie easily on our backs and their own hand rest lazily on their knees. Of course, such gentlemen have no control over a horse, if anything happens suddenly. If a horse shies, starts, or stumbles, they are nowhere, and cannot help the horse or themselves till the mischief is done.

Of course, for myself, I had no objection to it, as I was not in the habit either of starting or stumbling, and had only been used to depend on my driver for guidance and encouragement; still, one likes to feel the rein a little in going downhill, and likes to know that one's driver is not gone to sleep.

Besides, a slovenly way of driving gets a horse into bad, and often lazy, habits; and when he changes hands he has to be whipped out of them with more or less pain and trouble. Squire Gordon always kept us to our best paces and our best manners. He said that spoiling a horse and letting him get into bad habits was just as cruel as spoiling a child, and both had to suffer for it afterwards.

Moreover, these drivers are often altogether careless, and will attend to anything else rather than to their horses. I went out in the phaeton one day with one of them; he had a lady and two children behind. He flopped the reins about as we started, and, of course, gave me several unmeaning cuts with the whip, though I was fairly off. There had been a good deal of road-mending going on, and even where the stones were not freshly laid down there were a great many loose ones about. My driver was laughing and joking with the lady and the children, and talking about the country to the right and to the left; but he never thought it worth while to keep an eye on his horse, or to drive on the smoothest parts of the road; and so it easily happened that I got a stone in one of my forefeet.

Now, if Mr Gordon or John, or, in fact, any good driver had been there, he would have seen that something was wrong before I had gone three paces. Or, even if it had been dark, a practised hand would have felt by the rein that there was something wrong in the step, and would have got down and picked out the stone. But this man went on laughing and talking, whilst at every step the stone became more firmly wedged between my shoe and the frog of my foot. The stone was sharp on the inside and round on the outside, which, as everyone knows, is the most dangerous kind that a horse can pick up, as it cuts his foot and at the same time makes him most liable to stumble and fall.

Whether the man was partly blind or only very careless I can't say; but he drove me with that stone in my foot for a good half-mile before he saw anything was wrong. By that time I was going so lame with the pain that at last he saw it, and called out, 'Well, here's a go! Why, they have sent us out with a lame horse! What a shame!'

He then jerked the reins and flipped about with the whip, saying, 'Now, then, it's no use playing the old soldier with me; there's the journey to go, and it's no use turning lame and lazy.'

Just at this time a farmer came riding up on a brown cob; he lifted his hat and pulled up.

'I beg your pardon, sir,' he said, 'but I think there is something the matter with your horse; he goes very much as if he had a stone in his shoe. If you will allow me, I will look at his feet; these loose, scattered stones are very dangerous things for the horses.'

'He's a hired horse,' said the driver. 'I don't know what's the matter with him, but it's a great shame to send out a lame beast like this.'

The farmer dismounted, and, slipping his rein over his arm, at once took up my near foot.

'Bless me, there's a stone. Lame! I should think so!'

At first he tried to dislodge it with his hand, but as it was now very tightly wedged, he drew a stonepick out of his pocket, and very carefully, and with some trouble, got it out. Then, holding it up, he said, 'There, that's the stone your horse has picked up; it is a wonder he did not fall down and break his knees into the bargain!'

'Well, to be sure!' said my driver. 'That is a queer thing!

I never knew before that horses picked up stones.'

'Didn't you?' said the farmer rather contemptuously; 'but they do, though, and the best of them will do it, and can't help it sometimes on such roads as these. And if you don't want to lame your horse, you must look sharp and get them out quickly. This foot is very much bruised,' he said, setting it gently down and patting me. 'If I may advise, sir, you had better drive him gently for a while; the foot is a good deal hurt, and the lameness will not go off directly.'

Then, mounting his cob, and raising his hat to the lady, he drove off.

When he was gone, my driver began to flop the reins about and whip the harness, by which I understood that I was to go on, which of course I did, glad that the stone was gone, but still in a good deal of pain.

This was the sort of experience we job-horses often had.

CHAPTER TWENTY-NINE

Cockneys

Then there is the steam-engine style of driving; these drivers were mostly people from towns, who never had a horse of their own, and generally travelled by rail.

They always seemed to think that a horse was something like a steam engine, only smaller. At any rate, they think that if only they pay for it, a horse is bound to go just as far, and just as fast, and with just as heavy a load, as they please. And be the roads heavy and muddy, or dry and good, be they stony or smooth, uphill or downhill, it is all the same – on, on, on, one must go at the same pace, with no relief and no consideration.

These people never think of getting out to walk up a steep hill. Oh, no, they have paid to ride, and ride they will! The horse? Oh, he's used to it! What were horses made for, if not to drag people uphill? Walk! A good joke, indeed! And so the whip is plied and the rein is jerked, and often a rough, scolding voice cries out, 'Go along, you lazy beast!' And then comes another slash of the whip, when all the time we are doing our very best to get along, uncomplaining and obedient, though often sorely harassed and down-hearted.

This steam-engine style of driving wears us up faster than any other kind. I would far rather go twenty miles with a good, considerate driver than ten with some of these; it would take less out of me.

Another thing – they scarcely ever put on the drag, however steep the hill may be, and thus bad accidents sometimes happen; or if they do put it on, they often forget to take it off at the bottom of the hill; and more than once I have had to pull half-way up the next hill with one of the wheels lodged fast in the dragshoe before my driver chose to think about it; and that is a terrible strain on a horse.

Then these Cockneys, instead of starting at an easy pace as a gentleman would do, generally set off at full speed from the very stable yard; and when they want to stop, they first whip us and then pull up so suddenly that we are nearly thrown on our haunches, and our mouths are jagged with the bit; they call that pulling up with a dash! And when they turn a corner they do it as sharply as if there was no right side or wrong side of the road.

I well remember one spring evening. Rory and I had been out for the day (Rory was the horse that mostly went with me when a pair was ordered, and a good honest fellow he was). We had our own driver, and, as he was always considerate and gentle with us, we had a very pleasant day. About twilight we were coming home at a good smart pace.

Our road turned sharp to the left; but as we were close to the hedge on our own side, and there was plenty of room to pass, our driver did not pull us in. As we neared the corner I heard a horse and two wheels coming rapidly down the hill towards us. The hedge was high, and I could see nothing; but the next moment we were upon each other. Happily for me, I was on the side next the hedge. Rory was on the right side of the pole, and had not even a shaft to protect him.

The man who was driving was making straight for the corner, and when he came in sight of us he had no time to pull over to his own side. The whole shock came upon Rory. The gig shaft ran right into his chest, making him stagger back with a cry that I shall never forget. The other horse was thrown upon its haunches, and one shaft broken. It turned out that it was a horse from our own stables, with the high-wheeled gig that the young men were so fond of.

The driver was one of those random, ignorant fellows who don't even know which is their own side of the road, or, if they know, don't care. And there was poor Rory, with his flesh torn open and bleeding and the blood streaming down. They said if it had been a little more to one side, it would have killed him; and a good thing for him, poor fellow, if it had.

As it was, it was a long time before the wound healed, and then he was sold for coal carting; and what that is, up and down those steep hills, only horses know. Some of the sights I saw there, where a horse had to come downhill with a heavily loaded two-wheel cart behind him, on which no drag could be placed, make me sad even now to think of.

After Rory was disabled I often went in the carriage with a mare named Peggy, who stood in the stall next to mine. She was a strong, well-made animal, of a bright dun colour, beautifully dappled, and with a dark-brown mane and tail. There was no high-breeding about her, but she was very pretty, and remarkably sweet-tempered and willing. Still, there was an anxious look about her eye, by which I knew that she had some trouble. The first time we went out together I thought she had a very odd pace; she seemed to go partly in a trot, partly in a canter – three or four paces, and then to make a little jump forward.

It was very unpleasant for any horse who pulled with her, and made me quite fidgety. When we got home, I asked her what made her go in that odd, awkward way.

'Ah,' she said in a troubled manner, 'I know my paces are very bad, but what can I do? It really is not my fault, it is just because my legs are so short. I stand nearly as high as you, but your legs are a good three inches longer above your knees than mine, and of course you can take a much longer step, and go much faster. You see, I did not make myself; I wish I could have done so, I would have had long legs then; all my troubles come from my short legs,' said Peggy, in a desponding tone.

'But how is it,' I said, 'when you are so strong and good-tempered and willing?'

'Why, you see,' said she, 'men will go so fast, and if one can't keep up to other horses, it is nothing but whip, whip, whip, all the time. And so I have had to keep up as I could, and have got into this ugly, shuffling pace. It was not always so; when I lived with my first master I always went a good regular trot, but then he was not in such a hurry. He was a young clergyman in the country, and a good, kind master he was. He had two churches a good way apart, and a great deal of work, but he never scolded or whipped me for not going faster. He was very fond of me. I only wish I was with him now; but he had to leave and go to a large town, and then I was sold to a farmer.

'Some farmers, you know, are capital masters; but I think this one was a low sort of man. He cared nothing about good horses or good driving; he only cared for going fast. I went as fast as I could, but that would not do, and he was always whipping; so I got into this way of making a spring forward to keep up. On market nights he used to stay very late at the inn, and then drive home at a gallop.

'One dark night he was galloping home as usual, when all on a sudden the wheel came against some great, heavy thing in the road, and turned the gig over in a minute. He was thrown out and his arm broken, and some of his ribs, I think. At any rate, it was the end of my living with him, and I was not sorry. But you see it will be the same everywhere for me, if men *must* go so fast. I wish my legs were longer!'

Poor Peggy! I was very sorry for her, and I could not comfort her, for I knew how hard it was upon slow-paced horses to be put with fast ones; all the whipping comes to their share, and they can't help it.

She was often used in the phaeton, and was very much liked by some of the ladies, because she was so gentle; and some time after this she was sold to two ladies who drove themselves, and wanted a safe, good horse.

I met her several times out in the country, going a good, steady pace, and looking as gay and contented as a horse could be. I was very glad to see her, for she deserved a good place.

After she left us, another horse came in her stead. He was young, and had a bad name for shying and starting, by which he had lost a good place. I asked him what made him shy.

'Well, I hardly know,' he said. 'I was timid when I was young, and several times was a good deal frightened. If I saw anything strange, I used to turn and look at it – you see, with our blinkers one can't see or understand what a thing is unless one looks round – and then my master always gave me a whipping, which, of course, made me start on and did not make me less afraid. I think if he would have let me just look at things quietly to see that there was nothing to hurt me, it would have been all right and I should have got used to them.

'One day an old gentleman was riding with him, and a large piece of white paper or rag blew across just on one side of me. I shied and started forward – my master as usual whipped me smartly, but the old man cried out, "You're wrong! you're wrong! You should never whip a horse for shying: he shies because he is frightened, and you only frighten him more, and make the habit worse." So I suppose all men don't do so.

'I am sure I don't want to shy for the sake of it, but how should one know what is dangerous and what is not if one is never allowed to get used to anything? I am never afraid of what I know. Now I was brought up in a park where there were deer. Of course, I knew them as well as I did a sheep or a cow; but they are not common, and I know many sensible horses who are frightened at them and kick up quite a shindy before they will pass a paddock where there are deer.'

I knew what my companion said was true, and I wished that every young horse had as good masters as Farmer Grey and Squire Gordon.

Of course we sometimes came in for good driving here. I remember one morning I was put into the light gig, and taken to a house in Pulteney Street. Two gentlemen came out; the taller of them came round to my head. He looked at the bit and bridle, and just shifted the collar with his hand, to see if it fitted comfortably.

'Do you consider this horse wants a curb?' he said to the ostler.

'Well,' said the man, 'I should say he would go just as well without, for he has an uncommonly good mouth, and though he has a fine spirit, he has no vice; but we generally find people like the curb.'

'I don't like it,' said the gentleman; 'be so good as to take it off, and put the rein in at the cheek. An easy mouth is a great thing on a long journey, is it not, old fellow?' he said, patting my neck.

Then he took the reins, and they both got up. I can remember now how quietly he turned me round, and then with a light feel of the rein, and a gentle drawing of the whip across my back, we were off.

I arched my neck and set off at my best pace. I found I had someone behind me who knew how a good horse ought to be driven. It seemed like old times again, and made me feel quite gay.

This gentleman took a great liking to me, and after trying me several times with the saddle, he prevailed upon my master to sell me to a friend of his who wanted a safe, pleasant horse for riding. And so it came to pass that in the summer I was sold to Mr Barry.

CHAPTER THIRTY

A Thief

My new master was an unmarried man. He lived at Bath, and was much engaged in business. His doctor advised him to take horse exercise, and for this purpose he bought me. He hired a stable a short distance from his lodgings, and engaged a man named Filcher as groom. My master knew very little about horses, but he treated me well, and I should have had a good and easy place but for circumstances of which he was ignorant. He ordered the best hay, with plenty of oats, crushed beans, and bran, with vetches or rye grass, as the man might think needful. I heard the master give the order, so I knew there was plenty of good food, and

I thought I was well off.

For a few days all went on well; I found that my groom understood his business. He kept the stable clean and airy, groomed me thoroughly, and was never otherwise than gentle. He had been an ostler in one of the great hotels in Bath. This he had given up, and now cultivated fruit and vegetables for the market; and his wife reared and fattened poultry and rabbits for sale.

After a while it seemed to me that my oats became very short. I had the beans, but bran was mixed with them with a few oats, certainly there were not more than a quarter of the oats there should have been. In two or three weeks this began to tell upon my strength and spirits. The grass food, though very good, was not the thing without corn to keep up my condition. However, I could not complain nor make known my wants. So it went on for about two months; and I wondered my master did not see that something was the matter.

However, one afternoon he rode out into the country to see a friend of his – a gentleman farmer who lived on the road to Wells. This gentleman had a very quick eye for horses; and after he had welcomed his friend, casting his eye over me, he said:

'It seems to me, Barry, that your horse does not look so well as he did when you first had him: has he been well?'

'Yes, I believe so,' said my master, 'but he is not nearly so lively as he was. My groom tells me that horses are always dull and weak in the autumn, and that I must expect it.'

'Autumn! fiddlestick!' said the farmer; 'why, this is only August; and with your light work and good food, he ought not to go down like this, even if it were autumn. How do you feed him?'

My master told him. The other shook his head slowly, and began to feel me over.

'I can't say who eats your corn, my dear fellow, but I am

much mistaken if your horse gets it. Have you ridden very fast?'

'No, very gently.'

'Then just put your hand here,' said he, passing his hand over my neck and shoulders; 'he is as warm and damp as a horse just come up from grass. I advise you to look into your stable a little more. I hate to be suspicious, and, thank Heaven, I have no cause to be, for I can trust my men, present or absent; but there are mean scoundrels wicked enough to rob a dumb beast of his food. You must look into it.' And turning to his man who had come to take me, 'Give this horse a good feed of bruised oats, and don't stint him.'

'Dumb beasts!' yes, we are; but if I could have spoken, I could have told my master where his oats went to. My groom used to come every morning about six o'clock with a little boy, who always had a covered basket with him. The boy used to go with his father into the harness-room where the corn was kept, and I could see them, when the door stood ajar, fill a little bag with oats out of the bin, and then the boy used to be off.

Five or six mornings after this, just as the boy had left the stable, the door was pushed open and a policeman walked in, holding the child tight by the arm. Another policeman followed, and locked the door on the inside, saying, 'Show me the place where your father keeps his rabbits' food.'

The boy looked very frightened and began to cry; but there was no escape, and he led the way to the corn-bin. Here the policeman found another empty bag like that which was found full of oats in the boy's basket.

Filcher was cleaning my feet at the time, but they soon saw him, and though he blustered a good deal, they walked him off to the 'lock-up', and his boy with him. I heard afterwards that the boy was not held to be guilty, but the man was sentenced to prison for two months.

CHAPTER THIRTY-ONE

A Humbug

My master was not immediately suited, but in a few days my new groom came. He was a tall, good-looking fellow enough; but if ever there was a humbug in the shape of a groom, Alfred Smirk was the man. He was very civil to me, and never used me ill; in fact, he did a great deal of stroking and patting, when his master was there to see it. To make me look smart he always brushed my mane and tail with water, and my hoofs with oil, before he brought me to the door, but as to clearing my feet, looking to my shoes, or grooming me thoroughly, he thought no more of these than if I had been a cow. He left my bit rusty, my saddle damp, and my crupper stiff.

Alfred Smirk considered himself very handsome; he spent a great deal of time before a little looking-glass in the harness-room, attending to his hair, whiskers, and necktie. When his master was speaking to him, it was always, 'Yes, sir; yes, sir,' touching his hat at every word; and everyone thought he was a very nice young man, and that Mr Barry was very fortunate to meet with him. I should say he was the laziest, most conceited fellow I ever came near.

Of course it was a great thing not to be ill-used, but then a horse wants more than that. I had a loose-box, and might have been very comfortable if he had not been too indolent to clean it out. He never took all the straw away, and the smell from what lay underneath was very bad, while the strong vapours that rose up from it made my eyes smart and inflame, and I had not the same appetite for my food.

One day my master came in and said, 'Alfred, the stable smells rather strong; should you not give that stall a good scrub, and throw down plenty of water?'

'Well, sir,' he said, touching his cap, 'I'll do so if you please, sir, but it is rather dangerous, sir, throwing down water in a horse's box; horses are very apt to take cold, sir. I should not like to do him an injury, but I'll do it if you please, sir.'

'Well,' said his master, 'I should not like him to take cold, but I don't like the smell of this stable; do you think the drains are all right.'

'Well, sir, now you mention it, I think the drain does sometimes send back a smell; there may be something wrong, sir.'

'Then send for the bricklayer and have it seen to,' said his master.

'Yes, sir, I will.'

The bricklayer came and pulled up a great many bricks, and found nothing amiss; so he put down some lime and charged the master five shillings; but the smell in my box was as bad as ever. This was not all. Standing as I did on a quantity of moist straw, my feet grew unhealthy and tender, and the master used to say:

'I don't know what is the matter with this horse, he goes very fumble-footed. I am sometimes afraid he will stumble.'

'Yes, sir,' said Alfred, 'I have noticed the same myself, when I have exercised him.'

Now the fact was that he hardly ever did exercise me, and when the master was busy, I often stood for days together without stretching my legs at all, and yet was fed just as high as if I were at hard work. This often disordered my health, and made me sometimes heavy and dull, but more often restless and feverish.

He never even gave me a meal of green meat or a bran

mash, which would have cooled me, for he was altogether as ignorant as he was conceited; and then, instead of exercise or change of food, I had to take horse balls and draughts; which, beside the nuisance of having them poured down my throat, used to make me feel ill and uncomfortable.

One day my feet were so tender that, trotting over some fresh stones with my master on my back, I made two such serious stumbles that as we came down Lansdown into the city, master stopped at the farrier's and asked him to see what was the matter with me. The man took up my feet one by one and examined them; then standing up and dusting his hands one against the other, he said –

'Your horse has got the "thrush", and badly too; his feet are very tender; it is fortunate that he has not been down. I wonder your groom has not seen to it before. This is the sort of thing we find in foul stables where the litter is never properly cleared out. If you will send him here tomorrow I will attend to the hoof, and I will direct your man how to apply some liniment which I will give him.'

The next day I had my feet thoroughly cleansed and stuffed with tow soaked in some strong lotion, and a very unpleasant business it was.

The farrier ordered all the litter to be taken out of my box day by day, and the floor to be kept very clean. Then I was to have bran mashes, a little green meat, and not so much corn, till my feet were well again. With this treatment I soon regained my spirits, but Mr Barry was so much disgusted at being twice deceived by his grooms that he determined to give up keeping a horse and to hire when he wanted one. I was therefore kept till my feet were quite sound, and was then sold again.

CHAPTER THIRTY-TWO

A Horse Fair

No doubt a horse fair is a very amusing place to those who have nothing to lose; at any rate, there is plenty to see – long strings of young horses out of the country, fresh from the marshes; droves of shaggy little Welsh ponies, no higher than Merrylegs; hundreds of cart horses of all sorts, some of them with their long tails braided up and tied with scarlet cord; and a good many, like myself, handsome and high-bred, but fallen into the middle class through some accident or blemish, unsoundness of wind, or some other complaint.

There were some splendid animals quite in their prime and fit for anything, who were throwing out their legs and showing off their paces in high style as they were trotted out with a leading rein, the groom running by the side. But round in the background were a number of poor things, sadly broken down with hard work, their knees knuckling over, and their hind legs swinging out at every step; some were very dejected-looking old horses, with the upper lip hanging down and the ears laying back heavily, as if there was no pleasure in life and no more hope; again, some were so thin you could see all their ribs; and some had old sores on their backs and hips. These were sad sights for a horse who knows not but that he may come to the same sad state.

There was a great deal of bargaining, running up and beating down; and if a horse may speak his mind so far as he understands, I should say there were more lies told and more trickery carried on at that horse fair than a clever man could give an account of. I was put with two or three other strong, useful-looking horses, and a good many people came to look at us. The gentlemen always turned from me when they saw my broken knees, though the man who had me swore it was only a slip in the stall.

To examine me, buyers began to pull my mouth open, then to look at my eyes, next to feel all the way down my legs, and to give me a hard feel of the skin and flesh, and, lastly, to try my paces. What a difference there was in the way these things were done! Some did it in a rough, offhand way, as if one was only a piece of wood; while others would take their hands gently over one's body, with a pat now and then, as much as to say, 'By your leave.' Of course, I judged the buyers a good deal by their manners to myself.

There was one man of whom I thought that if he would buy me I should be happy. He was not a gentleman, nor yet one of the loud, flashy sort that called themselves so. He was a rather small man, but well made, and quick in all his motions. I knew in a moment by the way he handled me that he was used to horses; he spoke gently, and his grey eye had a kindly, cheery look in it. It may seem strange – but it is true all the same – that the clean, fresh smell there was about him made me take to him. There was no smell of old beer and tobacco, which I hated, but a fresh smell as if he had come out of a hay-loft. He offered twenty-three pounds for me; but that was refused, and he walked away. I looked after him, but he was gone.

A very hard-looking, loud-voiced man came next. I was dreadfully afraid he would have me; but he walked off. One or two more came who did not mean business. Then the hard-faced man came back again and offered twenty-three pounds. A very close bargain was being driven, for my salesman began to think he should not get all he asked, and must come down; but just then the grey-eyed man came back again. I could not help reaching out my head towards him. He stroked my face kindly.

'Well, old chap,' he said, 'I think we should suit each other. I'll give twenty-four for him.'

'Say twenty-five and you shall have him.'

'Twenty-four ten,' said my friend, in a very decided tone, 'and not another sixpence – yes or no?'

'Done,' said the salesman, 'and you may depend upon it there's a monstrous deal of quality in that horse, and if you want him for cab work, he's a bargain.'

The money was paid on the spot, and my new master took my halter and led me out of the fair to an inn, where he had a saddle and bridle ready. He gave me a good feed of oats, and stood by whilst I ate it, talking to himself and talking to me. Half an hour after we were on our way to London, through pleasant lanes and country roads, until we came into the great London thoroughfare, on which we travelled steadily till in the twilight we reached the great City. The gas lamps were already lighted; there were streets to the right, streets to the left, and streets crossing each other for mile upon mile. I thought we should never come to the end of them. At last, in passing through one, we came to a long cab-stand, when my rider called out in a cheery voice, 'Good-night, Governor!'

'Halloo!' cried a voice, 'have you got a good one?'

'I think so,' replied my owner.

'I wish you luck with him.'

'Thank ye, Governor'; and he rode on. We soon turned up one of the side streets, and about half-way up turned again into a very narrow one, with rather poor-looking houses on one side and what seemed to be coach-houses and stables on the other.

My owner pulled up at one of the houses and whistled. The door flew open, and a young woman, followed by a little girl and boy, ran out. There was a very lively greeting as my rider dismounted.

'Now then, Harry, my boy, open the gates, and mother will bring us the lantern.'

The next minute they were all standing round me in a small stable yard.

'Is he gentle, father?'

'Yes, Dolly, as gentle as your own kitten; come and pat him.'

At once the little hand was patting about fearlessly all over my shoulder. How good it felt !

'Let me get him a bran mash while you rub him down,' said the mother.

'Do, Polly, it's just what he wants, and I know you've got a beautiful mash ready for me.'

'Sausage dumpling and apple turnover,' shouted the boy: this set them all laughing. I was led into a comfortable, clean-smelling stall with plenty of dry straw, and, after a capital supper, I lay down, thinking I was going to be happy.

CHAPTER THIRTY-THREE

A London Cab Horse

My new master's name was Jeremiah Barker, but as everyone called him Jerry, I shall do the same. Polly, his wife, was just as good a match as a man could have. She was a plump, trim, tidy little woman, with smooth, dark hair, dark eyes, and a merry little mouth. The boy was nearly twelve years old – a tall, frank, good-tempered lad; and little Dorothy (Dolly they called her) was her mother over again at eight years old. They were all wonderfully fond of each other; I never, before or since, knew such a happy, merry family.

Jerry had a cab of his own and two horses, which he drove and attended to himself. His other horse was a tall, white, rather large-boned animal, called Captain. He was old now, but when he was young he must have been splendid; there was still the proud way of holding his head and arching his neck; in fact, he was a high-bred, fine-mannered, noble old horse, every inch of him.

He told me that in his early youth he went to the Crimean War, for he belonged to an officer in the cavalry, and used to lead the regiment: I will tell more of that hereafter.

The next morning, when I was well groomed, Polly and Dolly came into the yard to see me and to make friends. Harry had been helping his father since the early morning, and had stated his opinion that I should turn out 'a regular brick.' Polly brought me a slice of apple, and Dolly a piece of bread, and they made as much of me as if I had been the 'Black Beauty' of olden time. To be petted again and talked to in a gentle voice was a great treat; and I let them see as well as I could that I wished to be friendly. Polly thought I was very handsome and a great deal too good for a cab, if it was not for the broken knees.

'Of course, there's no one to tell us whose fault that was,' said Jerry, 'and as long as I don't know, I shall give him the benefit of the doubt; for a firmer, neater stepper I never rode. We'll call him "Jack", after the old one – shall we, Polly?'

'Do,' she said, 'for I like to keep a good name going.'

Captain went out in the cab all the morning. Harry came in after school to feed me and give me water. In the afternoon I was put into the cab. Jerry took as much pains to see if the collar and bridle fitted comfortably as if he had been John Manly over again. When the crupper was let out a hole or two, it all fitted well. There was no bearing rein or curb, nothing but a plain ring snaffle.

What a blessing that was!

After driving through the side street we came to the large cab-stand where Jerry had said 'Good-night'. On one side of this wide street were high houses with wonderful shop fronts, and on the other was an old church and churchyard surrounded by iron palisades. Alongside these iron rails a number of cabs were drawn up, waiting for passengers. Bits of hay were lying about on the ground. Some of the men were standing together talking; others were sitting on their boxes reading the newspaper; and one or two were feeding their horses with bits of hay and a drink of water. We pulled up in the rank at the back of the last cab. Two or three men came round and began to look at me and to pass their remarks.

'Very good for a funeral,' said one.

'Too smart-looking,' said another, shaking his head in a very wise way; 'you'll find out something wrong one of these fine mornings, or my name isn't Jones.'

'Well,' said Jerry pleasantly, 'I suppose I need not find it out till it finds me out, eh? and, if so, I'll keep up my spirits a little longer.'

Then came up a broad-faced man dressed in a great grey coat with great grey capes and great white buttons, a grey hat, and a blue comforter loosely tied round his neck. His hair was grey too, but he was a jolly-looking fellow, and the other men made way for him. He looked me all over, as if he had been going to buy me; and then, straightening himself up, he said with a grunt, 'He's the right sort for you, Jerry; I don't care what you gave for him, he'll be worth it.' Thus my character was established on the stand.

This man's name was Grant, but he was called 'Grey Grant', or 'Governor Grant'. He had been the longest of any of the men on that stand, and he took it upon himself to settle matters and stop disputes. He was generally a good-humoured, sensible man; but if his temper was a little out, as it was sometimes when he had drunk too much, nobody liked to come too near his fist, for he could deal a very hard blow.

The first week of my life as a cab horse was very trying; I had never been used to London, and the noise, the hurry, the crowds of horses, carts, and carriages through which I had to make my way, made me feel anxious and harassed; but I soon found that I could perfectly trust my driver, and then I made myself easy and got used to it

Jerry was as good a driver as I had ever known; and, what was better, he took as much thought for his horses as he did for himself. He soon found out that I was willing to work and to do my best; and he never laid the whip on me, unless it was to draw the end of it gently over my back when I was to go on. Generally I knew this quite well by the way in which he took up the reins; and I believe his whip was more frequently stuck up by his side than in his hand.

In a short time my master and I understood each other as well as horse and man could do. In the stable, too, he did all that he could for our comfort. The stalls were of the old-fashioned style – too much on the slope; but he had two movable bars fixed across the back of our stalls, so that at night and when we were resting, he just took off our halters and put up the bars, and thus we could turn about and stand whichever way we pleased: this is a great comfort.

Jerry kept us very clean, and gave us as much change of food as he could, and always plenty of it; and not only that, but he always gave us plenty of clean fresh water, which he allowed to stand by us both night and day, except of course when we came in warm.

Some people say that a horse ought not to drink as much as he wishes; but I know if we are allowed to drink when we want it, we drink only a little at a time, and it does us a great deal more good than swallowing it down half a bucketful at a time, as we do if we have been left without water till we are thirsty and miserable.

Some grooms will go home to their beer and leave us for hours with our dry hay and oats, with nothing to moisten them; then, of course, we gulp down too much water at once, which helps to spoil our breathing and sometimes chills our stomachs.

But the best thing that we had here was our Sundays for rest. We worked so hard during the week that I do not think we could have kept up to it but for that day's rest; besides, we then had time to enjoy each other's company. It was on these days that I learned my companion's history.

CHAPTER THIRTY-FOUR

An Old War Horse

Captain had been broken in and trained for an army horse, his first owner being an officer of cavalry going out to the Crimean War. He said he quite enjoyed the training with all the other horses – trotting together, turning together to the right hand or the left, halting at the word of command, or dashing forward at full speed at the sound of the trumpet or signal of the officer. When young, he was a dark, dappled iron grey, and was considered very handsome. His master, a young, high-spirited gentleman, was very fond of him, and from the first treated him with the greatest care and kindness. He told me he thought the life of an army horse was very pleasant; but when it came to being sent abroad in a great ship over the sea, he almost changed his mind.

'That part of it,' he said, 'was dreadful! Of course we could not walk off the land into the ship; so they were obliged to put strong straps under our bodies, and then we were lifted off our legs in spite of our struggles, and were swung through the air, over the water, to the deck of the great vessel. There we were placed in small, close stalls, and never for a long time saw the sky, or were able to stretch our legs. The ship sometimes rolled about in high winds, and we were knocked about, and felt very ill. However, at last it came to an end, and we were hauled up, and swung over again to the land. We were very glad, and snorted and neighed for joy when we once more felt firm ground under our feet.

'We soon found that the country to which we had come was very different from our own, and that we had many hardships to endure besides the fighting; but many of the men were so fond of us that they did everything they could to make us comfortable, in spite of snow, wet, and the fact that all things were out of order.'

'But what about that fighting?' said I; 'was not that worse than anything else?'

'Well,' said he, 'I hardly know. We always liked to hear the trumpet sound, and to be called out, and were impatient to start off, though sometimes we had to stand for hours, waiting for the word of command. But when the word was given, we used to spring forward as gaily and eagerly as if there were no cannon-balls, bayonets, or bullets. I believe so long as we felt our rider firm in the saddle, and his hand steady on the bridle, not one of us gave way to fear, not even when the terrible bombshells whirled through the air and burst into a thousand pieces.

'With my noble master, I went into many actions without a wound; and though I saw horses shot down with bullets, others pierced through with lances or gashed with fearful sabre-cuts, though I left them dead on the field, or dying in the agony of their wounds, I don't think I feared for myself. My master's cheery voice as he encouraged his men made me feel as if he and I could not be killed. I had such perfect trust in him that whilst he was guiding me, I was ready to charge up to the very cannon's mouth.

'I saw many brave men cut down, and many fall from their saddles mortally wounded. I have heard the cries and groans of the dying, cantered over ground slippery with blood, and frequently had to turn aside to avoid trampling on wounded man or horse; but, until one dreadful day, I had never felt terror: that day I shall never forget.'

Here old Captain paused for a while and drew a long breath; I waited, and he went on.

'It was one autumn morning, and, as usual, an hour before daybreak our cavalry had turned out, ready caparisoned for the day's work, whether fighting or waiting. The men stood waiting by their horses, ready for orders. As the light increased, there seemed to be some excitement among the officers; and before the day was well begun, we heard the firing of the enemy's guns.

'Then one of the officers rode up and gave the word for the men to mount, and in a second every man was in his saddle, and every horse stood expecting the touch of the rein, or the pressure of his rider's heels – all animated, all eager. But still we had been trained so well, that, except by the champing of our bits, and by the restive tossing of our heads from time to time, it could not be said that we stirred.

'My dear master and I were at the head of the line, and as all sat motionless and watchful, he took a little stray lock of my mane which had turned over the wrong side, laid it over on the right and smoothed it down with his hand; then, patting my neck, he said, "We shall have a day of it today, Bayard, my beauty; but we'll do our duty as we always have done."

'That morning he stroked my neck more, I think, than he had ever done before; quietly on and on, as if he were thinking of something else. I loved to feel his hand on my neck, and arched my crest proudly and happily; but I stood very still, for I knew all his moods, and when he liked me to be quiet and when gay.

'I cannot tell all that happened that day, but I will tell of the last charge that we made together: it was across a valley right in front of the enemy's cannon. By this time we were well used to the roar of heavy guns, the rattle of musket fire, and the flying of shot near us; but never had I been under such a fire as we rode through that day. From right, left, and front, shot and shell poured in upon us. Many a brave man went down, many a horse fell, flinging his rider to the earth; many a horse without a rider ran wildly out of the ranks; then, terrified at being alone with no hand to guide him, came pressing in amongst his old companions, to gallop with them to the charge.

'Fearful as it was, no one stopped, no one turned back. Every moment the ranks were thinned, but as our comrades fell we closed in to keep the others together; and instead of being shaken or staggered in our pace, our gallop became faster and faster as we neared the cannon, all clouded in white smoke, while the red fire flashed through it.

'My master, my dear master, was cheering on his comrades, with his right arm raised on high, when one of the balls, whizzing close to my head, struck him. I felt him stagger with the shock, though he uttered no cry. I tried to check my speed, but the sword dropped from his right hand, the rein fell loose from the left, and sinking backward from the saddle, he fell to the earth; the other riders swept past us, and by the force of their charge I was driven from the spot where he fell.

'I wanted to keep my place at his side, and not to leave

him under that rush of horses' feet, but it was in vain. And now, without a master or a friend, I was alone on that great slaughter-ground. Then fear took hold of me, and I trembled as I had never trembled before. Then I, too, as I had seen other horses do, tried to join in the ranks and to gallop with them; but I was beaten off by the swords of the soldiers.

'Just then, a soldier whose horse had been killed under him caught at my bridle and mounted me, and with this new master I was again going forward. But our gallant company was cruelly overpowered, and those who remained alive after the fierce fight for the guns came galloping back over the same ground.

'Some of the horses had been so badly wounded that they could scarcely move from loss of blood; other noble creatures were trying on three legs to drag themselves along; and others were struggling to rise on their forefeet when their hind legs had been shattered by shot. Their groans were piteous to hear, and the beseeching look in their eyes as those who escaped passed by and left them to their fate I shall never forget. After the battle, the wounded men were brought in, and the dead were buried.'

'And what about the wounded horses?' I said; 'were they left to die?'

'No, the army farriers went over the field with their pistols, and shot all that were ruined. Some that had only slight wounds were brought back and attended to, but the greater part of the noble, willing creatures that went out that morning never came back! In our stables there was only about one in four that returned.

'I never saw my dear master again. I believe he fell dead from the saddle. Never did I love another master so well. I went into many other engagements, but was only once wounded, and then not seriously; and when the war was over, I came back again to England, as sound and strong as when I went out.'

I said, 'I have heard people talk about war as if it was a very fine thing.'

'Ah!' said he, 'I should think they have never seen it. No doubt it is very fine when there is no enemy, only just exercise, parade, and sham-fight. Yes, it is very fine then; but when thousands of good, brave men and horses are killed or crippled for life, then it has a very different look.'

'Do you know what they fought about?' said I.

'No,' he said, 'that is more than a horse can understand; but the enemy must have been awfully wicked people if it was right to go all that way over the sea on purpose to kill them.'

CHAPTER THIRTY-FIVE

Jerry Barker

I never knew a better man than my new master – kind and good, as strong for the right as John Manly, and so good-tempered and merry that very few people could pick a quarrel with him. He was very fond of making little songs, which he would sing to himself. His favourite was this:

> Come, father and mother,
> And sister and brother,
> Come, all of you, turn to
> And help one another.

And so they did; Harry was as clever at stable-work as a much older boy, and always wanted to do what he could. Then Polly and Dolly used to come in the morning to help with the cab – to brush and beat the cushions and rub the glass, while Jerry was giving us a cleaning in the yard and Harry was cleaning the harness. There used to be a great deal of laughing and fun between them, and it put Captain and me in much better spirits than if we had heard scolding and hard words. They were always early in the morning, for Jerry would say:

> If you in the morning
> Throw minutes away,
> You can't pick them up
>   In the course of the day.
> You may hurry and skurry,
>   And flurry and worry,
> You've lost them for ever,
>   For ever and ay.

He could not bear any careless loitering and waste of time; and nothing was so near making him angry as to find people who were always late wanting a cab horse to be driven hard to make up for their idleness.

One day two wild-looking young men came out of a tavern close by the stand, and called Jerry.

'Here, cabby! look sharp, we are rather late; put on the steam, will you, and take us to Victoria in time for the one o'clock train. You shall have a shilling extra.'

'I will take you at the regular pace, gentlemen; shillings don't pay for putting on the steam like that.'

Larry's cab was standing next to ours. He flung open the door and said, 'I'm your man, gentlemen! Take my cab, my horse will get you there all right'; and as he shut them in, with a wink towards Jerry, he said, 'It's against his conscience to go beyond a jog-trot.' Then, slashing his jaded horse, he set off as hard as he could. Jerry patted me on the neck – 'No, Jack, a shilling would not pay for that sort of thing, would it, old boy?'

Although Jerry was steadfastly set against hard driving to please careless people, he always went at a good fair pace, and was not against putting on the steam, as he said, if only he knew *why*.

I well remember one morning, as we were on the stand waiting for a fare, that a young man carrying a heavy portmanteau trod on a piece of orange-peel which lay on the pavement and fell down with great force.

Jerry was the first to run and lift him up. He seemed much stunned, and as they led him into a shop, he walked as if he were in great pain. Jerry, of course, came back to the stand, but in about ten minutes one of the shopmen called him, so he drew up to the pavement.

'Can you take me to the South-Eastern Railway?' said the young man. 'This unlucky fall has made me late, I fear; but it is of great importance that I should not lose the twelve o'clock train. I should be most thankful if you could get me there in time, and will gladly pay you an extra fare.'

'I'll do my very best,' said Jerry heartily, 'if you think you are well enough, sir,' for he looked dreadfully white and ill.

'I *must* go,' he said earnestly. 'Please open the door, and let us lose no time.'

The next minute Jerry was on the box. He gave a cheery chirrup to me, and a twitch to the rein that I well understood.

'Now then, Jack, my boy,' said he, 'spin along; we'll show them how we can get over the ground if we only know why.'

It is always difficult to drive fast in the city in the middle of the day, when the streets are full of traffic, but we did what could be done; and when a good driver and a good horse, who understand each other, are of one mind, it is wonderful what they can do. I had a very good mouth – that is, I could be guided by the slightest touch of the rein, and that is a great thing in London, amongst carriages, omnibuses, carts, vans, trucks, cabs, and great wagons creeping along at a walking pace; some going one way, some another, some going slowly, others wanting to pass them, omnibuses stopping short every few minutes to take up a passenger, obliging the horse that is coming behind to pull up too, or to pass and get before them: perhaps you try to pass, but just then something else comes dashing in through the narrow opening, and you have to keep in behind the omnibus again; presently you think you see a chance, and manage to get to the front, going so near the wheels on each side that half an inch nearer and they would scrape. Well, you get along for a bit, but soon find yourself in a long train of carts and carriages all obliged to go at a walk; perhaps you come to a regular block-up and have to stand still for minutes together, till something clears out into a side street, or the policeman interferes; you have to be ready for any chance – to dash forward if there be an opening, and be quick as a rat dog to see if there be room, and if there be time, lest you get your own wheels locked, or smashed, or the shaft of some other vehicle run into your chest or shoulder. All this is what you have to be ready for. If you want to get through London fast in the middle of the day, it wants a deal of practice.

Jerry and I were used to the thickest traffic, and no one could beat us at getting through when we were set on it. I was quick and bold, and could always trust my driver; Jerry was quick and patient at the same time, and could trust his horse, which was a great thing too. He very seldom used the whip; I knew by his voice and his click, click, when he wanted to get on fast, and the rein told me where I was to go, so there was no need for whipping.

The streets were very full that day, but we got on pretty well as far as the bottom of Cheapside, where there was a block for three or four minutes. The young man put his head out and said anxiously: 'I think I had better get out and walk; I shall never get there if this goes on.'

'I'll do all that can be done, sir,' said Jerry. 'I think we shall be in time; this block-up cannot last much longer, and your luggage is very heavy for you to carry, sir.'

Just then the cart in front of us began to move on, and then we had a good turn. In and out, in and out we went, as fast as horseflesh could do it, and for a wonder, we had a good clear time on London Bridge, for there was a whole train of cabs and carriages all going our way at a quick trot – perhaps wanting to catch that very train. At any rate, with many others, we whirled into the station just as the great clock pointed to eight minutes to twelve.

'Thank God! we are in time,' said the young man; 'and thank you, too, my friend, and your good horse. You have saved me more than money can ever pay for; take this extra half-crown.'

'No, sir, no, thank you all the same. So glad we hit the time, sir; but don't stay now, sir, the bell is ringing. Here, porter! take this gentleman's luggage – Dover line – twelve o'clock train – that's it'; and without waiting for another word, Jerry wheeled me round to make room for other cabs that were dashing up at the last minute, and draw up on one side till the crush was past.

'So glad!' he said, 'so glad! poor young fellow! I wonder what it was that made him so anxious.'

Jerry often talked to himself, quite loud enough for me to hear when we were not moving.

On Jerry's return to the rank there was a good deal of laughing and chaffing at him for driving hard to the train for an extra fare, as they said all against his principles; and they wanted to know how much he had pocketed.

'A good deal more than I generally get,' said he, nodding slyly; 'what he gave me will keep me in little comforts for several days.'

'Gammon!' said one.

'He's a humbug,' said another, 'preaching to us, and then doing the same himself.'

'Look here, mates,' said Jerry. 'The gentleman offered me half a crown extra, but I didn't take it; 'twas quite pay enough for me to see how glad he was to catch that train; and if Jack and I choose to have a quick run now and then to please ourselves, that's our business and not yours.'

'Well,' said Larry, '*you'll* never be a rich man.'

'Most likely not,' said Jerry, 'but I don't know that I shall be the less happy for that. I have heard the commandments read a great many times, and I never noticed that any of them said, "Thou shalt be rich"; and there are a good many curious things said in the New Testament about rich men that, I think, would make me feel rather queer if I was one of them.'

'If you ever do get rich,' said Governor Grant, looking over his shoulder across the top of his cab, 'you'll deserve it, Jerry, and you won't find a curse come with your wealth. As for you, Larry, you'll die poor, you spend too much in whipcord.'

'Well,' said Larry, 'what is a fellow to do if his horse won't go without it?'

'You never take the trouble to see if he will go without it; your whip is always going as if you had the St Vitus's dance in your arm; and if it does not wear you out, it wears your horse out. You know you are always changing your horses, and why? because you never give them any peace or encouragement.'

'Well, I have not had good luck,' said Larry, 'that's where it is.'

'And you never will,' said the Governor. 'Good Luck is rather particular with whom she rides, and mostly prefers those who have common sense and a good heart; at least, that is my experience.'

Governor Grant turned round again to his newspaper, and the other men went to their cabs.

CHAPTER THIRTY-SIX

The Sunday Cab

One morning, as Jerry had just put me into the shafts and was fastening the traces, a gentleman walked into the yard. 'Your servant, sir,' said Jerry.

'Good-morning, Mr Barker,' said the gentleman. 'I should be glad to make some arrangement with you for taking Mrs Briggs regularly to church on Sunday mornings. We go to the New Church now, and that is rather farther than she can walk.'

'Thank you, sir,' said Jerry, 'but I have only taken out a six days' licence, and therefore I could not take a fare on a Sunday, it would not be legal.'

'Oh!' said the other, 'I did not know yours was a six days' cab; but of course it would be very easy to alter your licence. I would see that you did not lose by it; the fact is, Mrs Briggs very much prefers you to drive her.'

'I should be glad to oblige the lady, sir, but I had a seven days' licence once, and the work was too hard for me and too hard for my horses. Year in and year out, not a day's rest, never a Sunday with my wife and children, and never able to go to a place of worship, which I had always been used to do before I took to the driving box; so for the last five years I have taken only a six days' licence, and I find it better all the way round.'

'Well, of course,' replied Mr Briggs, 'it is very proper that every person should have rest and be able to go to church on Sundays, but I should have thought you would not have minded such a short distance for the horse, and only once a day; you would have all the afternoon and evening for yourself, and we are very good customers, you know.'

'Yes, sir, that is true, and I'm grateful for all favours, I am sure, and anything that I could do to oblige you or the lady, I should be proud and happy to do; but I can't give up my Sundays, sir, indeed I can't. I read that God made man, and He made horses and all the other beasts; and as soon as he had made them, He made a day of rest, and bade that all should rest one day in seven. I think, sir, he must have known what was good for them, and I am sure it is good for me. I am stronger and healthier altogether now that I have a day of rest; the horses are fresh too, and do not wear up nearly so fast. The six-day drivers all tell me the same, and I have laid more money in the Savings Bank than ever I did before; and as for my wife and children, sir – why, heart alive! they would not go back to the seven days' work for all they could get by it.'

'Oh, very well,' said the gentleman. 'Don't trouble yourself, Mr Barker, any further; I will enquire somewhere else'; and he walked away.

'Well,' says Jerry to me, 'we can't help it, Jack, old boy, we must have our Sundays.'

'Polly!' he shouted, 'Polly! come here.'

She was there in a minute.

'What is it all about, Jerry?'

'Why, my dear, Mr Briggs wants me to take Mrs Briggs to church every Sunday morning. I said I had only a six days' licence. He said, "Get a seven days' licence, and I'll make it worth your while"; and you know, Polly, they are very good customers to us. Mrs Briggs often goes out shopping for hours, or makes calls, and then she pays down fair and honourable like a lady; there's no beating down, or making three hours into two hours and a half, as some folks do. Besides, it is easy work for the horses; not like tearing along to catch trains for people that are always a quarter of an hour too late. If I don't oblige her in this matter, it is very likely we shall lose them altogether. What do you say, little woman?'

'I say, Jerry,' says she, speaking very slowly, 'I say, if Mrs Briggs would give you a sovereign every Sunday morning, I would not have you a seven days' cabman again. We have known what it was to have no Sundays, and now we know what it is to call them our own. Thank God! you earn enough to keep us, though it is sometimes close work to pay for all the oats and hay, in addition to the licence and the rent.

'But Harry will soon be earning something, and I would rather struggle on harder than we do than go back to those horrid times when you hardly had a minute to look at your own children, and we never could go to a place of worship together, or have a happy, quiet day. God forbid that we should ever turn back to those times! that's what I say, Jerry.'

'And that is just what I told Mr Briggs, my dear,' said Jerry, 'and that is what I mean to stick to; so don't go and fret yourself, Polly' (for she had begun to cry); 'I would not go back to the old times if I earned twice as much; so that is settled, little woman. Now cheer up, and I'll be off to the stand.'

Three weeks had passed away after this conversation, and no order had come from Mrs Briggs; so there was nothing but taking jobs from the stand. Jerry took it to heart a good deal, for of course the work was harder for horse and man. But Polly would always cheer him up and say, 'Never mind, father, never mind –

> Do your best,
> And leave the rest,
> 'Twill all come right
> Some day or night.'

It soon became known that Jerry had lost his best customer, and for what reason; most of the men said he was a fool, but two or three took his part.

'If working men don't stick to their Sunday,' said Truman, 'they'll soon have none left; it is every man's right, and every beast's right. By God's law we have a day of rest, and by the law of England we have a day of rest, and I say we ought to hold to the rights these laws give us, and keep them for our children.'

'All very well for you religious chaps to talk so,' said Larry, 'but I'll turn a shilling when I can. I don't believe in religion, for I don't see that your religious people are any better than the rest.'

'If they are not better,' put in Jerry, 'it is because they are not religious. You might as well say that our country's laws are not good because some people break them. If a man gives way to his temper, and speaks evil of his neighbour, and does not pay his debts, he is *not* religious; I don't care how much he goes to church. If some men are shams and humbugs, that does not make religion untrue. Real religion is the best and the truest thing in the world, and the only thing that can make a man really happy, or make the world any better.'

'If religion was good for anything,' said Jones, 'it would prevent your religious people from making us work on Sundays as you know many of them do, and that's why I say religion is nothing but a sham – why, if it was not for the church and chapel goers it would be hardly worth while our coming out on a Sunday; but they have their privileges, as they call them, and I go without. I shall expect them to answer for my soul, if I can't get a chance of saving it.'

Several of the men applauded this, till Jerry said:

'That may sound well enough, but it won't do; every man must look after his own soul; you can't lay it down at another man's door like a foundling, and expect him to take care of it; and don't you see, if you are always sitting on your box, waiting for a fare, they will say, "If we don't take him, someone else will, and he does not look for any Sunday." Of course they don't go to the bottom of it, or they would see if they never came for a cab, it would be no use your standing there; but people don't always like to go to the bottom of things; it may not be convenient to do it; but if you Sunday drivers would all strike for a day of rest, the thing would be done.'

'And what would all the good people do if they could not get to their favourite preachers?' said Larry.

' 'Tis not for me to lay down plans for other people,' said Jerry, 'but if they can't walk so far, they can go to what is nearer; and if it should rain they can put on their mackintoshes as they do on a weekday. If a thing is right, it *can* be done, and if it is wrong, it *can be done without*; and a good man will find a way; and that is as true for us cabmen as it is for the church-goers.'

CHAPTER THIRTY-SEVEN

The Golden Rule

Two or three weeks after this, as we came into the yard rather late in the evening, Polly came running across the road with the lantern (she always brought it to him if it was not very wet).

'It has all come right, Jerry; Mrs Briggs sent her servant this afternoon, to ask you to take her out tomorrow at eleven o'clock. I said, yes, I thought you could, but we supposed she employed someone else now.

' "Well," says he, "the real fact is, master was put out because Mr Barker refused to come on Sundays, and he has been trying other cabs, but there's something wrong with them all; some drive too fast, and some too slow; and the mistress says there is not a cab so nice and clean as yours; so nothing will suit her but Mr Barker's cab again." '

Polly was almost out of breath, and Jerry broke out into a merry laugh:

> 'All will come right
> Some day or night.

You were right, my dear; you generally are. Run in and get the supper, and I'll have Jack's harness off and make him snug and happy in no time.'

After this Mrs Briggs wanted Jerry's cab quite as often as before; never, however, on a Sunday. But there came a day when we had Sunday work, and this was how it happened.

We had all come home on the Saturday night very tired, and very glad to think that the next day would be all rest; but it was not to be so.

On Sunday morning Jerry was cleaning me in the yard, when Polly stepped up to him, looking very full of something.

'What is it?' said Jerry.

'Well, my dear,' she said, 'poor Dinah Brown has just received a letter to say that her mother is dangerously ill, and that she must go directly if she wishes to see her alive. The place is more than ten miles away from here, right out in the country; and she says if she took the train she should still have four miles to walk; and so weak as she is, and the baby only four weeks old, of course that would be impossible. She wants to know if you would take her in your cab, and she promises to pay you faithfully as soon as she can get the money.'

'Tut, tut, we'll see about that. It was not the money I was thinking about, but of losing our Sunday; the horses are tired, and I am tired too – that's where it pinches.'

'It pinches all round, for that matter,' said Polly, 'for it's only half Sunday without you. But you know we should do to other people as we would like them to do to us. I know very well what I should like if my mother was dying; and Jerry, dear, I am sure it won't break the Sabbath; for if pulling a poor beast or donkey out of a pit would not spoil the Sabbath, I am quite sure taking poor Dinah would not.'

'Why, Polly, you are as good as the minister; so, as I've had my Sunday morning sermon early today, you may go and tell Dinah that I'll be ready for her as the clock strikes ten. But stop – just step round to Butcher Braydon's, with my compliments, and ask him if he would lend me his light trap; I know he never uses it on the Sunday, and it would make a wonderful difference to the horse.'

Away she went, and soon returned, saying that he could have the trap and welcome.

'All right,' said he; 'now put me up a bit of bread and cheese, and I'll be back in the afternoon as soon as I can.'

'And I'll have the meat pie ready for an early tea instead of for dinner,' said Polly. And away she went, whilst he made his preparations to the tune of 'Polly, the woman and no mistake', of which tune he was very fond.

I was selected for the journey, and at ten o'clock we started in a light, high-wheeled gig, which ran so easily that, after the four-wheeled cab, it seemed like nothing.

It was a fine May day, and as soon as we were out of the

town the sweet air, the smell of the fresh grass, and the soft country roads were as pleasant as they used to be in the old times, and I soon began to feel quite fresh.

Dinah's family lived in a small farmhouse up a green lane, close by a meadow with some fine shady trees: there were two cows feeding in it. A young man asked Jerry to bring his trap into the meadow, and he would tie me up in the cowshed; he wished he had a better stable to offer.

'If your cows would not be offended,' said Jerry, 'there is nothing my horse would like so well as to have an hour or two in your beautiful meadow. He's quiet, and it would be a rare treat for him.'

'Put him there and welcome,' said the young man. 'The best we have is at your service for your kindness to my sister; we shall be having some dinner in an hour, and I hope you'll come in, though with mother so ill we are all out of sorts in the house.'

Jerry thanked him kindly, but said as he had some dinner with him, there was nothing he should like so well as walking about in the meadow.

When my harness was taken off, I did not know what I should do first – eat the grass, roll over on my back, lie down and rest, or have a gallop across the meadow out of sheer spirits at being free; so I did all by turns. Jerry seemed to be quite as happy as I was. He sat down by a bank under a shady tree, and listened to the birds; then he sang to himself, and read out of the little brown book he is so fond of; next he wandered round the meadow and down by a little brook, where he picked the flowers and the hawthorn, and tied them up with long sprays of ivy; lastly he gave me a good feed of the oats which he had brought with him. But the time seemed all too short – I had not been in a field since I left poor Ginger at Earlshall.

We came home at a gentle pace, and Jerry's first words were as we came into the yard, 'Well, Polly, I have not lost my Sunday after all, for the birds were singing hymns in every bush, and I joined in the service; and as for Jack, he was like a young colt.'

When he handed Dolly the flowers she jumped about for joy.

CHAPTER THIRTY-EIGHT

Dolly and a Real Gentleman

The winter came in early with a great deal of cold and wet. There was snow, sleet, or rain almost every day for weeks, changing only to keen driving winds or sharp frosts. We all felt it very much. When it is a dry cold, a couple of good thick rugs will keep the warmth in us; but when it is a soaking rain, they soon get wet through and are no good. Some of the drivers had a waterproof cover to throw over us; this was a fine thing.

But some of the men were so poor that they could not protect either themselves or their horses, and many of them suffered very much that winter. When we horses had worked half the day we went to our dry stables, and could rest; whilst the drivers had to sit on their boxes, sometimes staying out as late as one or two o'clock in the morning if they had to wait for a party.

When the streets were slippery with frost or snow, that was the worst of all for us horses; one mile of such travelling, with a weight to draw and no firm footing, would take more out of us than four on a good road. Every nerve and muscle of our body is on the strain to keep our balance; and added to this, the fear of falling is more exhausting than anything else. If the roads are very bad indeed, our shoes are roughed, but this makes us feel nervous at first.

When the weather was very bad, many of the men would go and sit in the tavern close by, and get someone to watch for them; but they often lost a fare in this way, and could not, as Jerry said, be there without spending money.

He never went to the 'Rising Sun'. There was a coffee-shop near, where he now and then went; or he bought of an old man who came to our rank with tins of hot coffee and pies. It was Jerry's opinion that spirits and beer made a man colder afterwards, and that dry clothes, good food, cheerfulness, and a comfortable wife at home were the best things to keep a cabman warm.

Polly always supplied him with something to eat when he could not get home, and sometimes he would see little Dolly peeping from the corner of the street, to make sure if 'Father' was on the stand. If she saw him, she would run off at full speed and soon come back with something in a tin or basket – some hot soup or pudding that Polly had ready.

It was wonderful how such a little thing could get safely across the street, often thronged with horses and carriages; but she was a brave little maid, and felt it quite an honour to bring 'Father's first course', as he called it. She was a general favourite on the stand, and there was not a man who would not have seen her safely across the street, if Jerry had not been able to do so.

One cold, windy day, Dolly had brought Jerry a basin of something hot, and was standing by him whilst he ate it. He had scarcely begun, when a gentleman walking towards us very quickly held up his umbrella. Jerry touched his hat in return, gave the basin to Dolly, and was taking off my cloth, when the gentleman, hastening up, cried out, 'No, no, finish your soup, my friend; I have not much time to spare, but I can wait till you have done, and have set your little girl safely on the pavement.' So saying, he seated himself in the cab.

Jerry thanked him kindly, and came back to Dolly.

'There, Dolly, that's a gentleman; that's a real gentleman, Dolly; he has both time and thought for the comfort of a poor cabman and a little girl.'

Jerry finished his soup, saw the child safely across the road, and then took his orders to drive to Clapham Rise. Several times after this the same gentleman took our cab. I think he was very fond of dogs and horses, for whenever we took him to his own door, two or three dogs would come bounding out to meet him. Sometimes he came round and patted me, saying in his quiet, pleasant way, 'This horse has a good master, and he deserves it.'

It was a very rare thing for anyone to notice the horse that had been working for him. I have known ladies do it now and then, and this gentleman, and one or two others have given me a pat and a kind word; but ninety-nine out of a hundred would as soon think of patting the steam-engine that drew the train.

This gentleman was not young, and there was a forward stoop in his shoulders as if he was always going at something. His lips were thin and close shut, though they had a very pleasant smile; his eye was keen, and there was something in his jaw and the motion of his head that made one think he was very determined in anything he set about doing. His voice was pleasant and kind; any horse would trust that voice, though it was just as decided as everything else about him.

One day, he and another gentleman took our cab. They stopped at a shop in R— Street, and whilst his friend went in he stood at the door. A little ahead of us, on the other side of the street, a cart with two very fine horses was standing before some wine-vaults; the carter was not with them, and I cannot tell how long they had been standing, but they seemed to think they had waited long enough, and began to move off. Before they had gone many paces the carter came running out and caught them. He seemed furious at their having moved, and with whip and rein punished them brutally, even beating them about the head.

Our gentleman saw it all, and stepping quickly across the street, said in a decided voice, 'If you don't stop that directly, I'll have you summoned for leaving your horses and for brutal conduct.'

The man, who had clearly been drinking, poured forth some abusive language, but he left off knocking the horses about, and taking the reins, got into his cart. Meanwhile our friend had quietly taken a notebook from his pocket, and looking at the name and address painted on the cart, he wrote something down.

'What do you want with that?' growled the carter, as he cracked his whip and was moving on. A nod and a grim smile was the only answer he got.

On returning to the cab, our friend was joined by his companion, who said laughingly, 'I should have thought, Wright, you had enough business of your own to look after without troubling yourself about other people's horses and servants.'

Our friend stood still for a moment, and throwing his head a little back, said, 'Do you know why this world is as bad as it is?'

'No,' said the other.

'Then I'll tell you. It is because people think *only* about their own business, and won't trouble themselves to stand up for the oppressed, nor bring the wrong-doer to light. I never see a wicked thing like this without doing what I can, and many a master has thanked me for letting him know how his horses have been used.'

'I wish there were more gentlemen like you, sir,' said Jerry, 'for they are wanted badly enough in this city.'

After this we continued our journey, and as they got out of the cab our friend was saying, 'My doctrine is this, that if we see cruelty or wrong that we have the power to stop, and yet do nothing, we make ourselves sharers in the guilt.'

CHAPTER THIRTY-NINE

Seedy Sam

I should say that for a cab-horse I was very well off indeed; my driver was my owner, and it was to his interest to treat me well and not to overwork me, even had he not been so good a man as he was: but there were a great many horses which belonged to the large cab-owners, who let them out to their drivers for so much money a day. As the horses did not belong to these men, the only thing they thought of was how to get their money out of the horses, first to pay the master, and then to provide their own living; and a dreadful time some of these horses had of it. Of course I understood but little, but it was often talked over on the stand, and the Governor, who was a kind-hearted man and fond of horses, would sometimes speak his mind if a horse came in very much jaded or ill-used.

One day, a shabby, miserable-looking driver, who went by the name of 'Seedy Sam', brought in his horse looking dreadfully beat, and the Governor said, 'You and your horse look more fit for the police-station than for this rank.'

The man flung his tattered rug over the horse, turned full round upon the Governor, and said, in a voice that sounded almost desperate:

'If the police have any business with the matter, it ought to be with the masters who charge us so much, or with the fares that are fixed so low. If a man has to pay eighteen shillings a day for the use of a cab and two horses, as many of us have to do in the season, and must make that up before he earns a penny for himself – I say, 'tis more than hard work. Nine shillings a day to get out of each horse before you begin to get your own living! You know that's true, and if the horses don't work we must starve.

'My children and I have known what that is before now. I've six of 'em, and only one earns anything. I am on the stand fourteen or sixteen hours a day, and I haven't had a Sunday these ten or twelve weeks. You know, Skinner never gives a day if he can help it; and if I don't work hard, tell me who does! I want a warm coat and a mackintosh, but with so many to feed, how can a man get it? I had to pledge my clock a week ago to pay Skinner, and I shall never see it again.'

Some of the other drivers stood round nodding their heads, and saying he was right. The man went on, 'You that have your own horses and cabs, or drive for good masters, have a chance of getting on, and a chance of doing right; I haven't. Within the four-mile radius we can't charge more than sixpence a mile after the first mile.

'This very morning I had to go a clear six miles and took only three shillings. I could not get a return fare, and had to come half the way back; there's twelve miles for the horse and three shillings for me.

'After that I had a three-mile fare, and there were bags and boxes enough to have brought in a good many two-pences if they had been put outside. But you know how people do – all that could be piled up inside on the front seat were put in, and three heavy boxes went on the top – that was sixpence, and the fare one and sixpence. Then I got a return for a shilling; now that makes eighteen miles for the horse and six shillings for me. There's three shillings still for that horse to earn, and nine shillings for the afternoon horse before I touch a penny.

'Of course it is not always as bad as that, but you know it often is; and I say 'tis mockery to tell a man that he must not overwork his horse, for when a beast is downright tired, there's nothing but the whip that will keep his legs going – you can't help yourself. You must put your wife and children before the horse; the masters must look to that, we can't. I don't ill-use my horse for the sake of doing so; none of you can say I do.

'There's wrong lying somewhere – never a day's rest, never a quiet hour with the wife and children. I often feel like an old man, though I'm only forty-five. You know how quick some of the gentry are to suspect us of cheating and over-charging. Why, they stand with their purses in their hands, counting the fare over to a penny, and looking at us as if we were pickpockets. I wish some of 'em had got to sit on my box sixteen hours a day, and had to get a living out of it and eighteen shillings besides, and to do it in all weathers: they would not then be so uncommonly particular never to give us a sixpence over, nor would they then cram all the luggage inside. Of course, some of 'em tip us pretty handsomely now and then, or else we could not live: but we can't *depend* upon that.'

The men who stood round much approved of this speech. One of them said, 'It is desperate hard; and if a man sometimes does what is wrong, it is no wonder; and if he gets a dram too much, who's to blow him up?'

Jerry had taken no part in this conversation, but I never saw his face look so sad before. The Governor had stood with both his hands in his pockets; now he took his handkerchief out of his hat, and wiped his forehead.

'You've beaten me, Sam,' he said, 'for it's all true, and I won't cast it up against you any more about the police. It was the look in that horse's eye that came over me. It is hard lines for both man and beast, and who's to mend it I don't know; but anyway you might tell the poor beast that you were sorry to take it out of him in that way. Sometimes a kind word is all we can give 'em, poor brutes, and 'tis wonderful what they understand.'

A few mornings after this talk a new man came on the stand with Sam's cab.

'Halloo!' said one, 'what's up with Seedy Sam?'

'He's ill in bed,' said the man; 'he was taken ill last night in the yard, and could scarcely crawl home. His wife sent a boy this morning to say his father was in a high fever and could not get out; so I'm here instead.'

The next morning the same man came again.

'How is Sam?' enquired the Governor.

'He's gone,' said the man.

'What! gone? You don't mean to say he's dead?'

'Just snuffed out,' said the other; 'He died at four o'clock this morning. All yesterday he was raving – raving about Skinner and about having no Sundays. "I never had a Sunday's rest," these were his last words.'

No one spoke for a while, and then the Governor said, 'I tell you what, mates, this is a warning to us all.'

CHAPTER FORTY

Poor Ginger

One day, whilst our cab and many others were waiting outside one of the parks where a band was playing, a shabby old cab drove up beside ours. The horse was an old worn-out chestnut with an ill-kept coat, and with bones that showed plainly through it. The knees knuckled over, and the forelegs were very unsteady.

I had been eating some hay, and the wind rolling a little lock of it that way, the poor creature put out her long, thin neck and picked it up, and then turned round and looked about for more. There was a hopeless look in the dull eye that I could not help noticing; and then, as I was thinking where I had seen that horse before, she looked full at me and said, 'Black Beauty, is that you?'

It was Ginger! but how changed! The beautifully arched and glossy neck was now straight, lank, and fallen in; the clean, straight legs and delicate fetlocks were swollen; the joints were grown out of shape with hard work; the face that was once so full of spirit and life was now full of suffering; and I could tell by the heaving of her sides and by her frequent cough how bad her breath was.

Our drivers were standing together a little way off, so I sidled up to her a step or two that we might have a little quiet talk. It was a sad tale that she had to tell.

After a twelvemonth's run off at Earlshall, she was considered to be fit for work again, and was sold to a gentleman. For a little while she got on very well, but after a longer gallop than usual, the old strain returned, and, after being rested and doctored, she was again sold. In this way she changed hands several times, but always getting lower down.

'And so at last,' said she, 'I was bought by a man who keeps a number of cabs and horses, and lets them out. You look well off, and I am glad of it; but I cannot tell you what my life has been. When they found out my weakness, they said I was not worth what they gave for me, and that I must go into one of the low cabs and just be used up; that is what they are doing – whipping and working me, with never one thought of what I suffer. They paid for me, and must get the money out of me, they say. The man who hires me now pays a deal of money to the owner every day, and so he has to get it out of me first; and so it goes on all the weeks round, with never a Sunday rest.'

I said, 'You used to stand up for yourself if you were ill-used.'

'Ah!' she said, 'I did once, but it's no use; men are stronger, and if they are cruel and have no feeling, there is nothing that we can do but just bear it – bear it on and on to the end. I wish the end was come; I wish I was dead. I have seen dead horses, and I am sure they do not suffer pain; I hope I may drop down dead at my work, and not be sent off to the knacker's.'

I was very much troubled, and I put my nose up to hers, but I could say nothing to comfort her. I think she was pleased to see me, for she said, 'You are the only friend I ever had.'

Just then her driver came up, and with a tug at her mouth backed her out of the line and drove off, leaving me very sad indeed.

A short time after this a cart with a dead horse in it passed our cab-stand. The head hung out of the cart tail, the lifeless tongue was slowly dropping blood; and the sunken eyes I – but I can't speak of them, the sight was too dreadful. It was a chestnut horse with a long, thin neck. I saw a white streak down the forehead. I believe it was Ginger; I hoped it was, for then her troubles would be over. Oh! if men were more merciful, they would shoot us before we come to such misery.

CHAPTER FORTY-ONE

The Butcher

I saw a great deal of trouble amongst the horses in London, much of which might have been prevented by a little common sense. We horses do not mind hard work if we are treated reasonably; and I am sure there are many driven by quite poor men who have a happier life than I had when, with my silver-mounted harness, I used to go in the Countess of W—'s carriage.

It often went to my heart to see how badly the little ponies were used – straining along with heavy loads, or staggering under heavy blows from some low, cruel boy. Once I saw a little grey pony with a thick mane and a pretty head, and so much like Merrylegs that if I had not been in harness I should have neighed to him. He was doing his best to pull a heavy cart, while a strong, rough boy was cutting him under the belly with his whip, and chucking cruelly at his little mouth.

Could it be Merrylegs? It was just like him; but then Mr Blomefield was never to sell him, and I do not think he would have done so. Yet this may have been quite as good a little fellow, and have had as happy a place when he was young.

I often noticed the great speed at which butcher's horses were made to go, though I did not know why they were driven so fast till one day when we had to wait some time in St John's Wood. There was a butcher's shop next door, and as we were standing a butcher's cart came dashing up at a great pace. The horse was hot and much exhausted; he hung his head down, while his heaving sides and trembling legs showed how hard he had been driven. The lad jumped out of the cart and was getting the basket when the master came out of the shop much displeased. After looking at the horse, he turned angrily to the lad.

'How many times shall I tell you not to drive in this way? You ruined the last horse and broke his wind, and you are going to ruin this in the same way. If you were not my own son, I would dismiss you on the spot; it is a disgrace to have a horse brought to the shop in such a condition. You are liable to be taken up by the police for furious driving, and if you are, you need not look to me for bail, for I have spoken to you till I am tired; you must look out for yourself.'

During this speech the boy had stood by, sullen and dogged; but when his father ceased, he broke out angrily, 'It wasn't my fault, and I won't take the blame: I am only going by orders all the time.

'You always say, "Now be quick; now look sharp!" And when I go to the houses, one person wants a leg of mutton for an early dinner, and I must be back with it in a quarter of an hour; another has forgotten to order the beef, and I must go and fetch it and be back in no time or the mistress will scold; the third says they have company coming unexpectedly and must have some chops sent up directly; and the lady at No. 4 in the Crescent *never* orders her dinner till the meat comes in for lunch – it's nothing but hurry, hurry, all the time. If the gentry would think of what they want, and order their meat the day before, there need not be this blow up!'

'I wish to goodness they would,' said the butcher; ' 'twould save me a wonderful deal of harass, and I could suit my customers much better if I knew beforehand. But there – what's the use of talking? Whoever thinks of a butcher's convenience, or a butcher's horse? Now then, take him in, and look to him well. Mind, he does not go out again today, and if anything else is wanted, you must carry it yourself in the basket.' With that he went in, and the horse was led away.

But all boys are not cruel. I have seen some as fond of their pony or donkey as if it had been a favourite dog; and the little creatures have worked away as cheerfully and willingly for their young drivers as I work for Jerry. It may be hard work sometimes, but a friend's hand and voice make it easy.

There was a young coster-boy who came up our street with greens and potatoes. He had an old pony, not very handsome, but the most cheerful and plucky little thing I ever saw; and to see how fond those two were of each other was a treat. The pony followed his master like a dog; and when the boy got into his cart, the pony would trot off without a whip or a word and rattle down the street as merrily as if he had come out of the Queen's stables. Jerry liked the boy and called him 'Prince Charlie', for he said he would make a king of drivers someday.

There was an old man, too, who used to come up our street with a little coal cart. He wore a coal-heaver's hat, and looked rough and black. He and his old horse used to plod together along the street like two good partners who understood each other. The horse would stop of his own accord at the doors where they took coal of him. He used to keep one ear bent towards his master. The old man's cry could be heard up the street long before he came near. I never knew what he said, but the children called him 'Old Ba-a-ar Hoo', for it sounded like that. Polly bought her coal of him, and was very friendly; and Jerry said it was a comfort to think how happy an old horse may be in a poor place.

CHAPTER FORTY-TWO

The Election

As we came into the yard one afternoon, Polly came out.
'Jerry! I've had Mr B— here asking about your vote, and he
wants to hire your cab for the election; he will call for an
answer.'

'Well, Polly, you may say that my cab will be otherwise
engaged; I should not like to have it pasted over with their
great bills, and as to make Jack and Captain race about to
the public-houses to bring up half-drunken voters, why, I
think 'twould be an insult to the horses. No, I sha'n't do it.'

'I suppose you'll vote for the gentleman? He said he was
of your politics.'

'So he is in some things, but I shall not vote for him,
Polly; you know what his trade is?'

'Yes.'

'Well, a man who gets rich by that trade may be all very
well in some ways, but he is blind as to what working men
want: I could not in my conscience send him up to make
the laws. I dare say they'll be angry, but every man must do
what he thinks to be the best for his country.'

On the morning before the election Jerry was putting me
into the shafts, when Dolly came into the yard sobbing and
crying, with her little blue frock and white pinafore spat-
tered all over with mud.

'Why, Dolly, what is the matter?'

'Those naughty boys,' she sobbed, 'have thrown the dirt
all over me, and called me a little raga – raga – '

'They called her a little blue ragamuffin, father,' said

Harry, who ran in looking very angry; 'but I have given it to them, they won't insult my sister again. I have given them a thrashing they will remember; a set of cowardly, rascally, orange blackguards!'

Jerry kissed the child and said, 'Run in to mother, my pet, and tell her I think you had better stay at home today and help her.'

Then, turning gravely to Harry:

'My boy, I hope you will always defend your sister, and give anybody who insults her a good thrashing – that is as it should be; but mind, I won't have any election blackguarding on my premises. There are as many blue blackguards as there are orange, and as many white as there are purple, or any other colour, and I won't have any of my family mixed up with it. Even women and children are ready to quarrel for the sake of a colour, and not one in ten of them knows what it is about.'

'Why, father, I thought blue was for Liberty.'

'My boy, Liberty does not come from colours, they only show party, and all the liberty you can get out of them is, liberty to get drunk at other people's expense, liberty to ride to the poll in a dirty old cab, liberty to abuse anyone that does not wear your colour, and to shout yourself hoarse at what you only half understand – that's your liberty!'

'Oh, father, you are laughing.'

'No, Harry, I am serious, and I am ashamed to see how men go on that ought to know better. An election is a very serious thing; at least, it ought to be, and every man ought to vote according to his conscience, and let his neighbour do the same.'

CHAPTER FORTY-THREE

A Friend in Need

It was the day of the election. Jerry would not let his cab to either party, but there was no lack of work for us.

First came a stout, puffy gentleman with a carpet-bag, who wanted to go to the Bishopsgate Station; then we were called by a party who wished to be taken to the Regent's Park; and next we were wanted in a side street, where a timid, anxious old lady was waiting to be taken to the Bank. There we had to stop to take her back again; and just as we had set her down, a red-faced gentleman with a handful of papers came running up, out of breath; and before Jerry could get down, he had opened the door, popped himself in, and called out, 'Bow Street Police Station, quick!' So off we went with him; and when after another turn or two we came back, there was no other cab on the stand. Jerry put on my nosebag, for, as he said, 'We must eat when we can on such days as these; so munch away, Jack, and make the best of your time, old boy.'

I found I had a good feed of crushed oats, wetted with a little bran; this would be a treat any day, but was specially refreshing now. Jerry was so thoughtful and kind – what horse would not do his best for such a master? Then he took out one of Polly's meat pies, and standing near me, he began to eat it.

The streets were very full, and the cabs with the candidates' colours on them were dashing about through the crowd as if life and limb were of no consequence. We saw two people knocked down that day, and one was a woman.

The horses were having a bad time of it, poor things! but the voters inside thought nothing of that, for many of them were half drunk, hurrahing out of the cab windows if their own party came by. It was the first election I had seen, and I don't want to be in another, though I have heard things are better now.

Jerry and I had not eaten many mouthfuls before a poor young woman, carrying a heavy child, came along the street. She was looking this way and that way, and seemed quite bewildered. Presently she made her way up to Jerry and asked if he could tell her the way to St Thomas's hospital, and how far it was to get there. She had come from the country that morning in a market cart, and did not know it was the election. She was quite a stranger in London, but had got an order for the hospital for her little boy, who was crying with a feeble, pining cry.

'Poor little fellow!' she said, 'he suffers a deal of pain. He is four years old, and can't walk any more than a baby; but the doctor said if I could get him into the hospital, he might get well. Pray, sir, how far is it? and which way must I go?'

'Why, missis,' said Jerry, 'you can't get there walking through crowds like this! Why, it is three miles away, and that child is heavy.'

'Yes, bless him, he is, but I am strong, thank God; and if I knew the way, I think I could get on somehow: please tell me the way.'

'You can't do it,' said Jerry; 'you might be knocked down and the child be run over. Now look here, just get into this cab, and I'll drive you safely to the hospital: don't you see the rain is coming on?'

'No, sir, no, I can't do that, thank you; I have only just money enough to get back with. Please tell me the way.'

'Look you here, missis,' said Jerry, 'I've got a wife and dear children at home, and I know a father's feelings. Now get into that cab and I'll take you there for nothing; I'd be ashamed of myself to let a woman and a sick child run a risk like that.'

'Heaven bless you!' said the woman, and she burst into tears.

'There, there, cheer up, my dear, I'll soon take you there. Come, let me put you inside.'

As Jerry went to open the door, two men with colours in their hats and button-holes ran up, calling out, 'Cab!'

'Engaged!' cried Jerry. But one of the men, pushing past the woman, sprang into the cab, followed by the other. Jerry looked as stern as a policeman: 'This cab is already engaged, gentleman, by that lady.'

'Lady!' said one of them; 'oh! she can wait: our business is very important: besides, we were in first. It is our right, and we shall stay in.'

A droll smile came over Jerry's face as he shut the door upon them. 'All right, gentlemen; pray stay in as long as it suits you. I can wait while you rest yourselves'; and turning his back upon them, he walked up to the young woman, who was standing near me. 'They'll soon be gone,' he said, laughing; 'don't trouble yourself, my dear.'

And they soon were gone; for when they understood Jerry's dodge, they got out, calling him all sorts of bad names, and blustering about his number and getting a summons. After this little stoppage we were soon on our way to the hospital, going as much as possible through by-streets. Jerry rang the great bell, and helped the young woman out.

'Thank you a thousand times,' she said; 'I could never have got here alone.'

'You're kindly welcome, and I hope the dear child will soon be better.'

He watched her go in at the door, and he said to himself quietly, ' "Inasmuch as ye have done it to one of the least of these." ' Then he patted my neck; this was always his way when anything pleased him.

The rain was now coming down fast, and just as we were leaving the hospital the door opened again, and the porter called out, 'Cab!' We stopped, and a lady came down the steps. Jerry seemed to know her at once. She put back her veil, and said, 'Barker! Jeremiah Barker! is it you? I am very glad to find you here; you are just the friend I want, for it is very difficult to get a cab in this part of London today.'

'I shall be proud to serve you, ma'am; I am right glad I happened to be here. Where may I take you to, ma'am?'

'To the Paddington Station, and then if we are in good time, as I think we shall be, you shall tell me all about Mary and the children.'

We got to the station in good time, and being under shelter, the lady stood a good while talking to Jerry. I found she had been Polly's mistress, and after many enquiries about her, she said, 'How do you find the cab-work suit you in winter? I know Mary was rather anxious about you last year.'

'Yes, ma'am, she was; I had a bad cough that followed me up quite into the warm weather, and when I am kept out late she does worry herself a good deal. You see, ma'am, my work is at all hours and in all weathers, and that does try a man's constitution; but I am getting on pretty well, and I should feel quite lost if I had not horses to look after. I was brought up to it, and I am afraid I should not do as well at anything else.'

'Well, Barker,' she said, 'it would be a great pity that you should seriously risk your health in this work, not only for your own but for Mary's and the children's sake. There are many places where good drivers or good grooms are wanted; and if ever you think you ought to give up this cab-work, let me know.' Then sending some kind messages to Mary, she put something into his hand, saying, 'There are five shillings each for the two children; Mary will know how to spend it.'

Jerry thanked her and seemed much pleased; then, turning out of the station, we at last reached home: I, at least, was tired.

CHAPTER FORTY-FOUR

Old Captain and his Successor

Captain and I were great friends. He was a noble old fellow, and a very good companion. I never thought that he would have to leave his home and go down the hill, but his turn came; and this is how it happened. I was not there, but I heard all about it.

Jerry and he had taken a party to the great railway station over London Bridge, and were coming back, somewhere between the bridge and the Monument, when Jerry saw a brewer's empty dray coming along, drawn by two powerful horses. The drayman was lashing his horses with his heavy whip. The dray was light, and they were going at a furious rate. The man had no control over them.

The street was full of traffic; one young girl was knocked down and run over, and the next moment the dray dashed up against our cab; both the wheels were torn off, and the cab was thrown over. Captain was dragged down, the shafts splintered, and one of them ran into his side. Jerry, too, was thrown, but was only bruised. Nobody could tell how he escaped; he always said 'twas a miracle.

When poor Captain was got up, he was found to be very much cut and knocked about. Jerry led him home gently, and a sad sight it was to see the blood soaking into his white coat and dropping from his side and shoulder. The drayman being proved to be very drunk, was fined, and the brewer had to pay damages to our master; but there was no one to pay damages to poor Captain.

The farrier and Jerry did the best they could to ease his pain and make him comfortable. The fly had to be mended; and for several days I did not go out; so Jerry earned nothing. The first time we went to the stand after the accident the Governor came up to hear how Captain was.

'He'll never get over it,' said Jerry – 'at least, not for my work, so the farrier said this morning. He says he may do for carting and that sort of work. It has put me out very much. Carting indeed! I've seen what horses come to at that work round London. I only wish all the drunkards could be put in a lunatic asylum, instead of being allowed to run foul of sober people.

'If they would break their *own* bones, and smash their *own* carts, and lame their *own* horses, that would be their own affair, and we might let them alone; but it seems to me that the innocent always suffer; and then they talk about compensation! You can't make compensation – there's all the trouble and vexation and loss of time, besides losing a good horse that's like an old friend – it's nonsense talking of compensation! If there's one devil more than another that I should like to see in the bottomless pit, it's the drink devil.'

'I say, Jerry,' said the Governor, 'you are treading pretty hard on my toes, you know; I'm not as good as you are, more shame for me, I wish I were.'

'Well,' said Jerry, 'why don't you cut the drink, Governor? You are too good a man to be the slave of such a thing.'

'I'm a great fool, Jerry, but I tried once for two days, and I thought I should have died: how did you do?'

'I had hard work at it for several weeks. You see, I never

did get drunk, but I found that I was not my own master, and that when the craving came on, it was hard work to say "no". I saw that one of us must knock under – the drink devil or Jerry Barker; and I said that it should not be Jerry Barker, God helping me.

'But it was a struggle, and I wanted all the help I could get; for till I tried to break the habit, I did not know how strong it was. Polly took pains that I should have good food, and when the craving came on, I used to get a cup of coffee, or some peppermint, or I used to read a bit in my book, and that was a help to me.

'Sometimes I had to say over and over to myself, "Give up the drink or love your soul? Give up the drink or break Polly's heart." But thanks be to God and my dear wife, my chains were broken, and now for ten years I have not tasted a drop, and never wish for it.'

'I've a great mind to try it,' said Grant, 'for 'tis a poor thing not to be one's own master.'

'Do, Governor, do; you'll never repent it; and what a help it would be to some of the poor fellows in our rank if they saw you do without it! I know there are two or three would like to keep out of that tavern if they could.'

At first Captain seemed to do well, but he was a very old horse, and it was only his wonderful constitution and Jerry's care that had kept him up at the cab-work so long; now he broke down very much. The farrier said he might mend up enough to sell for a few pounds, but Jerry said, No! a few pounds got by selling a good old servant into hard work and misery would canker all the rest of his money. He thought the kindest thing he could do for the fine old fellow would be to put a sure bullet through his heart, and then he would never suffer more; for he did not know where to find him a kind master for the rest of his days.

The day after this was decided Harry took me to the

forge for some new shoes. When I returned Captain was gone. The family and I all felt it very much.

Jerry had now to look out for another horse, and he soon heard of one through an acquaintance who was under-groom in a nobleman's stables. He was a valuable young horse, but he had run away, smashed into another carriage, flung his lordship out, and so cut and blemished himself that he was no longer fit for a gentleman's stables, and the coachman had orders to look round and sell him as well as he could.

'I can do with high spirits,' said Jerry, 'if a horse is not vicious or hard-mouthed.'

'There is not a bit of vice in him,' said the man; 'his mouth is very tender, and I think myself that was the cause of the accident. You see, he had just been clipped, and the weather was bad, and he had not had exercise enough, and when he did go out, he was as full of spring as a balloon. Our governor (the coachman, I mean) had him harnessed in as tight and strong as he could, with the martingale, and the bearing rein, a very sharp curb, and the reins put in at the bottom bar; it is my belief that it made the horse mad, being tender in the mouth and so full of spirit.'

'Likely enough; I'll come and see him,' said Jerry.

The next day, Hotspur – that was his name – came home; he was a fine brown horse, without a white hair in him, as tall as Captain, with a very handsome head, and only five years old. I gave him a friendly greeting by way of good-fellowship, but did not ask him any questions. The first night he was very restless; instead of lying down, he kept jerking his halter rope up and down through the ring, and knocking the block about against the manger so that I could not sleep. However, the next day, after five or six hours in the cab, he came in quiet and sensible. Jerry patted and talked to him a good deal, and very soon they under-stood each other, and Jerry said that with an easy bit and plenty of work he would be as gentle as a lamb, and that it was an ill wind that blew nobody good, for if his lordship had lost a hundred-guinea favourite, the cabman had gained a good horse with all his strength in him.

Hotspur thought it a great comedown to be a cab-horse, and was disgusted at standing in the rank, but he confessed to me at the end of the week that an easy mouth and a free head made up for a great deal, and, after all, the work was not so degrading as having one's head and tail fastened to each other at the saddle. In fact, he settled in well, and Jerry liked him very much.

CHAPTER FORTY-FIVE

Jerry's New Year

Christmas and the New Year are very merry times for some people; but for cabmen and cabmen's horses these times are no holiday, though they may be a harvest. There are so many parties, balls, and places of amusement open that the work is hard and often late. Sometimes driver and horse, shivering with cold, have to wait for hours in the rain or frost, whilst the merry people within are dancing to the music. I wonder if the beautiful ladies ever think of the weary cabman waiting on his box, and of his patient beast standing till his legs get stiff with cold!

I had now most of the evening work as I was well accustomed to standing, and Jerry was also more afraid of Hotspur, the new horse, taking cold. We had a great deal of late work in the Christmas week, and Jerry's cough was bad, but, however late we were, Polly sat up for him, and, looking anxious and troubled, she came out with the lantern to meet him.

On the evening of the New Year we had to take two gentlemen to a house in one of the West End squares. We sat them down at nine o'clock, and were told to come again at eleven. 'But,' said one of them, 'as it is a card party, you may have to wait a few minutes, but don't be late.'

As the clock struck eleven we were at the door, for Jerry was always punctual. The clock chimed the quarters – one, two, three, and then struck twelve; but the door did not open.

The wind had been very changeable, with squalls of rain during the day, but now it came on sharp, driving sleet, which seemed to come all the way round one; it was very cold, and there was no shelter. Jerry got off his box and came and pulled one of my cloths a little more over my neck; then, stamping his feet, he took a turn or two up and down; then he began to beat his arms, and that set him on coughing; so he opened the cab door and sat at the bottom with his feet on the pavement, and was thus a little sheltered. Still the clock chimed the quarters, but no one came. At half-past twelve he rang the bell, and asked the servant if he would be wanted that night.

'Oh! yes, you'll be wanted safe enough,' said the man; 'you must not go, it will soon be over.' And again Jerry sat down, but his voice was so hoarse I could hardly hear him.

At a quarter past one the door opened, and the two gentlemen came out; they got into the cab without a word, and told Jerry where to drive; it was nearly two miles away. My legs were numb with cold, and I thought I should have stumbled. When the men got out, they never said they were sorry to have kept us waiting so long, but were angry at the charge. However, as Jerry never charged more than was his due, he never took less, and so they had to pay for the two hours and a quarter of waiting but it was hard-earned money to Jerry.

At last we got home. He could hardly speak, and his cough was dreadful. Polly asked no questions, but opened the door and held the lantern for him.

'Can't I do something?' she said.

'Yes; get Jack something warm, and then boil me some gruel.'

This was said in a hoarse whisper. He could hardly get his breath, but he gave me a rub down as usual, and even went up into the hayloft for an extra bundle of straw for my bed. Polly brought me a warm mash that made me comfortable; and then they locked the door.

It was late the next morning before anyone came, and then it was only Harry. He cleaned and fed us, and swept out the stalls; then he put the straw back again as if it was Sunday. He was very still, and neither whistled nor sang. At noon he came again and gave us our food and water: this time Dolly came with him. She was crying, and I could gather from what they said that Jerry was dangerously ill, and the doctor said it was a bad case. So two days passed, and there was great trouble indoors. We saw only Harry and sometimes Dolly. I think she came for company, for Polly was always with Jerry, who had to be kept very quiet.

On the third day, whilst Harry was in the stable, a tap came at the door, and Governor Grant came in.

'I wouldn't go to the house, my boy,' he said, 'but I want to know how your father is.'

'He is very bad,' said Harry, 'he can't be much worse. They call it bronchitis, and the doctor thinks it will turn one way or another tonight.'

'That's bad, very bad,' said Grant, shaking his head. 'I know two men who died of that last week. It takes 'em off in no time; but whilst there's life there's hope, so you must keep up your spirits.'

'Yes,' said Harry quickly, 'and the doctor said that father had a better chance than most men, because he didn't drink. He said yesterday the fever was so high that if father had been a drinking man, it would have burnt him up like a piece of paper; but I believe he thinks he will get over it; don't you think he will, Mr Grant?'

The Governor looked puzzled.

'If there's any rule that good men should get over these things, I am sure he will, my boy. He's the best man I know. I'll look in early tomorrow.'

Early next morning he was there.

'Well?' said he.

'Father is better,' said Harry. 'Mother hopes he will get over it.'

'Thank God!' said the Governor; 'and now you must keep him warm, and keep his mind easy. And that brings me to the horses. You see, Jack will be all the better for the rest of a week or two in a warm stable, and you can easily take him a turn up and down the street to stretch his legs; but this young one, if he does not get work, will soon be all up on end as you may say, and will be rather too much for you; and when he does go out, there'll be an accident.'

'He is like that now,' said Harry; 'I have kept him short of corn, but he's so full of spirit I don't know what to do with him.'

'Just so,' said Grant. 'Now look here. Will you tell your mother that, if she is agreeable, I will come for him every day till something is arranged, and take him for a good spell of work; and whatever he earns, I'll bring your mother half of it, and that will help with the horses' feed. Your father is in a good club, I know, but that won't keep the horses, and they'll be eating their heads off all this time: I'll come at noon to hear what she says'; and without waiting for Harry's thanks, he was gone.

At noon I think he went and saw Polly, for Harry and he came to the stable together, harnessed Hotspur, and took him out.

For a week or more he came for Hotspur, and when Harry thanked him or said anything about his kindness, he laughed it off, saying, it was all good luck for him, for his horses were wanting a little rest which they could not otherwise have had.

Jerry steadily grew better, but the doctor said that he must never go back to the cab-work again if he wished to be an old man. The children had many consultations together about what father and mother would do, and how they could help to earn money.

One afternoon Hotspur was brought in very wet and dirty.

The streets are nothing but slush,' said the Governor; 'it will give you a good warming, my boy, to get him clean and dry.'

'All right, Governor,' said Harry, 'I shall not leave him till he is; you know I have been trained by my father.'

'I wish all the boys had been trained like you,' said the Governor.

While Harry was sponging off the mud from Hotspur's body and legs, Dolly came in, looking very full of something.

'Who lives at Fairstowe, Harry? Mother has got a letter from Fairstowe; she seemed so glad, and ran upstairs to father with it.'

'Don't you know? Why, it is the name of Mrs Fowler's place – mother's old mistress, you know – the lady that father met last summer, who sent you and me five shillings each.'

'Oh! Mrs Fowler; of course I know all about her. I wonder what she is writing to mother about.'

'Mother wrote to her last week,' said Harry. 'You know she told father if ever he gave up the cab-work, she would like to know. I wonder what she says; run in and see, Dolly.'

Harry scrubbed away at Hotspur with a 'huish! huish!' like any old ostler.

In a few minutes Dolly came dancing into the stable.

'Oh, Harry! was there ever anything so beautiful? Mrs Fowler says we are all to go and live near her. There is a cottage now empty that will just suit us, with a garden, a hen-house, apple trees, and everything! Her coachman is going away in the spring, and then she will want father in his place. And there are good families round, where you can get a place in the garden or stable, or as a page-boy; and there's a good school for me. Mother is laughing and crying by turns, and father does look *so* happy!'

'That's uncommon jolly,' said Harry, 'and just the right thing, I should say. It will suit father and mother both; but I don't intend to be a page-boy with tight clothes and rows of buttons. I'll be a groom or a gardener.'

It was quickly settled that, as soon as Jerry was well enough, they should remove to the country, and that the cab and horses should be sold as soon as possible.

This was heavy news for me, for I was not young now, and could not look for any improvement in my condition. Since I left Birtwick I had never been so happy as with my dear master, Jerry; but three years of cab-work, even under the best conditions, will tell on one's strength, and I felt that I was not the horse that I had been.

Grant said at once that he would take Hotspur. There were men on the stand who would have bought me; but Jerry said I should not go to cab-work again with just anybody, and the Governor promised to find a place for me where I should be comfortable.

The day came for going away. Jerry had not been allowed to go out yet, and I never saw him after that New Year's Eve. Polly and the children came to bid me goodbye. 'Poor old Jack! dear old Jack! I wish we could take you with us,' she said; and then, laying her hand on my mane, she put her face close to my neck and kissed me. Dolly was crying, and she kissed me too. Harry stroked me a great deal, but said nothing, only he seemed very sad; and so I was led away to my new place.

CHAPTER FORTY-SIX

Jakes and the Lady

I was sold to a corn dealer and baker whom Jerry knew, and with him he thought I should have good food and fair work. In the first he was quite right, and if my master had always been on the premises, I do not think I should have been overloaded; but there was a foreman who was always hurrying and driving everyone, and frequently when I had quite a full load, he would order something else to be taken on. My carter, whose name was Jakes, often said it was more than I ought to take, but the other always overruled him, saying, ' 'Tis no use going twice when once will do, and I choose to get business forward.'

Jakes, like the other carters, always had the bearing rein up, which prevented me from drawing easily; and by the time I had been there three or four months, I found the work telling very much on my strength.

One day, I was loaded more than usual, and part of the road was up a steep hill: I used all my strength, but I could not get on, and was obliged continually to stop. This did not please my driver, and he laid his whip on badly. 'Get on, you lazy fellow,' he said, 'or I'll make you.'

Again I started the heavy load, and struggled on a few yards; again the whip came down, and again I struggled forward. The pain of that great cart whip was sharp, but my mind was hurt quite as much as my poor sides. To be punished and abused when I was doing my very best was so hard that it took the heart out of me. A third time he was flogging me cruelly, when a lady stepped quickly up to him, and said in a sweet, earnest voice:

'Oh! pray do not whip your good horse any more; I am sure he is doing all he can. The road is very steep, and I am sure he is doing his best.'

'If doing his best won't get this load up, he must do something more than his best; that's all I know, ma'am,' said Jakes.

'But is it not a very heavy load?' she said.

'Yes, yes, too heavy,' he said, 'but that's not my fault; the foreman came just as we were starting, and would have three hundredweight more put on to save him trouble. I must get on with it as well as I can.'

He was raising the whip again, when the lady said:

'Pray, stop, I think I can help you if you will let me.'

The man laughed.

'You see,' she said, 'you do not give him a fair chance. He cannot use all his power with his head held back as it is with that bearing rein; if you would take it off, I am sure he would do better – *do* try it,' she said persuasively; 'I should be very glad if you would.'

'Well, well,' said Jakes, with a short laugh, 'anything to please a lady, of course. How far would you wish it down, ma'am?'

'Quite down; give him his head altogether.'

The rein was taken off, and in a moment I put my head down to my very knees. What a comfort it was! Then I tossed it up and down several times to get the aching stiffness out of my neck.

'Poor fellow! that is what you wanted,' said she, patting and stroking me with her gentle hand; 'and now if you will speak kindly to him and lead him on, I believe he will be able to do better.'

Jakes took the rein – 'Come on, Blackie.' I put down my head, and threw my whole weight against the collar. I spared no strength; the load moved on, and I pulled it steadily up the hill, and then stopped to take breath.

The lady had walked along the footpath, and now came across into the road. She stroked and patted my neck, as I had not been patted for many a long day.

'You see, he was quite willing when you gave him the chance; I am sure he is a fine-tempered creature, and I dare say has known better days. You won't put that rein on again, will you?' for he was just going to hitch it up on the old plan.

'Well, ma'am, I can't deny that having his head has helped him up the hill, and I'll remember it another time, and thank you, ma'am; but if he went without a bearing rein, I should be the laughing-stock of all the carters; it is the fashion, you see.'

'Is it not better,' she said, 'to lead a good fashion than to follow a bad one? A great many gentlemen do not use bearing reins now; our carriage horses have not worn them for fifteen years, and work with much less fatigue than those which have them; besides,' she added in a very serious voice, 'we have no right to distress any of God's creatures without a very good reason; we call them dumb animals, and so they are, for they cannot tell us how they feel, but they do not suffer less because they have no words. But I must not detain you now; I thank you for trying my plan with your good horse, and I am sure you will find it far better than the whip. Good-day.' And with another soft pat on my neck, she stepped lightly across the path, and I saw her no more.

'That was a real lady, I'll be bound for it,' said Jakes to himself; 'she spoke just as politely as if I was a gentleman. I'll try her plan, uphill, at any rate.'

I must do him the justice to say that he let my rein out several holes, and after that, going uphill, he always gave me my head; but the heavy loads went on.

Good food and fair rest will keep up one's strength under full work, but no horse can stand against overloading; and I was getting so thoroughly pulled down from this cause that a younger horse was bought in my place. I may as well mention here what I suffered at this time from another cause. I had heard horses speak of it, but had never myself had experience of the evil of a badly-lighted stable. There was only one very small window at the end, and the consequence was that the stalls were almost dark.

Besides the depressing effect this had on my spirits, it very much weakened my sight, and when I was suddenly brought out of the darkness into the glare of daylight, it was very painful to my eyes. Several times I stumbled over the threshold, and could scarcely see where I was going.

I believe, had I stayed there very long, I should have become purblind, and that would have been a great misfortune; for I have heard men say that a stone-blind horse is safer to drive than one which has imperfect sight, as purblindness generally makes them very timid. However, I escaped without any permanent injury to my sight, and was sold to a large cab-owner.

CHAPTER FORTY-SEVEN

Hard Times

I shall never forget my new master. He had black eyes and a hooked nose; his mouth was as full of teeth as a bulldog's, and his voice was as harsh as the grinding of cart wheels over gravel-stones. His name was Nicholas Skinner, and I believe he was the same man for whom poor Seedy Sam had driven.

I have heard men say that seeing is believing; but I should say that *feeling* is believing; for much as I had seen before, I never knew till now the utter misery of a cab-horse's life.

Skinner had a low set of cabs and a low set of drivers; he was hard on the men, and the men were hard on the horses. In this place we had no Sunday rest, and it was in the heat of summer.

Sometimes on a Sunday morning a party of fast men would hire a cab for the day – four of them inside and another with the driver, and I had to take them ten or fifteen miles out into the country, and back again: never would any of them get down to walk up a hill, let it be ever so steep or the day ever so hot – unless indeed, when the driver was afraid I should not manage it, and sometimes I was so fevered and worn that I could hardly touch my food. How I used to long for the nice bran mash with nitre in it that Jerry used to give us on Saturday nights in hot weather, that used to cool us down and make us so comfortable. Then we had two nights and a whole day for unbroken rest, and on Monday morning we were as fresh as young horses again; but here, there was no rest, and my driver was just as hard as his master.

He had a cruel whip with something so sharp at the end that it sometimes drew blood, and he would even whip me under the belly, and flip out the lash at my head. Indignities like these took the heart out of me terribly, but still I did my best and never hung back; for, as poor Ginger said, it was no use; men are the stronger.

My life was now so utterly wretched that I wished I might, like Ginger, drop down dead at my work, and so be out of my misery; and one day my wish very nearly came to pass.

I went on the stand at eight in the morning, and had done a good share of work when we had to take a fare to the railway. A long train was just expected in, so my driver pulled up at the back of some of the outside cabs to take the chance of a return fare. It was a very heavy train, and as all the cabs were soon engaged, ours was called for.

There was a party of four: a noisy, blustering man with a lady, a little boy, a young girl, and a great deal of luggage. The lady and the boy got into the cab, and while the man ordered about the luggage, the young girl came and looked at me.

'Papa,' she said, 'I am sure this poor horse cannot take us and all our luggage so far; he is so very weak and worn out; do look at him.'

'Oh! he's all right, miss,' said my driver, 'he's strong enough.'

The porter, who was pulling about some heavy boxes, suggested to the gentleman that, as there was so much luggage, he should take a second cab.

'Can your horse do it, or can't he?' said the blustering man.

'Oh! he can do it all right, sir. Send up the boxes, porter; he can take more than that.' Saying this, he helped to haul up a box so heavy that I could feel the springs go down.

'Papa, papa, do take a second cab,' said the young girl in a beseeching tone; 'I am sure we are wrong; I am sure it is very cruel.'

'Nonsense, Grace, get in at once, and don't make all this fuss; a pretty thing it would be if a man of business had to examine every cab-horse before he hired it – the man knows his own business of course: there, get in and hold your tongue!'

My gentle friend had to obey; and box after box was dragged up and lodged on the top of the cab, or settled by the side of the driver. At last all was ready, and with his usual jerk of the rein and slash of the whip, he drove out of the station.

The load was very heavy, and I had had neither food nor rest since the morning; but I did my best, as I always had done in spite of cruelty and injustice.

I got along fairly till we came to Ludgate Hill; but there, the heavy load and my own exhaustion were too much. I was struggling to keep on, goaded by constant chucks of the rein and use of the whip, when, in a single moment – I cannot tell how – my feet slipped from under me, and I fell heavily to the ground on my side. The suddenness and the force with which I fell seemed to beat all the breath out of my body.

I lay perfectly still; indeed, I had no power to move, and I thought now I was going to die. I heard a sort of confusion round me – loud, angry voices, and the getting down of the luggage; but it was all like a dream. I thought I heard that sweet, pitiful voice saying, 'Oh! that poor horse! it is all our fault.'

Someone came and loosened the throat strap of my bridle, and undid the traces which kept the collar so tight upon me. Someone said, 'He's dead, he'll never get up again.' Then I could hear a policeman giving orders, but I did not even open my eyes; I could only draw a gasping breath now and then. Some cold water was thrown over my head, some cordial was poured into my mouth, and something was covered over me.

I cannot tell how long I lay there, but I found my life coming back, and a kind-voiced man was patting me and encouraging me to rise. After some more cordial had been given me, and after one or two attempts, I staggered to my feet, and was gently led to some stables which were close by. Here I was put into a well-littered stall, and some warm gruel was brought to me: this I drank thankfully.

In the evening I was sufficiently recovered to be led back to Skinner's stables, where I think they did the best for me they could. In the morning Skinner came with a farrier to look at me. He examined me very closely, and said:

'This is a case of overwork more than disease, and if you could give him a run off for six months, he would be able to work again; but now there is not an ounce of strength in him.'

'Then he must just go to the dogs,' said Skinner. 'I have no meadows to nurse sick horses in – he may get well or he may not; that sort of thing does not suit my business. My plan is to work 'em as long as they'll go, and then sell 'em for what they'll fetch at the knacker's or elsewhere.'

'If he was broken-winded,' said the farrier, 'you had better have had him killed out of hand, but he is not; there is a sale of horses coming off in about ten days; if you rest him and feed him up, he may pick up, and you may at any rate get more than his skin is worth.'

Upon this advice Skinner, rather unwillingly, I think, gave orders that I should be well fed and cared for; and the stableman, happily for me, carried out the orders with a much better will than his master had shown in giving them.

Ten days of perfect rest, plenty of good oats, hay, and bran mashes with boiled linseed mixed in them, did more to get up my condition than anything else could have done.

Those linseed mashes were delicious, and I began to think that after all it might be better to live than go to the dogs. When the twelfth day after the accident came, I was taken to the sale, a few miles out of London. I felt that any change from my present place must be an improvement; so I held up my head, and hoped for the best.

CHAPTER FORTY-EIGHT

Farmer Thoroughgood and his Grandson Willie

At this sale of course I found myself in company with the old broken-down horses – some lame, some broken-winded, some old, and some that I am sure it would have been merciful to shoot.

The buyers and sellers, too, many of them, looked not much better off than the poor beasts for which they were bargaining. There were poor old men trying to get a horse or pony for a few pounds to drag about some little wood or coal cart. There were poor men trying to sell a worn-out beast for two or three pounds, rather than have the greater loss of killing him.

Some of them looked as if poverty and hard times had hardened them all over; but there were others for whom I would willingly have used the last of my strength – poor and shabby, but kind and human, with voices that I could trust. There was one tottering old man that took a great fancy to me, and I to him, but I was not strong enough – it was an anxious time!

Coming from the better part of the fair, I noticed a man who looked like a gentleman farmer, with a young boy by his side. He had a broad back and round shoulders, a kind, ruddy face, and he wore a broad-brimmed hat. When he came up to me and my companions, he stood still and gave a pitiful look round upon us. I saw his eye rest on me; I had still a good mane and tail, which did something for my appearance. I pricked my ears and looked at him.

'There's a horse, Willie, that has known better days.'

'Poor old fellow!' said the boy. 'Do you think, grandpapa, he was ever a carriage horse?'

'Oh, yes, my boy,' said the farmer, coming closer, 'he might have been anything when he was young. Look at his nostrils and his ears, and the shape of his neck and shoulders; there's a deal of breeding about that horse.' He put out his hand and gave me a kind pat on the neck. I put out my nose in answer to his kindness, and the boy stroked my face.

'Poor old fellow! See, grandpapa, how well he understands kindness. Could you not buy him and make him young again, as you did Ladybird?'

'My dear boy, I can't make all old horses young. Besides, Ladybird was not so old as she was run down and badly used.'

'Well, grandpapa, I don't believe that this one is old; look at his mane and tail. I wish you would look into his mouth, and then you could tell. Though he is so very thin, his eyes are not sunken like some old horses.'

The old gentleman laughed. 'Bless the boy! he is as horsy as his old grandfather.'

'But do look at his mouth, grandpapa, and ask the price; I am sure he would grow young in our meadows.'

The man who had brought me for sale now put in his word.

'The young gentleman's a real knowing one, sir. Now the fact is, this 'ere hoss is just pulled down with overwork in the cabs. He's not an old one, and I heard as how the vet.

should say that a six months' run off would set him right up, being as how his wind was not broken. I've had the tending of him these ten days past, and a more grateful and pleasant animal I never met. 'Twould be worth a gentleman's while to give a five-pound note for him and let him have a chance. I'll be bound he'd be worth twenty pounds next spring.'

The old gentleman laughed, and the little boy looked up eagerly.

'Oh! grandpapa, did you not say that the colt sold for five pounds more than you expected? You would not be poorer if you did buy this one.'

The farmer slowly felt my legs, which were much swollen and strained; then he looked at my mouth – 'Thirteen or fourteen, I should say. Just trot him out, will you?'

I arched my poor thin neck, raised my tail a little, and threw out my legs as well as I could, for they were very stiff.

'What is the lowest you will take for him?' said the farmer as I came back.

'Five pounds, sir; that was the lowest price my master set.'

' 'Tis a speculation,' said the old gentleman, shaking his head, but at the same time slowly drawing out his purse – 'quite a speculation! Have you any more business here?' he said, counting the sovereigns into the man's hand.

'No, sir, I can take him for you to the inn if you please.'

'Do so; I am now going there.'

They walked forward, and I was led behind. The boy could hardly control his delight, and the old gentleman seemed to enjoy his pleasure. I had a good feed at the inn, and was then gently ridden home by a servant of my new master and turned into a large meadow with a shed in one corner of it.

Mr Thoroughgood, for that was the name of my benefactor, gave orders that I should have hay and oats every night and morning, and the run of the meadow during the day. 'You, Willie,' said he, 'must take the oversight of him; I give him into your charge.'

The boy was proud of his charge, and undertook it in all seriousness. There was not a day when he did not pay me a visit, picking me out from among the other horses to give me a bit of carrot or some other good thing, or sometimes to stand by me whilst I ate my oats. He always came with kind words and caresses, and of course I grew very fond of him. He called me Old Crony, as I used to come to him in the field and follow him about. Sometimes he brought his grandfather, who always looked closely at my legs.

'That is our point, Willie,' he would say; 'but he is improving so steadily that I think we shall see a change for the better in the spring.'

The perfect rest, the good food, the soft turf, and gentle exercise soon began to tell on my condition and my spirits. I had a good constitution from my mother, and I was never strained when I was young, so that I had a better chance than many horses who have been worked before they came to their full strength.

During the winter my legs improved so much that I began to feel quite young again. The spring came round, and one day in March Mr Thoroughgood determined that he would try me in the phaeton. I was well pleased, and he and Willie drove me a few miles. My legs were not stiff now and I did the work with perfect ease.

'He's growing young, Willie; we must give him a little gentle work now, and by midsummer he will be as good as Ladybird; he has a beautiful mouth and good paces; these could not be better.'

'Oh, grandpapa, how glad I am you bought him!'

'So am I, my boy, but he has to thank you more than me. We must now be looking out for a quiet, genteel place for him where he will be valued.'

CHAPTER FORTY-NINE

My Last Home

One day during this summer the groom cleaned and dressed me with such extraordinary care that I thought some new change must be at hand. He trimmed my fetlocks and legs, passed the tarbrush over my hoofs, and even parted my forelock. I think the harness also had an extra polish. Willie seemed half anxious, half merry, and he got into the chaise with his grandfather.

'If the ladies take to him,' said the old gentleman, 'they'll be suited, and he'll be suited: we can but try.'

At the distance of a mile or two from the village we came to a pretty, low house with a lawn and shrubbery at the front and a drive up to the door. Willie rang the bell, and asked if Miss Blomefield or Miss Ellen was at home. Yes, they both were. So whilst Willie stayed with me, Mr Thoroughgood went into the house.

In about ten minutes he returned, followed by three ladies. One tall, pale lady, wrapped in a white shawl, leaned on a younger lady with dark eyes and a merry face; the third, a very stately-looking person, was Miss Blomefield. They all came to look at me and ask questions. The younger lady – this was Miss Ellen – took to me very much; she said she was sure she should like me, for I had such a good face. The tall, pale lady said that she should always be nervous in riding behind a horse that had once been down, as I might come down again; and if I did, she should never get over the fright.

'You see, ladies,' said Mr Thoroughgood, 'many first-rate

horses have had their knees broken through the carelessness of their drivers, without any fault of their own; and from what I see of this horse, I should say that is his case: but of course I do not wish to influence you. If you wish, you can have him on trial, and then your coachman will see what he thinks of him.'

'You have always been such a good adviser to us about our horses,' said the stately lady, 'that your recommendation would go a long way with me, and if my sister Lavinia sees no objection, we will accept with thanks your offer of a trial.'

It was then arranged that I should be sent for the next day.

In the morning a smart-looking young man came for me. At first he looked pleased, but when he saw my knees, he said in a disappointed voice: 'I didn't think, sir, you would have recommended my ladies a blemished horse like this.'

'Handsome is that handsome does,' said my master. 'You are only taking him on trial, and I am sure you will do fairly by him, young man; and if he is not as safe as any horse you ever drove, send him back.'

I was led home, placed in a comfortable stable, fed, and left to myself. The next day, when my groom was cleaning my face, he said: 'That is just like the star that Black Beauty had, and he is much the same height, too; I wonder where he is now.'

A little farther on he came to the place in my neck where I was bled, and where a little knot was left in the skin. He almost started, and began to look me over carefully, talking to himself.

'White star in the forehead, one white foot on the off side, this little knot just in that place'; then, looking at the middle of my back – 'and as I am alive, there is that little patch of white hair that John used to call "Beauty's three-penny-bit". It *must* be Black Beauty! Why, Beauty! Beauty! do you know me, little Joe Green that almost killed you?'

And he began patting and patting me as if he was quite overjoyed.

I could not say that I remembered him, for now he was a fine grown young fellow with black whiskers and a man's voice, but I was sure he knew me, and that he was Joe Green; so I was very glad. I put my nose up to him, and tried to say that we were friends. I never saw a man so pleased.

'Give him a fair trial! I should think so indeed! I wonder who the rascal was that broke your knees, my old Beauty! You must have been badly served out somewhere. Well, well, it won't be my fault if you haven't good times of it now. I wish John Manly were here to see you.'

In the afternoon I was put into a low park chair and brought to the door. Miss Ellen was going to try me, and Green went with her. I soon found that she was a good driver, and she seemed pleased with my paces. I heard Joe telling her about me, and that he was sure I was Squire Gordon's old Black Beauty.

When we returned, the other sisters came out to hear how I had behaved myself. She told them what she had just heard, and said, 'I shall certainly write to Mrs Gordon to tell her that her favourite horse has come to us. How pleased she will be!'

After this I was driven every day for a week or so, and as I appeared to be quite safe, Miss Lavinia at last ventured out in the small close carriage. After this, it was quite decided to keep me and to call me by my old name of 'Black Beauty'.

I have now lived in this happy place a whole year. Joe is the best and kindest of grooms. My work is easy and pleasant, and I feel my strength and spirits all coming back again. Mr Thoroughgood said to Joe the other day, 'In your place he will last till he is twenty years old – perhaps more.'

Willie always speaks to me when he can, and treats me as his special friend. My ladies have promised that I shall never be sold, and so I have nothing to fear; and here my story ends. My troubles are all over and I am at home; and often before I am quite awake, I fancy I am still in the orchard at Birtwick, standing with my old friends under the apple trees.

MAN'S DISCOVERY OF HIS PAST

MAN'S DISCOVERY OF HIS PAST

Literary Landmarks in Archaeology

Edited by

Robert F. Heizer

A SPECTRUM BOOK

Prentice-Hall, Inc., *Englewood Cliffs, N. J.*

To Paul Fejos

Barát és collega

PREFACE

The present collection of reprinted articles or excerpts from longer works will provide, I hope, easy and inexpensive access to a number of significant literary landmarks in man's study of his past. The choice of items is my own, and doubtless reflects in some manner my own interests as they have developed in the course of twenty years of reading and teaching. Another archaeologist interested in the history of archaeology would, no doubt, have selected some of the same items, as well as others which I have not chosen.

Reading *about* an earlier student who recognized an important principle, or who tediously arrived at a significant conclusion is not the same thing as reading the article in the original author's words. Most of us can not readily secure the original works in which these contributions appear since they are often rare books which libraries hesitate to loan freely. One way to make older written works available is to reprint them. This process is limited, of course; we will never have all the works of the past at our fingertips in reprint form. Some of the rarer contributions important to the development of archaeological discipline are reprinted here in the hope that the students will be able to savor an original contribution better than they could by hearsay, as it were, in a lecture or a synthetic history.

Some of the authors in this volume will not be familiar to the reader, and the new acquaintance will, I hope, be a pleasant experience. Other authors will be known, by name at least, but the reader will probably not have read the original article.

I have benefited from the suggestions made by a number of my colleagues in assembling and organizing the contents of this book. In particular I wish to acknowledge the aid and encouragement of Paul Fejos, Director of Research of the Wenner-Gren Foundation for Anthropological Research, to whom this book is dedicated in recognition of my debt to him for stimulating me to learn about the history of archaeology. My more immediate colleagues, among whom I wish to thank Howel Williams, Earl Count, J. Desmond Clark, Loren Eiseley, Alex D. Krieger, and Sherwood L. Washburn, have been both encouraging and helpful.

R. F. H.

Table of Contents

Introduction

The Greeks and Romans were collectors, but not true archaeologists —they did not excavate in order to reconstruct the past—as the reader will learn from reading A. J. B. Wace's article in this volume. Although classical authors—Hesiod, Xenophon, Lucretius, Tacitus, and Herodotus —have left us useful and important accounts, their explanations of antiquity are speculative and mythological.[1] These works are chiefly of ethnographic significance in that they record contemporary peoples and situations as seen by or reported to the authors. As Peake (1940:116) states it, the Greeks "preferred to think out what was likely to have happened rather than search for evidence of what actually had taken place."

Ferdinand Lot (1961:170) summarizes the problem of Classical science by saying, "science as well as philosophy suffered from the formidable competition of the spirit of mythology, which offers at a smaller cost more attractive solutions to the problems of life and death." After Alaric's seizure of Rome on August 24, 410 A.D., which marked the fall and division of the Roman Empire, there followed, at least in the West, a long period during which the church preserved those few Classical works which have come down to our day. It was a long darkness in intellectual thought, and even at the end the light came only slowly and fitfully. This period of history is masterfully reviewed by Lot in his *The End of the Ancient World and the Beginnings of the Middle Ages* (1961, esp. Chap. IX, Part 1; Chap. XIII, Part 3; see also Sanford, 1944).

Knowledge was nearly lost during the Dark Ages, and all independent thinking about the history of the earth or of man was effectively suppressed by the universal adherence to the Bible as the supreme authority. Medieval scholars regarded all living forms as descendants of those which survived the Noachian Flood. Thus, we see why ancient stone tools were long thought not to be man-made but were explained by citing Classical authorities as the result of lightning striking the earth (Blinkenberg, 1911). Fossils found on mountains far distant from the sea were passed off as having been washed there by the waves of the biblical Flood. The first challenges of such explanations appeared in the fifteenth century, and slowly the idea developed that fossils of plants and animals were evidence

---

[1] Possible exceptions are Hesiod (*Works and Days*) and Homer (*Iliad*), who, according to some authorities (Myres, 1908:127-128; Land, 1908; Albright, 1940:41; Daniel, 1950:15; Page, 1959, chap. VI; Griffiths, 1956) but not others (Baldry, 1956), are describing a known chronological situation at the end of the Bronze Age.

of very ancient life forms which had once lived and since turned to stone. The Biblical chronology, which allowed only six thousand years since the creation in 4004 B.C. (Haber, 1959c),[2] was clearly insufficient, and intelligent individuals realized that the accepted ideas of the earth's age must be in error. Albert Einstein's statement, "Imagination is more important than knowledge," applies to men of all epochs.[3] The fascinating story of how men—brave as well as imaginative—discovered that the world's history differed from that given in the Book of Genesis is carefully told in J. C. Greene's *The Death of Adam* (1961; see also Haber, 1959a, 1959b, 1959c; Eiseley, 1961).

In the selections reprinted here the reader will be able to follow the steps which led to the development of a geological chronology, to the realization that prehistoric stone tools were made by man, and that the geological earth layers contained truly ancient remains of man himself and of his stone tools. Thus, for example, Mercatus' realization that some stone implements were man-made tools rather than *ceraunia* (thunderbolts) was a prerequisite to any study of prehistoric artifacts, and Steno's establishment of the basic principle of geological stratification, which stated that in any superimposed series of earth strata the order of deposition can be read from bottom to top, opened the way not only for a geological chronology but also provided a means of tying this chronology to the succession of life forms contained in the layers. Frere for the first time recognized and published (1800) clear evidence that chipped flint implements made by man were coeval with forms of animal life now extinct, and in so doing prematurely founded Paleolithic archaeology. No one person saw the grand vista of geological time and the evolution of life forms more clearly than Charles Darwin, who, in 1859, published his great book *On the Origin of Species by Means of Natural Selection or the Preservation of Favored Races in the Struggle for Life.*[4]

[2] As Haber (1959c:1) points out, the creation date was computed differently by authorities using different versions of the Scripture, but all were in general agreement. The Rabbinical chronology based on the Hebrew text accepted 3700 B.C.; the Roman Catholic Church accepted 5199 B.C. based upon the Clementine edition of the Vulgate; and the King James Authorized Version listed 4004 B.C. as determined by Archbishop Ussher.

[3] Flinders Petrie, the archaeologist, wrote: "Imagination is the fire of discovery," and T. Mommsen, the historian, said: "Imagination, mother of all poetry, is likewise mother of all history."

[4] For a survey of the influence of Darwin and ensuing accomplishments in the century 1859-1959 see *Evolution After Darwin*, S. Tax, ed., Vols. 1-3, (University of Chicago Press, 1960). Darwin in 1859 avoided direct discussion of the ancestry or evolution of man, and is reported to have admitted that he had been unwilling to accept the evidence of man's antiquity which the British geologists (Evans, Falconer, and Prestwich) had presented in 1859 after their return from France where they had inspected the Somme gravels with Boucher de Perthes (see chap. II of this volume). Darwin did take up the problem of human evolution in 1871 in his *The Descent of Man*. Darwin's 1859 book established the general principle of organic evolution and pointed out a new way of thinking about life forms.

The emergence of the study of the human past was part of the intellectual awakening that followed the Middle Ages. The antiquarians of the sixteenth, seventeenth, and eighteenth centuries were interested in prehistoric antiquities among other things, and they deserve an honorable rank as sincere, though often uninformed, students of the past. But the accurate study of the past could only come about through the application of a new method of looking at the external world which involved observation and deduction to replace the "prescientific" approach which was subjective and inductive. A variety of social, economic, industrial, and intellectual factors all had some influence in leading to the serious study of prehistory (see Crawford, 1932; Piggott, 1937; Childe, 1953; Clark, 1957:50-55).

O. G. S. Crawford (1953:21) has written, "Remember that the evolution of man from an ancestral primate, and the origins of civilization, are discoveries that have been made during the span of two lives, one of which is still running." And in this second life span, man is engaged not only in a massive world-wide study of the human past through archaeology, but also in an attempt to apply his knowledge to the problems of man's future on the earth. For instance, we have retrospective surveys of man's use of natural resources with future prospects estimated (Vogt, 1948; Brown, 1954; Nicholson, 1961), as well as attempts to calculate when the earth's human population will approach infinity.[5] A sort of ultramodern archaeological detection is to listen for signals from extraterrestrial civilizations (von Hoerner, 1961).

The relative newness of archaeology as a formal discipline with a special vocabulary is also shown in that the first use of the word "prehistoric" with reference to archaeology dates from 1851 (Putnam, 1899:3; Daniel, 1950:86); the coining of "Paleolithic" and "Neolithic" is attributed to Lubbock in 1865 (Lubbock, 1865); and the earliest use of the term "human paleontology" was by Marcel de Serres in 1853 (Hamy, 1870:2). The use of the word "archaeology," though not strictly in its modern sense, dates back to a book by Dionysius of Halicarnassus about 2,000 years ago [Rowe (n.d.)]. Caumont, in 1836, first used the term "chronological horizon" to indicate "the periods in the history of art remarkable for revolutions or for notable changes in the forms and character of the monuments" (Morlot, 1864:401; cf. Childe, 1944a). The familiar terms "dolichocephalic" and "brachycephalic" to denote skull shapes were invented by G. Retzius in 1842 (Peake, 1940:109), and use of the terms "Palaeanthropic" to refer to the Neanderthal type of man and "Neoanthropic" to designate fully evolved *Homo sapiens* came as late as 1916 (Smith, 1916:325).

[5] One prediction is Friday, November 13, 2026 A.D. (von Foerster, Mora and Amiot, 1960). See also Darwin, 1960.

✳ 1 ✳

OF TIME AND CHANGE

Archaeological age-dating by means of which we establish cultural chronology does not, as a whole, comprise a single field of endeavor. Instead it is a compartmentalized discipline composed of individuals who are expert, usually in one or at most a few, of the techniques and skills used to answer the question, "How old?"

There are a number of broad surveys of the time-reckoning methods used and the results secured; the reader is referred to the following publications for details: Heizer (1953), Griffin (1955), Smiley (1955), Zeuner (1958), Bowen (1958), and Aitken (1961).

The selections given here are all concerned with the early steps, methods, or outstanding conclusions which resulted from the application of those methods. This is not a comprehensive review of the vast field of age-dating but merely some of the historically significant contributions to it.

✳✳✳

Nicolaus Steno (1638-1686) was a Danish medical doctor attached to the court of Ferdinand II, Grand Duke of Tuscany. He was known in England, and his Prodromus, *first published in 1669, was translated into English two years later. Although his explanation of stratigraphy or the determination of the successive order of the earth strata may sound rather awkward to us, nearly three centuries later, the principle is nonetheless clear and is carefully illustrated with a diagram. Steno was one of the few in his day who were convinced that fossils are the remains of ancient organic forms. Admittedly, Steno glimpsed the possibility that the earth's history might be studied in the strata of its mantle, but more than a century passed before a clear conception of geological antiquity was brought forth. Steno's work is significant in that he formulated, for the first time, the concept of stratigraphy upon which paleontology depends Brunet (1950:78-79) suggests that the Englishman George Owen, in his* History of Pembrokeshire *which was written in 1570 but not published until 1796, was the first person to clearly set forth the orderly principle of geological stratigraphy. While this may be true, the appearance in print of Steno's* Prodromus *a hundred years before Owen's work gives Steno clear priority in the* effective *proposal of the idea. For further information see Woodford (1935), Lenoble (1954), Rowe (1961), and Greene (1961:57-61).*

The Strata of the Earth

Nicolaus Steno

The strata of the earth are due to the deposits of a fluid:

1. Because the comminuted matter of the strata could not have been reduced to that form unless, having been mixed with some fluid and then falling from its own weight, it had been spread out by the movement of the same superincumbent fluid.

2. Because the larger bodies contained in these same strata obey, for the most part, the laws of gravity, not only with respect to the position of any substance by itself, but also with respect to the relative position of different bodies to each other.

3. Because the comminuted matter of the strata has so adjusted itself to the bodies contained in it that it has not only filled all the smallest cavities of the contained body, but has also expressed the smoothness and luster of the body in that part of its own surface where it is in contact with the body, although the roughness of the comminuted matter by no means admits of similar smoothness and luster.

Sediments, moreover, are formed so long as the contents in a fluid fall to the bottom of their own weight, whether the said contents have been carried thither from some other where, or have been secreted gradually

"The Prodromus of Nicolaus Steno's Dissertation Concerning a Solid Body Enclosed by Process of Nature Within a Solid," translated by John Garrett Winter with a Foreword by William H. Hobbs. *University of Michigan Studies, Humanistic Series.* Vol. XI, Excerpt here from pp. 227-231, 262-263, 276. (New York and London: The Macmillan Company, 1916.) Reprinted by permission of The University of Michigan Press.

from the particles of the fluid, that too, either in the upper surface, or equally from all the particles of the fluid. Although a close relationship exists between crusts and sediments, they can nevertheless be distinguished easily because the upper surface of crusts is parallel to the lower surface, however rough this may be from various larger projections, while the upper surface of sediments is parallel to the horizon, or deviates but slightly therefrom. So in rivers, the mineral layers, now green, now yellow, now reddish, do not remove the unevenness of a stony bottom, while a sediment of sand or clay makes all level; and it is due to this fact that in the formation of the different composite strata of the earth I have easily distinguished crusts from sediments.

Concerning the matter of the strata the following can be affirmed:

1. If all the particles in a stony stratum are seen to be of the same character, and fine, it can in no wise be denied that this stratum was produced at the time of the creation from a fluid which at that time covered all things; and Descartes also accounts for the origin of the earth's strata in this way.

2. If in a certain stratum the fragments of another stratum, or the parts of animals and plants are found, it is certain that the said stratum must not be reckoned among the strata which settled down from the first fluid at the time of the creation.

3. If in a certain stratum we discover traces of salt of the sea, the remains of marine animals, the timbers of ships, and a substance similar to the bottom of the sea, it is certain that the sea was at one time in that place, whatever be the way it came there, whether by an overflow of its own or by the upheaval of mountains.

4. If in a certain stratum we find a great abundance of rush, grass, pine cones, trunks and branches of trees, and similar objects, we rightly surmise that this matter was swept thither by the flooding of a river, or the inflowing of a torrent.

5. If in a certain stratum pieces of charcoal, ashes, pumice-stone, bitumen, and calcined matter appear, it is certain that a fire occurred in the neighborhood of the fluid; the more so if the entire stratum is composed throughout of ash and charcoal, such as I have seen outside the city of Rome, where the material for burnt bricks is dug.

6. If the matter of all the strata in the same place be the same, it is certain that that fluid did not take in fluids of a different character flowing in from different places at different times.

7. If in the same place the matter of the strata be different, either fluids of a different kind streamed in thither from different places at different times (whether a change of winds or an unusually violent downpour of rains in certain localities be the cause) or the matter in the same sediment was of varying gravity, so that first the heavier particles, then the lighter, sought the bottom. And a succession of storms might have

given rise to this diversity, especially in places where a like diversity of soils is seen.

8. If within certain earthy strata stony beds are found, it is certain either that a spring of petrifying waters existed in the neighborhood of that place, or that occasionally eruptions of subterranean vapors occurred, or that the fluid, leaving the sediment which had been deposited, again returned when the upper crust had become hardened by the sun's heat.

Concerning the position of strata, the following can be considered as certain:

1. At the time when a given stratum was being formed there was beneath it another substance which prevented the further descent of the comminuted matter; and so at the time when the lowest stratum was being formed either another solid substance was beneath it, or if some fluid existed there, then it was not only of a different character from the upper fluid, but also heavier than the solid sediment of the upper fluid.

2. At the time when one of the upper strata was being formed, the lower stratum had already gained the consistency of a solid.

3. At the time when any given stratum was being formed it was either encompassed on its sides by another solid substance, or it covered the entire spherical surface of the earth. Hence it follows that in whatever place the bared sides of the strata are seen, either a continuation of the same strata must be sought, or another solid substance must be found which kept the matter of the strata from dispersion.

4. At the time when any given stratum was being formed, all the matter resting upon it was fluid, and, therefore, at the time when the lowest stratum was being formed, none of the upper strata existed.

As regards form, it is certain that at the time when any given stratum was being produced its lower surface, as also its lateral surfaces, corresponded to the surfaces of the lower substance and lateral substances, but that the upper surface was parallel to the horizon, so far as possible; and that all strata, therefore, except the lowest, were bounded by two planes parallel to the horizon. Hence it follows that strata either perpendicular to the horizon or inclined toward it, were at one time parallel to the horizon.

Moreover, the changed position of strata and their exposed sides, such as are seen to-day in many places, do not contradict my statement; since in the neighborhood of those places evident traces of fires and waters are to be found. For just as water disintegrating earthy material carries it down sloping places not only on the surface of the earth but also in the earth's cavities; so fire, breaking up whatever solids oppose it, not only drives out their lighter particles but also sometimes hurls forth their heaviest weights; and the result is that on the surface of the earth are formed steeps, channels, and hollows, while in the bowels of the earth subterranean passages and caverns are produced.

By reason of these causes the earth's strata can change position in two ways:

The first process is the violent thrusting up of the strata, whether this be due to a sudden burning of subterranean gases, or be brought about through the violent explosion of air due to other great downfalls near by. This thrusting up of the strata is followed by a scattering of the earthy matter as dust and the breaking up of rocky matter into lapilli and rough fragments.

The second process is the spontaneous slipping or downfall of the upper strata after they have begun to form cracks, in consequence of the withdrawal of the underlying substance, or foundation. Hence by reason of the diversity of the cavities and cracks the broken strata assume different positions; while some remain parallel to the horizon, others become perpendicular to it, many form oblique angles with it, and not a few are twisted into curves because their substance is tenacious. This change can take place either in all the strata overlying a cavity, or in certain lower strata only, the upper strata being left unbroken.

The altered position of the strata affords an easy explanation of a variety of matters otherwise obscure. Herein may be found a reason for that unevenness in the surface of the earth which furnishes occasion for so many controversies; an unevenness manifest in mountains, valleys, elevated bodies of water, elevated plains, and low plains. But passing over the rest I shall now treat briefly certain points concerning mountains.

THE DIFFERENT CHANGES WHICH HAVE TAKEN PLACE IN TUSCANY

In what way the present condition of any thing discloses the past condition of the same thing, is above all other places clearly manifest in Tuscany; inequalities of surface observed in its appearance today contain within themselves plain tokens of different changes, and these I shall review in inverse order, proceeding from the last to the first.

1. At one time the inclined plane A [Fig. 1, No. 20] was in the same plane with the higher, horizontal plane B, and the end of the same plane A thus raised, as also the end of the higher, horizontal place C, were continuous, whether the lower, horizontal plane E was in the same plane with the higher horizontal planes B, C, or another solid body existed there, supporting the exposed sides of the higher planes. Or, what is the same thing, in the place where today rivers, swamps, sunken plains, steeps, and planes inclined between sand hills are seen, all was once level, and at that time all the waters, both of rains and of springs, were flooding that plain, or had opened for themselves underground channels beneath it; at any rate, there were cavities under the upper strata.

2. At the time when the plane B, A, C [Fig. 1, No. 21] was being formed, and other planes under it, the entire plane B, A, C, was covered

with water; or, what is the same thing, the sea was at one time raised above sand hills, however high.

3. Before the plane *B, A, C* [Fig. 1, No. 22] was formed, the planes *F, G, I* [Fig. 1, No. 23] had the same position which they now hold; or, what is the same thing, before the strata of the sand hills were formed, deep valleys existed in the same places.

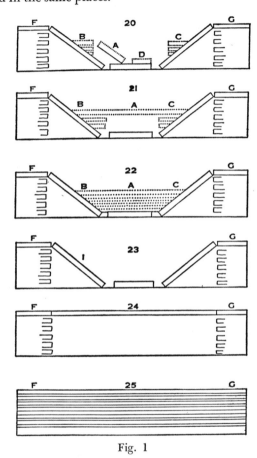

Fig. 1

4. At one time the inclined plane *I* [Fig. 1, No. 23] appeared in the same plane with the horizontal planes *F* and *G*, and either the exposed sides of the planes *I* and *G* were continuous, or another solid existed there, supporting the exposed sides when the planes were being formed; or, what is the same thing, where valleys are seen today between the plane summits of the highest mountains, there was at one time a single continuous plane under which huge caverns had been formed before the downfall of the upper strata.

5. When the plane F, G [Fig. 1, Nos. 24 and 25] was being formed, a watery fluid lay upon it; or, what is the same thing, the plane summits of the highest mountains were at one time covered with water.

Six distinct aspects of Tuscany [This summary takes up the figures in inverse order, figures 25, 24, etc.] we therefore recognize, two when it was fluid, two when level and dry, two when it was broken; and as I prove this fact concerning Tuscany by inference from many places examined by me, so do I affirm it with reference to the entire earth, from the descriptions of different places contributed by different writers. But in order that no one may be alarmed by the novelty of my view, in a few words I shall set forth the agreement of Nature with Scripture by reviewing the chief difficulties which can be urged regarding the different aspects of the earth.

The last six figures [of Fig. 1], while they show in what way we infer the six distinct aspects of Tuscany from its present appearance, at the same time serve for the readier comprehension of what we have said about the earth's strata. The dotted lines represent the sandy strata of the earth, so called from the predominant element, although various strata of clay and rock are mixed with them; the rest of the lines represent strata of rock, likewise named from the predominant element, although other strata of a softer substance are sometimes found among them. In the Dissertation itself I have explained the letters of the figures in the order in which the figures follow one another: here I shall briefly review the order of change.

Figure 25 shows the vertical section of Tuscany at the time when the rocky strata were still whole and parallel to the horizon.

Figure 24 shows the huge cavities eaten out by the force of fires or waters while the upper strata remained unbroken.

Figure 23 shows the mountains and valleys caused by the breaking of the upper strata.

Figure 22 shows new strata, made by the sea, in the valleys.

Figure 21 shows a portion of the lower strata in the new beds destroyed, while the upper strata remain unbroken.

Figure 20 shows the hills and valleys produced there by the breaking of the upper sandy strata.

✳ ✳ ✳

The effective formulation and presentation of the Three Age System,—the succession of the chief industrial materials from stone to bronze to iron—was made by C. J. Thomsen, curator of the Museum of Northern Antiquities (later the Danish National Museum) from 1816 to 1865. The proposal first appeared in an 1836 edition of the guidebook to the museum; the excerpt printed here is a translation from the German edition published a year later. Thomsen based his formulation upon the great collections in the museum where he worked; the theory resulted from the need to classify these collections in some meaningful system. The stratigraphic proof of the theory, based on excavation, came only later with the work of Worsaae, Steenstrup, Nilsson, and others (cf. Piggott, 1960:89). For penetrating analyses of Thomsen's scheme showing its earlier importance but present-day inapplicability see Childe (1944b) and Daniel (1943).

Thomsen's proposal was made at the precise instant when it could be profitably applied, and he is properly given credit for the effective presentation of the idea. But Thomsen is probably not independently responsible for the concept, since we know that he was a careful scholar and had read books and journals dealing with antiquities. For reviews of Thomsen's predecessors, of whom there were many dating back to Hesiod in the seventh century B.C., see Daniel (1943) and Heizer (1962). Among the scholars who anticipated Thomsen, and indeed one whose work may have directly helped Thomsen to formulate his hypothesis, was A. Y. Goguet whose three volume work was first published in Paris in 1758 and reprinted many times in France, Italy, and England until 1818. An extract from Goguet's work dealing with the succession of the stone, bronze, and iron industrial stages is given here, and with it are Goguet's prefatory remarks on the early history of mankind which he believed was traceable only as far back as the Noachian Deluge. The awakening from this "dogmatic slumber" was not to come until over half a century later.

The Ancient History of Mankind

A. Y. Goguet

OF THE STATE OF MANKIND IMMEDIATELY AFTER THE DELUGE

The family of Noah remained no longer united in one society on the plains of Shinar, than was necessary for their increase and security. As soon as they were become sufficiently numerous, God was pleased to disperse them into the different regions of the earth, about the time of the birth of Peleg, nearly 150 years after the deluge. It appears, that these new inhabitants of the earth had no design to separate. They were some-

The Origin of Laws, Arts, and Sciences, and their Progress among the Most Ancient Nations, translated from the French of the President De Goguet. 3 vols. [Vol. 1 translated by R. Henry: Vol. 2 translated by Dr. Dunn; Vol. 3 translated by A. Spearman.] (Excerpt here taken from Vol. I, pp. 1-6, 140-161). Edinburgh, 1761.

times forced to part in order to seek subsistence: but the fear of losing each other, in their various excursions, made them use all the precautions they could think of to prevent so great a misfortune. With this view they formed the design of building a city, and raising a tower in it to a prodigious height, that it might be seen at a great distance, and serve them for a signal and center of reunion. But Providence, judging their separation necessary for the more speedy repeopling of the earth, employed the most effectual means to oblige them to disperse. All mankind at that time spoke the same language. The Supreme Being dissolved this powerful bond of union, by confounding their tongues in such a manner, that, not understanding each other, they separated and directed their steps to different parts of the world.

I shall not undertake to describe the routes of the several colonies which were then formed. Such a disquisition would be altogether foreign to my present purpose. I shall only observe, that if we reflect ever so little, with how much ease and expedition the Savages, Tartars, and Arabians of our days, transport themselves and their whole families to very great distances, we shall soon be convinced, that those first men, naturally robust, accustomed to a life of labor, and having few wants, when forced to quit their native soil in search of new settlements, might in a very little time spread themselves over the different climates of our hemisphere.

But this dispersion of mankind must necessarily have considerably diminished the primitive knowledge which they had hitherto been able to preserve. All society being dissolved by this confusion of tongues, and families living detached from each other, they sunk in a little time into the profoundest ignorance. Add to this, the consideration of the tumult and disorder inseparable from new establishments, and we shall easily conceive how there was a time, in which almost all this world was plunged into the most deplorable barbarity. Men wandered in the woods and fields, without laws, without leaders, or any form of government. Their ferocity became so great, that many of them devoured each other. All kinds of knowledge, even the most common and necessary, were so much neglected, that not a few had forgot even the use of fire. It is to these unhappy times we must refer what profane historians relate of the miseries which afflicted the first ages of the world. All ancient traditions declare that the first men led a life very little different from that of beasts.

We shall find no difficulty in believing these relations, if we cast our eyes on what ancient authors tell us of the state of several countries even in their own times, a state the reality of which is confirmed by modern relations. Travellers inform us, that even at this day, in some parts of the world, they meet with men who are strangers to all social intercourse, of a character so cruel and ferocious, that they live in perpetual war, destroying, and even devouring each other. These wretched people, void of all the principles of humanity, without laws, polity, or government, live in dens and caverns, and differ but very little from the brute creation.

Their food consists of some fruits and roots with which the woods supply them; for want of skill and industry they seldom procure more solid nourishment. In a word, not having even the most common and obvious notions, they have nothing of humanity but the external figure.

These savage people exactly answer the description given us by historians of the ancient state of mankind. We see even from scripture, that, soon after the dispersion, the precepts and example of Noah were so generally forgotten, that even the ancestors of Abraham were plunged in idolatry. When Jacob went into Mesopotamia, he found idolatry mixed with the worship of the true God in the family of his uncle Laban. After such facts as these, it is not in the least surprising to find the primitive traditions so darkened and disfigured by the most ridiculous fables among the Heathen nations.

As to the arts and sciences, there is no doubt, but some families preserved themselves from that barbarity and ignorance which succeeded the confusion of languages, and the dispersion of mankind. The most useful and necessary discoveries were never entirely lost. The precious seeds of these were preserved by the families who remained in the plains of Shinar, and the adjacent countries, where mankind had been first planted after the flood. Neither were these branches of knowledge altogether forgotten by those colonies who took up an early fixed residence: for example, those who settled in Persia, Syria, and Egypt. By their means, the several parts of human knowledge were preserved, propagated, and improved. But all the rest of mankind, excepting these few families, I repeat it again, led the life of savages and barbarians. The ancient state of the human race may very well be compared to that of the Cyclops, that is to say, the ancient inhabitants of Sicily, as represented by Homer.

"The Cyclops," says this poet, "know no laws. Each governs his family, and rules over his wife and children. They trouble not themselves with the affairs of their neighbors, and think not themselves interested in them. Accordingly, they have no assemblies to deliberate on public affairs. They are governed by no general laws to regulate their manners and their actions. They neither plant nor sow. They are fed by the fruits which the earth produces spontaneously. Their abode is on the summits of mountains, and caverns serve them for a retreat." Behold a lively picture of the manner in which almost all the families of the world lived immediately after their dispersion.

This savage unsociable life could not be of long continuance with regard to a great part of mankind. So many motives concurred to induce families to associate and mingle with each other, that several of them must have united very early. This were the proper place to inquire in what manner this reunion of mankind was brought about. But as no certain monuments are now remaining of these first transactions, and as there is no end of forming conjectures and hypotheses, we shall not enter into any discussion concerning the origin of these first societies.

OF THE DISCOVERY AND WORKING OF METALS

The discovery of metals was probably owing to accident. But we owe the art of working them, and applying them to all their various uses, to the necessities and industry of those nations who lived by agriculture. Without the art of working metals, agriculture never could have made any great progress, or have arrived at that degree of perfection in which we find it in the very first ages, in some countries. We may say the same of all the mechanic arts. They owe almost all their improvements to the discovery and use of metals.

How, when, and by whom was this discovery made? It is difficult to answer these questions. Nor is it easier to explain the manner in which mankind found out the art of working metals, and applying them to their various uses. The ancients looked upon the invention of metallurgy as something so divine and marvellous, that they ascribed it to celestial beings.

Metals were discovered, and they understood the art, even of working iron, before the deluge. But that dreadful calamity deprived the greatest part of mankind of this, as well as of other arts. All antiquity agrees in saying that there was a time, when the use of metals was unknown to mankind. This is the more credible, as ancient authors speak of several nations to whom this important discovery was unknown. We see that these people used stones, flints, the horns of animals, the bones of beasts, and fishes, shells, reeds, and thorns for all the purposes for which civilized nations use metals at present. The savages set before us a striking picture of the ignorance of the ancient world, and the practices of primitive times. They have no idea of metals, and supply the want of them by the means I have just now mentioned.

Metallurgy, however, was an early discovery amongst the nations who applied to agriculture. Necessity forced them to study the working of metals, in order to form those tools they stood in need of. We see the use of metals established in Egypt and Palestine, a few ages after the flood. The Egyptians gave the honor of this discovery to their first sovereigns; the Phoenicians to their ancient heroes. These traditions are fully confirmed by the authority of the sacred books. In the days of Abraham, metals were common in Egypt and in several countries of Asia. The art of metallurgy had even then arrived at great perfection. Nor is it surprising, that this art made such rapid progress in Asia and Egypt. These countries were the first where mankind settled, and formed themselves into powerful monarchies. I am however of opinion, that, in these ages, they understood only the working of a few metals, as gold, silver, and copper. Iron, that metal so necessary, and at present so common, was long either quite unknown, or but little used by ancient nations. Let us trace the steps of the human mind on this important article, and collect all the light which ancient history affords us concerning the discovery and improvements of this necessary art. Let us also compare what probably happened in the primitive times, with what we see practiced in some places in our own age.

The discovery of metals would not cost the first descendants of Noah much searching for. It would not be necessary to dig into the bowels of the earth for what presented itself upon the surface. A thousand events, of which we might quote many examples, would put metals into the hands of the first men. The devastations occasioned by great rains and inundations, were probably the first means of the discovery of metals. In some countries, after violent rains, metals are found almost in every brook. Torrents pouring from the mountains, deposit great quantities of gold upon the land and gravel in the valleys. In the kingdom of Achem, it is not necessary to dig into the earth for that metal; it may be picked up on the sides of the mountains, and in gutters made by the torrents. The ancients speak also of several rivers very famous for rolling down gold, silver, copper, and tin, in their waters. We know of several rivers which still enjoy this advantage.

As to mines, several accidents might discover to mankind the mineral substances which the earth concealed in her bosom. Thunder might break off pieces of rocks or mountains, and thereby betray the precious metals they contained. A gold mine was discovered in Peru by such an accident about the end of the last century. Sometimes the winds, by tearing up trees by the roots, have discovered metals and minerals. It is well known how the famous mines of Potosi were discovered. An Indian climbing up some rocks covered with trees and bushes, took hold of a small tree, which grew in a cleft of a rock, and pulled it by the root; he observed something glitter in the hole, which upon examination he found to be an ingot of silver. Sometimes also torrents carrying away the earth by their impetuosity, lay open the veins of metals. Laborers, in digging, have sometimes hit, by accident, upon very rich mines. It was in this manner, as Justin relates, that the gold mines which formerly rendered Spain so famous, were discovered. In a word, small branches sometimes appear upon the surface, and point to the veins below.

When men afterwards came to search for mines, the observations they had made on the appearance and qualities of the soil where metals had been originally found, would serve them for a guide. Nature furnishes several indications and external marks, by which it is not very difficult to discover mines. These soils have particular characteristics which are easily observed and remembered. Their color, particularly, is different from that of other soils, and gives strong indications of the minerals they contain. By this, and the observation of the herbs they produce, a guess may be formed even of the kind of mineral they conceal. These soils are for the most part barren, rough, and steep. Very often they produce no grass. A careful inspection of one mine therefore would lead them to discover others.

If it is easy to imagine how the first men might discover metals, it is difficult to conceive, and still more difficult to explain how they arrived at the art of working them. It is only by means of fire that we can prepare metals for our use. But before they can be forged, they must be melted and refined, that is, separated from all other substances which are mixed with them, and cast into masses of pure metal, which may be afterwards divided at pleasure. These operations are very difficult, and require no little dexterity, knowledge, and reflection. Fusion is the first means used for these purposes.

We may suppose that volcanos might possibly give men some idea of metallurgy. The streams of melted minerals, which from time to time are thrown up from these natural furnaces, might probably put men upon trying to work metals by the help of fire. What renders this conjecture the more credible, is, that those persons who are represented as the inventors of metallurgy, both by the fables and histories of antiquity, lived in countries famous for volcanos. . . .

I will confess however, that after all the conjectures we can form about these and the like accidents, the mind would not be entirely satisfied; some doubts would still remain, if we supposed that these first mines were in the same state, and had the same qualities with ours at present. The refining of metals in our times, commonly requires much labor, and many precautions; but we ought to consider that this operation probably was not near so difficult in the times we are now speaking of. In the first ages after the deluge, metals were commonly found on the surface of the earth, or at a very moderate depth, whatever way they were brought thither, whether by torrents, or by some fire which made them run from the mountains. Now metals, in this state, are not much mixed with other bodies, and consequently are much more easily melted and refined, than those which are brought from the bosom of the earth. The ancients speak of several countries where they picked up gold which had no need of refining, and we know of some where this may still be done. In some parts of Africa they find virgin gold so pure, that it is cast into ingots of an excellent quality by fire alone, without the help of any dissolvent. Several writers mention grains of natural gold of a prodigious bigness. Some have even weighed more than an hundred marks. A modern traveller says, he has seen a massy branch of gold, a cubit in length. This ingot, which was very pure, had been found in the river Couesme, in the kingdom of Mozambique. They find frequently in Peru pieces of virgin gold, some weighing more than eight or ten marks, and some more than an ounce. This gold needs no melting nor refining. In the kingdom of Macassar, besides gold dust, which they gather in great quantities, they pick up in the valleys where the torrents have flowed, ingots of pure gold without any mixture. In several countries, even at present, they gather gold which requires no artificial refining, only by washing away the earth, in certain places, by streams of water. This operation is very simple, and needs neither the chisel, the hammer, the mill, nor quicksilver. There is nothing to do but to wash the earth well, and a few small pieces of wood are sufficient to stir and mix it properly. This gold got by washing, was not unknown to the ancients. Lastly, the gold which is found in great quantities in certain rivers, is very fine, and requires little preparation. There is even some found so very pure, that it is ductile and malleable the moment it is taken out of the water.

Men at first would find no greater difficulty in refining silver and copper. In those days they would meet with these metals naturally pure and unmixed with other bodies, which render the smelting art so difficult at present. They knew formerly, and we know now, of rivers which roll silver and copper in their streams. Frequently too these metals are brought to light by torrents, and spread upon the surface of the earth. They are then found even in large masses, pure and without any mixture. Threads of pure silver have been often found in clues, resembling burnt lace. In some places of Peru they pick up pieces of virgin silver, only by digging lightly in the sand. Some of these pieces weigh sixty, and even one hundred and fifty marks. This virgin silver is malleable, and requires no further preparation, before it is wrought. It is the same with copper. The ancients speak of countries where that metal was found naturally pure. In several parts of Canada and Louisiana, they gather red copper very pure. Masses of this metal, weighing one hundred and fifty quintals, fit for working, have been discovered. It appears often in slender threads or branches.

Even when they afterwards came to dig metals from mines, they would at first find little difficulty in refining them. They ordinarily find metals quite pure, or with very little mixture, in the tops of mines. It is even not uncommon to meet with pure, and even maleable gold in some mines . . .

Mankind then, in these first ages, might procure metals without so much skill and labor as are now necessary in digging mines and refining metals. Besides, the consumption could not be very great, so that the resources, we have mentioned would be sufficient for a long time.

As the world became more populous and civilized, the consumption of metals would be greater. We are assured both by scripture and profane history, that the use of metals was very common in Asia and Egypt, about the middle of the period we are now examining. We cannot suppose that this plenty was altogether the gift of nature. By this time, no doubt, men had begun to dig mines, and no longer procured them with the same facility as at first. It then became necessary to study the art of separating metals from the other bodies with which they are commonly mixed.

Besides, it is not enough to expose metals to the fire as they come out of the mine. Many other precautions must be taken to extricate them from the foreign bodies with which they are intangled. The ore must not only be pounded and washed, but it must also be mixed with certain earths, and certain salts, and in a certain proportion. These are the only means of smelting and refining the greatest part of metals. Those who first attempted to refine metals, must often have met with the same accidents which happened to the ancient inhabitants of Peru in smelting silver ore. The Incas had silver mines in many of their mountains, but at first they knew not the art of refining that metal. They only put the ore into the fire, but instead of smelting they saw it evaporate in smoke. Necessity, the mother of invention, after several experiments, furnished them with a method of preventing this accident. They thought of mixing a certain quantity of lead with the silver. The experiment was made, and succeeded to their wish.

As ores became more refractory, it would become necessary to study the art of using fire to the best advantage, and of gradually increasing its force and activity. It would cost them much study to find out what kind of fewel [fuel] was most proper, whether coals, turf, wood, &c. Furnaces were probably invented very early, but bellows were not. That instrument, so simple and so useful, was certainly unknown in these first ages, and is still so to a great many nations. They must therefore have supplied the want of this instrument by some means or other; but we have no tradition on that subject. . . .

Nature has indeed diffused iron over all the world; but still there is no metal so difficult to be known and discovered. Nothing discloses it. The most part of other metals frequently show themselves such as they are, that is, in the real form of metals. The ores of gold, silver, and copper, have commonly a certain color and brightness which discover them. But iron is almost always concealed under appearances, which do not indicate any metal to vulgar eyes. It is not commonly found but in the form of stone, and deep under ground. Even in those countries where it most abounds, and is most exposed to view, the people trample upon it without knowing it; it seems only a blackish sand or gravel, having no marks to distinguish it from other kinds of matter, which are not iron, and yet have the same appearances. One must be a good natural philosopher to know this metal in the mine, or to find it out in the earths and sands which contain it. How could it occur then to men, who had never seen iron, had no idea of it, and were not looking for it? How could they extract this metal from that sand and gravel, by a chain of operations as much hidden from the mind as the materials were from the eye.

In reality, the greatest obstacle to the use of iron was the difficulty of making it. Iron, of all metals, is the most difficult to bring into fusion. Besides, one single melting is sufficient to render gold, silver, or copper ductile and malleable. It is not so with iron. A piece of this metal once melted, is as untractable as ever, and not more ductile than a flint. In this state it is still hard and brittle, and cannot bear the hammer, either cold or hot. The file, the chisel, and the graver, can make no impression upon it. In order to forge iron, therefore, it was necessary to find out the art of softening it, and rendering it ductile. To do this, it must be melted a second time, then beat with very heavy hammers; this mass must be put into the furnace, and heated till it is upon the point of fusion, then put again in this state under the hammer; this operation must be repeated several times: at last this hard and brittle mass, by frequent heating and hammering, becomes forgeable. All these operations much more complicated than those on other metals, must have long retarded the use of iron. . . . The history of Mexico and Peru affords us an evident proof of all this. These nations had long possessed the art of working gold, silver, and copper, but had not the least idea of iron, though it abounds in these countries.

All nations were originally in the same state of ignorance. We have incontestable proofs of this, independent of the testimony of historians. A kind of stones commonly call *thunderstones,* are still preserved in a great many cabinets. They have the shape of axes, plough-shares, hammers, mallets, or wedges. For the most part they are of a substance like that of our gunflints, so hard that no file can make the least impression upon them. We ought particularly to take notice, that they are almost all pierced with a round hole in the place most proper for receiving a handle; and this hole is made in such a manner, that the handle being once forced in, will not come out again but with great difficulty, as it is with our hammers. It is evident from inspection alone, that these stones have been thus wrought by the hands of men. The holes for inserting the handles prove their destination, and the several uses that were made of them. This is something more than a mere conjecture.

It is well known, that tools of stone have been in use in America from time immemorial. They are found in the tombs of the ancient inhabitants of Peru, and several nations use them at this day. They shape and sharpen them upon a kind of grindstone, and, by length of time, labor, and patience, form them into any figure they please. They then fit them very dexterously with a handle, and use them nearly in the same manner we do our tools of iron. Asia and Europe are strewed with these sort of stones. They are frequently found. There must then have been a time, when the people of these countries were ignorant of the use of iron, as the people of America were before the arrival of the Europeans.

Let us add to these evidences, the testimony of ancient authors. They are unanimous in declaring, that the first generations had little or no knowledge of iron, and that they were the latest in learning to work this or any metal. Anciently they employed copper for all the purposes for which we now make use of iron. Arms, tools for husbandry, and the mechanic arts, were all of copper for many ages. The writings of Homer leave us no room to doubt of this. We see, that, at the time of the Trojan war, iron was very little used. Copper, in a word, supplied its place; and this metal was used both in making of arms, and all kinds of tools and utensils. It was the same for many ages amongst the Romans. Almost all the arms and tools of that people now extant, are of copper. The most convincing proof, that the use of copper preceded that of iron, is, that the ancients used brass in all their religious ceremonies. . . .

It was the same in America, the arms and tools of that part of the world were of copper. Hatchets of this metal have been found in the ancient tombs of the Peruvians. These hatchets differ nothing from ours in shape. In Japan, even at this day, all things which in other countries are made of iron, are there made of copper or brass. In a word, every thing proves, that no metal was so much used in ancient times as copper. Many reasons contributed to this. Copper is found in great quantities, is easily taken from the mine, not difficult to smelt, and next to gold and silver, is the most ductile of all metals. . . .

In maintaining however that, originally, copper supplied the place of iron, I do not pretend to affirm that this last metal was altogether unknown in the ages we are now upon. Several testimonies give us reason to believe that some nations knew the art of working iron in very ancient times. There was a tradition among the Egyptians that Vulcan had taught them to forge arms of iron. The Phoenicians also ranked among their most ancient heroes, two brothers, who were supposed to have discovered iron, and the manner of working it. The Cretans, as Diodorus relates, placed both the discovery of iron, and the art of working it, in the most remote periods of their history. The inhabitants of Mount Ida pretended to have learned the art of working this metal, from the mother of the gods. In a word, Prometheus in Aeschylus boasts of having taught mankind the fabrication of all metals. Some authors ascribe the discovery of the art of working iron, to the Cyclops, and some to the Chalybes, a very ancient people, renowned for their skill in working this metal. The Chalybes inhabited the south coasts of the Euxine sea, between Colchis and Paphlagonia. Clemens Alexandrinus pretends that the art of making iron malleable was found out by the Noropes. This nation was situated in Pannonia, along the banks of the Danube, between Noricum and Moesia. Without entering into any discussion of these traditions, which are all liable to great difficulties and contradictions; it appears from the book of Job, that the art of working iron was known in some countries in the ages we are now speaking of. The books of Moses also furnish us with a very strong proof of the antiquity of this discovery. From the manner in which this legislator speaks of iron, it appears that metal must have been long in use in Egypt before his time. He celebrates the great hardness of it; takes notice that the bedstead of Og, King of Bashan, was of iron; he speaks of mines of iron; he compares the severity of the servitude of the Israelites in Egypt, to the heat of a furnace for melting that metal. But what is most worthy of our attention is, that they then made swords, knives, axes, and tools for cutting stones, of iron. To make the blades of swords and knives, they must have known the arts of tempering and turning iron into steel. These facts seem to me sufficient to prove that the discovery of iron, and the arts of working it, were extremely ancient in Egypt and Palestine.

But at the same time that we acknowledge the antiquity of working iron in some few places, we must confess that in these ages the use of it was neither very common, nor very much diffused. All antiquity is unanimous in declaring, that all nations we know any thing of, once used copper in the place of iron, and that this practice subsisted many ages, in some very enlightened and civilized countries.

✻ ✻ ✻

The Various Periods to Which Heathen Relics Can Be Assigned

C. J. Thomsen

Before starting to discuss the relics of the Christian period in the North, we shall look back at the objects which we have already touched upon and make a few suggestions as to the various ages to which they most probably can be assigned. Our collections are too new and our experiences too limited to permit us to draw conclusions in most cases with certainty. What we want to establish can be regarded only as surmises which surely will be better clarified and either verified or modified by the observations and study of these objects by various scholars. To facilitate this survey, we shall assign particular names to the various periods whose boundaries nevertheless cannot be accurately defined.

The Stone Age, or the period when weapons and tools were made of stone, wood, bone, and similar materials, and in which metals were known either very little or not at all. Even though one can surmise that some of the stone articles were used later in religious rituals and consequently remained in the same form and made of the same material as they were in the more ancient past, they are nevertheless found so often in the North, and besides this, so many of them bear definite indications of having been worn by use and of having been resharpened several times, that one cannot doubt that there was a time when these things were in

Leitfaden zur Nordischen Alterthumskunde, Herausgegeben von der Königlichen Gesellschaft für Nordische Alterthumskunde. (Kopenhagen, 1837) Present extract from pp. 57-64. Authorship of this guidebook is not given in the work, but it is known to have been prepared by Thomsen.

general use here in the North. That this is the oldest [period] in which we find that a man has lived in our region appears to be beyond all doubt; likewise it seems certain that these inhabitants must have been similar to savages. It is natural that the kinds of stones used in different areas were those found in the areas themselves, and they were those kinds of stone which were suitable for the manufacture of stone artifacts; thus in Denmark flint was used most frequently; in the parts of Sweden and Norway where flint is not found other kinds of stone, which at times had had an influence on the form. In the northernmost part of Sweden and Norway stone relics appear rarely or not at all, and it appears that these regions in more remote times were very little inhabited or not at all.

Towards the time when the first metals gradually (and certainly sparingly) came into use in the North, it appears that the great stone burial chambers were built. In these there have often been discovered, as has been previously mentioned, unburned bodies and with these crude urns, very rarely some article made of metal—in the latter case something small made of bronze or gold and never things of silver or iron—but almost exclusively stone articles and rare ornaments of amber. The clothing appears to have been made for the most part of animal skins. The following period we believe should be called:

The Bronze Age, in which the weapons and cutting tools were made of copper or bronze, and when iron and silver have been either very little or not at all known. Not only in the North but also in the more southern lands one will find that the metal which is mentioned first and was first used is copper, or, as it was very often used in antiquity, with a small addition of tin which gave it better hardness and which alloy has been called bronze. Only much later people became acquainted with iron, the reason for this apparently being that raw copper is found in a state in which it is much more easily recognizable as metal than is iron, which, before it can be worked, must first undergo smelting by the application of high temperature—a process which must have been unknown in the oldest times. One would surely make a mistake in assuming that the bronze objects were imitations of Roman articles from Rome's "golden age" (*Blütezeit*), or that they were made during this period in the South and were brought from there through trade to Germany and the North. Most items of this kind are found in the more remote areas; for example in the North and in Ireland, where one can assume with probability that the contact with the Romans was the least. Besides, it was only with the conquest of Gaul by Julius Caesar and his advance to the Rhine that a solid and lasting connection with the interior of Germany developed; but at that time the Romans had for a long time possessed cutting weapons and tools of iron. If one could determine, therefore, that the northern peoples had at that same time cutting tools made of bronze, then these must have been imitations of an older time and of an older taste. It seems as if an earlier culture was distributed over a large part of

Europe long before iron came into general use, and that the products of this culture had an extraordinarily great similarity in widely separated regions. Through exact study of the cutting weapons and tools made of bronze and from study of the circumstances in which they are found, one will without doubt become convinced that these are relics of the old culture stage as well as coming to the conclusion that they are very ancient in the southern lands. Assuming that the (northern) people got articles from other countries or that they imitated these, then it can be deduced that the articles must have been at the time in use in these lands. On the other hand, if those connections were disrupted or simply arose because of migrations, later inventions and improvements could have remained unknown for a long time to nations which had known older forms but who were themselves not appreciably advanced in their culture, and who, on account of the long separation and the vast distance had not learned of that which other more culturally advanced nations later invented and improved. What is found in the Nordic countries, will, therefore, doubtless serve to clarify the quality and the appearance of similar articles coming from very ancient times in areas where greater cultural progress had taken place much earlier than in the North.

To this period belong the stone chests and the small grave chambers covered with stone piles; this was the real time of cremation and the great grave chambers were no longer necessary. The burned bones were preserved in urns or put in stone chests. At the top of the urns of this time one very often finds a pin, a tweezers, and a small bronze knife, and likewise in this period belong the very common so-called celts and paal-staves of bronze. Also things of gold and electrum, but never of silver, are found. There is no known article belonging to the bronze age which bears writing on it, despite the fact that the work shows a skill which leads one to suppose that writing was not unknown at the time.

The Iron Age, the third and last period of heathen times, in which iron was used for those objects for which it is particularly suitable, so that it took the place of bronze for those things. Things which must have been sought more than any others were cutting weapons and tools made of tempered iron. On the other hand, bronze was used at this later time just as it was before but in a different form: for ornamentation, for handles, for several kinds of domestic tools, such as spoons and the like. There-fore one can by no means conclude from such bronze articles that these articles belong to the earlier period (i.e. the Bronze Age) if they do not indicate this by their form and ornamentation. Assuming that there took place an immigration into the North by peoples from more southern lands at about the time of Julius Caesar, it is probable that the im-migrants, who knew about iron which was in general use at this time in the south, must have brought it with them to the North. The relics seem to show that there was a period of transition in which iron was more precious than copper; in this era it was used very economically, one made, for example, an axe of copper, then added to it a cutting edge of iron, or a bronze dagger was made and then iron edges were added to either side. On one axe from this transition period, that is from the oldest part of the Iron Age, there has been found a runic inscription. As such relics are very rare, this period was probably not of very long duration. When people became aware of iron ore and its usefulness, it would not have been long until this metal, which is so abundant in the mountains of Norway and Sweden, could take the place of the metals which were used formerly.

The grave chambers had undergone a change in their construction and wooden structures are often found in the grave mounds of this period. At times the corpses were burned, but they were also often buried un-burned—frequently sitting on chairs—and sometimes the horse of the dead man was buried with him. In this period, which extends to the introduction of Christianity, people had silver and also vessels of glass. Glass beads appear to have been introduced very early, perhaps even in the stone age, as this ornament belongs to that category of things which savage peoples try to get first of all from civilized ones. Of course we cannot show real buildings from this time, and one could easily guess that connections with neighboring nations and the frequent excursions to other countries could have brought many articles here to the North. But one must pay attention to the historical facts; and the building of ships of the size and quality as were built in these lands requires such an ability for other tasks that one cannot doubt that the old people of the North, at least in certain respects, were more than a little skillful. The skill of the smiths is often mentioned and they were held in high esteem since excellent weapons were of great importance and probably orna-ments and decorative objects were made by the same masters who made weapons and armor.

To determine the approximate age of the relics or at least to determine to which period they belong, there is another procedure which has up to now been little used with reference to the northern antiquities; this is to study the applied forms and designs in order to see through compari-son and observation which kinds are found associated with one another, to find out the sequence in which changes have taken place and which will lead to attribution to a particular age by the evidence of the ornamenta-tion. But here our experience is too limited and too new and we can only present here a plan which, we hope, will later become better de-veloped and more definite.

On the articles of the Stone Age there are found very insignificant de-signs, for the most part only a kind of pecked design such as flames, bands, and the like. The small amount of incised carving which has been found in grave chambers and on rocks and which seems to belong mostly to the older periods consists merely on crude outlines having a similarity to the hieroglyphs of primitive peoples.

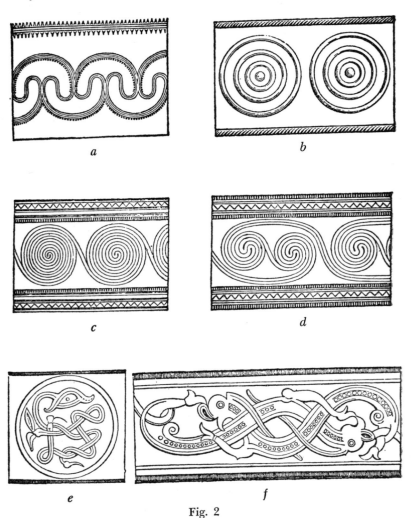

Fig. 2

In the Bronze Age we find in contrast to this the designs more fully developed. They do not seem to have undergone much change, since one finds only variations of the same kind. We give here samples of the most commonly appearing types [Fig. 2 a,b]. There are many variations of the first type. The second is still more common and seems, just as the first one, to belong to the older period; there are also smaller variations of these although in the main they resemble the designs pictured—these are variations in size, number of rings, center, and the like [Fig. 2 c,d]. The first seem to have derived from the ring designs and the doubled or paired ones are transitional to the later designs.

In the Iron Age or the last period of the heathen times two designs were particularly common, namely [those shown in Fig. 2 e,f]. Many rune stones are decorated with such designs, and in the serpent designs themselves the inscription is incorporated; but not seldom one finds them as frequently on jewelry and other articles of this time which are made of bronze and other materials. The design pictured here was applied to a gold bracteate. Many evidences have been found to show that the skillfully plaited work in gold, silver, and other metals which have been found commonly in the North belong to this period. In the very last part of heathen times and in the first part of the Christian period, the serpents are usually replaced by dragons and other fantastic animals, and our oldest buildings are decorated with designs of this kind—types which appear to have been in use over a large part of Europe until the more refined Gothic taste with its leaves and points replaced them.

❋ ❋ ❋

There was great public interest in the recent demonstration that the Piltdown skull and mandible, found in 1908 in England and believed by some to represent the oldest known direct ancestor of Homo sapiens, *were counterfeit. The perpetrator of the hoax never admitted his action. Many paleoanthropologists found it difficult to believe that the jaw, which was definitely apelike, and the skull, which was clearly that of a true man, could have belonged to the same individual (see Miller, 1915; MacCurdy, 1916; and Weidenreich, 1943:216-220). In 1949 Weiner suspected that the Piltdown bones were a hoax, and they were analyzed by the fluorine test.*

The fluorine test had been known since 1844 when Middleton published his famous paper on the method as a chronological technique. Carnot (1893), in France, further refined the method, but it lapsed and was more recently revived by Oakley who applied modern analytical methods of great precision to make the method more reliable and accurate.

The history of the Piltdown hoax is well told in a book by Weiner (1955), and the importance that the now discredited Piltdown skull and jaw had on the development of theories of human evolution can be seen in the brief papers by Washburn (1953) and Ehrich and Henderson (1954).

Presented here is Middleton's paper in 1844, the entire 1953 report on the Piltdown bones (except for the illustrations), and selected portions of Oakley's later (1955) and more detailed examination of the Piltdown human and animal remains and artifacts.

Fluorine Dating of Fossil Bones

J. Middleton

The accumulation of fluoride of calcium in fossil bones constitutes a very interesting and important subject of inquiry in reference to Geology, since it seems to involve the element of *time,* so interesting in all geological investigations. It was with a feeling of this importance that I some time ago commenced a series of investigations, which are not yet completed, in order to ascertain the proportion of fluoride of calcium in bones that had been preserved for various periods, with a view to infer, if possible, from the mineral condition, the relative ages of the specimens.

The bones hitherto examined by me with this view consisted of some from the Siwalik Hills, [India] furnished to me by my friend Dr. Falconer, and some, for the permission to examine which I am indebted to the authorities of University College, London, in the chemical laboratory of which institution my investigations have been conducted. Among these last were the bones of a Greek, who had lived, it is supposed, about the time of the second Peloponnesian war (a coin of that period being found under the jaw of the skeleton), and a part of an Egyptian mummy in a remarkably perfect state of preservation. The Siwalik fossils were of the soft kind (so named, I believe, by the gentlemen who found them, to distinguish them from those largely penetrated by oxide of iron or silica), those imbedded in the clay in that locality, as they seemed better suited for comparison with bones of recent and known age and with those of early tertiary periods.

On examining these bones, I found that those from India contained all of them nearly the same proportion of fluoride of calcium, viz. 11 per cent, while in the bones of the Greek the proportion was only a little more than 5 per cent., and in the mummy about 2 per cent. The difference in the two latter is accounted for, it would seem, by the circumstances of deposition, this being sufficiently evident from the appearance of the specimens; since the bone of the Greek has assumed a soft powdery character, tinged with peroxide of iron, the result of exposure to atmospheric and other influences, while that of the Egyptian exhibited all the structure of recent bone, having been preserved in a sarcophagus, and scarcely changed from its normal state.

"On Fluorine in Bones, Its Source and Its Application to the Determination of the Geological Age of Fossil Bones," by J. Middleton (London, R. and J. E. Taylor, 1844) *Proceedings of the Geological Society of London,* Vol. IV, Part II, No. 97, pp. 431-433.

From these results, and from having ascertained the presence of fluorine in the recent bones both of men and reptiles, I was led to suppose that the presence of fluorine must be due to some general condition, the same in ancient times as at present, for I could not believe that in this matter there could be any alteration in the laws of organic life, implying different proportions of the mineral at different periods. I was thus led to suspect that water might be the agent producing this apparent change; and this seemed to me to offer a ready solution of the whole problem. That there is a great tendency in fluoride of calcium to unite itself to phosphate of lime, is evident from the almost universal association of the two in nature; and thus, if the moisture constantly present at the earth's surface should contain the mineral in question, the bones might absorb it by simple exposure; a larger proportion being obtained, according as the bones had been longer exposed to its influence. Bearing this in mind, I was led to institute a series of experiments on aqueous deposits of different ages, and I found that, with one exception—a pure but incompact stalactite of carbonate of lime—fluorine exists in all, from the most recent deposit down to the old red sandstone, and that it is present in the older in larger proportion than in the newer beds. I think it is therefore beyond a doubt that it is present in water, though perhaps in very minute quantity; what its solvent may be I know not, but that it is so held in solution my own experiments have demonstrated; and if they had not, the simple fact that the blood conveys it to the bones, would, I apprehend, sufficiently refute any scepticism on the subject.

It now remains for me to show, that the relative geological age of rocks may be estimated by the proportion of fluoride of calcium which they contain; and for this purpose I append the following results of my analyses in the cases of recent bone, the bone of a Greek already alluded to, a fossil bone from the Siwalik Hills, and a bone of the Anoplotherium; the latter being given by Lassaigne:—

	Recent Bone	Bone of the Greek	Fossile Rumiment, from the Siwalik Hills	Bone of the Anoplotherium
Organic matter	33.43	9.97	—	
Phosphate of lime	52.11	70.01	78.00	37.00
Carbonate of lime	10.36	10.34	11.34	
Fluoride of calcium	1.99	5.04	10.65	15.00
Chloride of sodium	.60			
Soda	1.08	1.15		
Magnesia	.76		a trace	
Phosphate of magnesia	.00	1.34		
Silica	—	1.68	—	35.00
Peroxide of iron		about .25		
Alumina	—	—	—	10.00
Oxide of iron & manganese				3.00

In comparing together the quantities of fluoride of calcium in bones of different periods, we should be guided, I apprehend, by the proportion it bears, in each specimen, to the fixed basis of the bone, phosphate of lime, a substance which seems but liable to variation in amount. The comparisons stand thus:—

	Phosphate of Lime	Fluoride of Calcium
Recent bone	52.11	1.99
The Greek's bone	70.01	5.04
The Siwalik fossil bone	78.00	10.65
The Anoplotherium bone	37.00	15.00

When the animal matter, entirely obliterated in the fossil bones, has been suppressed in the recent bones, we have:—

	Phosphate of Lime	Fluoride of Calcium
Recent bone	77.84	2.97
The Greek's bone	78.55	5.62
The Siwalik fossil bone	78.00	10.65
The Anoplotherium bone	37.00	15.00

If now, for convenience of computation, we represent the phosphate in each case by 100, we obtain the following ratios of the fluoride:—

Recent bone	3.81
The Greek's bone	7.15
The Siwalik fossil bone	13.01
The Anoplotherium bone	40.54

Now, as the age of the Greek's bone is known to be 2000 years, we obtain, if my hypothesis be just, the following values, in time, of the above ratios of the fossil bones: viz. the Siwalik fossil, 7700 years; the Anoplotherium, 24,200 years.

❋ ❋ ❋

The Solution of the Piltdown Problem

J. S. Weiner, K. P. Oakley, and W. E. Le Gros Clark

Note—The curator of a palaeontological collection, which may contain rare specimens of great scientific importance, is frequently faced with the problem of whether to allow such specimens to be reinvestigated by treatment with acids, sectioning, removal of fragments for chemical analysis, or other methods which might seem to involve damage to a unique object. The cautious attitude of a previous generation has undoubtedly preserved for their successors many fossils which, for example, might have been damaged by mechanical treatment in the past, but can now be developed in perfection by more recently devised chemical methods. In the case of the Piltdown relics, one can be certain that after they came into the late Sir Arthur Smith Woodward's possession they would not have been treated or tampered with either chemically or physically. The decision to submit these specimens to a rigorous re-examination was made some years ago; the final result, unexpected at the time, will be found in the following pages.

W. N. Edwards, Keeper of Geology

Since the report, some forty years ago (Dawson & Woodward, 1913) of the discovery of several cranial fragments, a portion of a mandible and a canine tooth at Piltdown in Sussex, the problem of the "Piltdown skull" has been the subject of continuous controversy. Some authorities have accepted all the remains as those of an extinct type of hominid. But it is probably true to say that most anthropologists have remained sceptical or frankly puzzled by the contradictions which they present, for (apart altogether from other details) the combination of a cranium closely similar to that of *Homo sapiens* with a mandible and canine tooth of simian form seemed too incongruous. It has been suggested, indeed, that they really represent the fortuitous association of a Pleistocene human

"The Solution of the Piltdown Problem," by J. S. Weiner, K. P. Oakley, and W. E. Le Gros Clark. *The Bulletin of the British Museum* (*Natural History*), *Geology*, Vol. 2, No. 3, pp. 141-146 (London: Adland & Son, Ltd., Bartholemew Press, 1953). (The illustrations have not been reproduced here.) Reprinted by kind permission of the Trustees of the British Museum.

cranium with the remains of a fossil ape which had perhaps been second-arily derived from an earlier geological deposit. The application of the fluorine test (Oakley & Hoskins, 1950), however, made it quite clear that the mandible and canine were certainly not older than the cranium and, *on the assumption that they were all genuine fossils,* it naturally appeared to lend some support to those who held them to be contemporaneous and to belong to the same individual. It is also a fact that the remarkable flat wear of the molar teeth in the mandibular fragment is quite unlike that normally found in apes at a corresponding state of dental attrition (though similar to the type of wear characteristic of the hominid denti-tion), while the mode of wear of the large canine tooth is also different from that which occurs in apes. But there is another possible explanation of the apparent contradictions shown by the Piltdown remains: that the mandible and canine tooth are actually those of a modern ape (chim-panzee or orang) which have been deliberately faked to simulate fossil specimens. It was not till one of us (J.S.W.) in the course of personal discussion put forward this proposition fairly and squarely as the only possible solution of the Piltdown puzzle, pointed out that the organic content of the mandible had never been examined, and moreover dem-onstrated experimentally that artificial abrasion of the teeth of a chim-panzee combined with appropriate staining produced an appearance astonishingly similar to the Piltdown molars and canine, that we decided on a critical restudy of all the Piltdown material with this specific possi-bility directly in view. The results of our investigations have now demon-strated quite clearly that the mandible and canine are indeed deliberate fakes. The evidence for this conclusion is briefly as follows:

EVIDENCE OF THE ARTIFICIAL ABRASION OF THE PILTDOWN TEETH

Molar Teeth of the Mandible

(1) The occlusal surfaces (particularly of M_2) are planed down over almost their whole extent to a flatness which is much more even than that normally produced by natural wear.

(2) The borders of the flat occlusal surfaces—particularly the lateral borders—are sharp-cut and show no evidence of the bevelling which is usually produced by natural wear.

(3) The center of the talonid basin in M_2 is unworn, and is bounded by a sharp-cut and unbevelled border of the planed surface of the crown. This appearance would be produced by artificial abrasion but would not be expected in natural wear.

(4) The surface of the areas of dentine exposed on the anteromedial cusps of the two molars is quite flat and flush with the surrounding

enamel, instead of forming a depression as would be expected in natural wear.

(5) In both molars much more dentine has been exposed on the antero-internal than the anteroexternal cusps. But in the course of natural attrition the lateral cusps of lower molar teeth are normally worn down more rapidly (and thus usually show a greater exposure of dentine) than the medial cusps (Pl. 9, fig. 1).

(6) The degree of wear in the two molars, M_1 and M_2, is almost identical. But in early stages of natural attrition M_1 is commonly (though not always) more severely worn than M_2.

(7) The planes of the flat occlusal surfaces of the two molars are not congruous, i.e., they do not fit together to form a uniform contour. Unless the teeth have been displaced from their natural position after death (for which there is no evidence), this congruity is difficult to explain by natural wear.

(8) Inspection of the isolated molar tooth (referred to the specimen called Piltdown II) with a binocular microscope shows surface of the enamel has been finely scratched, as though by an abrasive.

Canine Tooth

(1) The mode of wear of this tooth is unlike that found normally either in ape or human canines, for the abraded surface has exposed the dentine over the entire lingual surface from medial to distal border and at one point actually reaches the apex of the pulp cavity.

(2) The condition of the apex of the root, and the wide and open pulp cavity seen in an X-ray photograph, indicate fairly certainly that the canine was still incompletely erupted or had only just recently completed its eruption. But this would be incompatible with the severe attrition of the crown if the latter were naturally produced.

(3) X-ray examination shows no evidence of the deposition of secondary dentine (with a constriction of the pulp cavity) which might be expected if the severe abrasion of the lingual surface of the crown were the result of natural attrition.

(4) The abraded surface of the crown shows fine vertically disposed scratches (as seen under a binocular microscope) which suggest the application of an abrasive.

EVIDENCE OF THE FLUORINE CONTENT

The fluorine method as applied in 1949 (and reported in full in 1950) served well enough to establish that neither the Piltdown cranium nor the mandible was Lower Pleistocene. It did not distinguish (nor at that time was it intended to distinguish) Upper Pleistocene from later material.

The rate of fluoridation at this site has probably not been high enough to give a clear separation between Upper Pleistocene and, say, Early Post-glacial bones. Moreover the method of analysis used in 1949 was accurate only within rather wide limits when applied to samples weighing less than 10 milligrams, with the consequence that even the difference between the fluorine contents of fossil and modern specimens was obscured where the samples were of that order of magnitude. Improvements in technique have since led to greater accuracy in estimating small amounts of fluorine, and it therefore seemed worth while submitting further samples of the critical Piltdown specimens for analysis in the Government Laboratory. The new estimations, based mainly on larger samples, were made by Mr. C. F. M. Fryd. The following summary of the results leaves no doubt that, whereas the Piltdown cranium may well be Upper Pleistocene as claimed in 1950, the mandible, canine tooth and isolated molar are quite modern.

	$\% F$	$\dfrac{\% F}{\% P_2O_5} \times 100$
Minimum F-content of local U. Pleistocene bones	0.1	0.4
Ditto. Upper Pleistocene teeth[*]	0.1	0.4
Piltdown cranium I	0.1	0.8
Piltdown cranium II: frontal	0.1	0.8
Piltdown cranium II: occipital	0.03	0.2
Piltdown mandible (bone)	<0.03	<0.2
Molar of Piltdown mandible	<0.04	<0.2
Piltdown canine	<0.03	<0.2
Isolated molar (Piltdown II)	<0.01	<0.1
Molar of Recent chimpanzee	<0.06	<0.3

[*] All the tooth samples are *dentine*.

Evidence of the Organic Content

To regard the organic content of bones and teeth as a measure of their antiquity has long been regarded as fallacious, and for that reason no serious attempt has ever been made to test the relative ages of the various Piltdown specimens by that means. However, extensive chemical studies of bones from early occupation sites in North America by Cook & Heizer (1947) have shown that in bones preserved under broadly the same conditions the nitrogen of their protein (ossein) is lost at a relatively slow, and on an average almost uniformly declining, rate. Thus, N-analysis, used with discretion, can be an important supplement to F-analysis, and also for the relative dating of specimens too recent to be within the range of the fluorine method. Dr. J. D. H. Wiseman and Mrs. A. Foster in the Department of Minerals of the British Museum have devised a method of estimating very small quantities of nitrogen, and Mrs. Foster, using this new method, determined the nitrogen content of a series of samples of the Piltdown material and of selected controls. The following is a summary of the results of this work which agree with all the other evidence indicating that the Piltdown mandible, canine, and isolated molar (II) are modern. (The possibility that the Piltdown specimens were steeped in a gelatinous preservative has been borne in mind; if this had been the explanation of their nitrogen-content, the cranial bones which are porous would have shown *more* nitrogen than the highly compact dentine of the teeth; whereas the reverse is true.)

Nitrogen Content of Bone Samples

	% N
Fresh bone	4.1
Piltdown mandible	3.9
Neolithic bone (Kent)	1.9
Piltdown I cranial bones (*average*)	1.4
Piltdown II frontal	1.1
Piltdown II occipital	0.6
U. Pleistocene bone (London)	0.7

Nitrogen Content of Dentine Samples

	% N
Chimpanzee molar	3.2
Piltdown canine	5.1
Piltdown I molar	4.3
Piltdown II molar	4.2
U. Pleistocene equine molar (Piltdown)	1.2
U. Pleistocene human molar (Surrey)	0.3

EVIDENCE OF THE COLORING OF THE PILTDOWN SPECIMENS

A black coating—ferruginous according to Dawson & Woodward (1914:87)—covers most of the surface of the Piltdown canine. When this tooth and the molars were sampled in 1948, one of us (K.P.O.) noted that "below an extremely thin ferruginous surface stain the dentine was pure white, apparently no more altered than the dentine of recent teeth from the soil." Examination by Dr. G. F. Claringbull in the Department of Minerals has now shown that the coating on the canine is in fact nonmetallic, it is a tough, flexible paint-like substance, insoluble in the common organic solvents, and with only a small ash content. The extreme whiteness of the dentine and the nature of the black skin are thus both consistent with the evidence presented above for the essential modernity of the canine.

The mandible is of a reddish-brown color which, though rather patchy, matches closely enough that of the cranial fragments to raise no suspicion that all the remains (from the original Piltdown site) might not belong to one skull. The frontal fragment stated to have been found at a second site (Piltdown II) is also of a similar brown color but differs noticeably from the darker greyish-brown occipital fragment from the same site. That the color of all these fragments is due to iron oxides has been confirmed by direct analysis in the Government Laboratory. But whereas the cranial fragments are all deeply stained (up to 8% of iron) throughout their thickness, the iron staining of the mandible is quite superficial. A small surface sample analyzed in 1949 contained 7% iron, but, when in the course of our re-examination this bone was drilled more deeply, the sample obtained was lighter in color and contained only 2/3% of iron. The difference in iron staining is thus also in keeping with the other evidence that the jaw and the cranium are not naturally associated.

Smith Woodward recorded (1948:59; see also 1935:134) that "the color of the pieces which were first discovered was altered a little by Mr. Dawson when he dipped them in a solution of bichromate of potash in the mistaken idea that this would harden them." Direct chemical analysis carried out by Drs. M. H. Hey and A. A. Moss in the Department of Minerals at the British Museum (Natural History), as well as the X-ray spectrographic method of Mr. E. T. Hall in the Clarendon Laboratory, Oxford University, confirmed that all the cranial fragments seen by Smith Woodward in the spring of 1912 (before he commenced systematic excavations) do contain chromate; on the other hand, there is no chromate in the cranial fragments subsequently collected that summer—either in the right parietal, or in the small occipital fragment found *in situ* by Smith Woodward himself. This being so, it is not to be expected that the mandible (which was excavated later and in the presence of Smith Woodward, 1948:11) would be chromate stained. In fact, as shown by direct chemical analysis carried out in the Department of Minerals of the British Museum, the jaw does contain chromate. It is clear from Smith Woodward's statement about the staining of the cranial fragments of Piltdown I (which we have verified), that a chromate staining of the jaw could hardly have been carried out without his knowledge *after* excavation. The iron and chromate staining of the Piltdown jaw seems to us to be explicable only as a necessary part of the deliberate matching of the jaw of a modern ape with the mineralized cranial fragments.

This grave interpretation, which we have found difficult to avoid, receives support from the finding that the frontal and occipital fragments labelled Piltdown II (and found three years later) contain small amounts of chromate. The piece of frontal bone, anatomically, could form part of the cranium of Piltdown I, and in color and in its content of nitrogen and fluorine it resembles the first occipital of Piltdown I rather than that of Piltdown II. Just as the isolated molar almost certainly comes from the Piltdown mandible, it seems only too likely that this frontal fragment originally belonged to the cranium of Piltdown I.

From the evidence which we have obtained, it is now clear that the distinguished palaeontologists and archaeologists who took part in the excavations at Piltdown were the victims of a most elaborate and carefully prepared hoax. Let it be said, however, in exoneration of those who have assumed the Piltdown fragments to belong to a single individual, or who, having examined the original specimens, either regarded the mandible and canine as those of a fossil ape or else assumed (tacitly or explicitly) that the problem was not capable of solution on the available evidence, that the faking of the mandible and canine is so extraordinarily skillful, and the perpetration of the hoax appears to have been so entirely unscrupulous and inexplicable, as to find no parallel in the history of palaeontological discovery.

Lastly, it may be pointed out that the elimination of Piltdown jaw and teeth from any further consideration clarifies very considerably the problem of human evolution. For it has to be realized that "Piltdown Man" (*Eoanthropus*) was actually a most awkward and perplexing element in the fossil record of the Hominidae, being entirely out of conformity both in its strange mixture of morphological characters and its time sequence with all the palaeontological evidence of human evolution available from other parts of the world.

References

Cook, S. F. & Heizer, R. F. 1947. The quantitative investigation of aboriginal sites: Analyses of human bone. Amer. J. Phys, Anthrop., Washington (n.s.) 5:201-220.

Dawson, C. & Woodward, A. S. 1913. On the Discovery of a Palaeolithic Human Skull and Mandible in a Flint-bearing Gravel overlying the Wealden (Hastings Beds) at Piltdown, Fletching (Sussex). Quart. J. Geol. Soc. Lond., 69:117-144.

——— 1914. Supplementary note on the Discovery of a Palaeolithic Skull and Mandible at Piltdown (Sussex). Quart. J. Geol. Soc. Lond., 70:82-93.

Nature, Lond., 165:379-382.

Oakley, K. P. & Hoskins, C. R. 1950. New Evidence on the Antiquity of Piltdown Man.

Woodward, A. S. 1935. Recent Progress in the Study of Early Man. Rep. Brit. Ass., London, 105:129-142.

——— 1948. The Earliest Englishman. 118 pp., 3 pls. London.

❄ ❄ ❄

The more detailed examination in 1955 of the Piltdown artifacts (a pointed tool made of elephant bone and several chipped flint pieces), the animal bones said to have been found in the discovery pit, and the several human bones found made it abundantly clear that the whole Piltdown discovery was an ingenious and total hoax. None of the artifacts or bones alleged to have come from Piltdown is of a type otherwise known to occur in the gravels there, and in many cases there is proof of deliberate faking and "planting" of pieces the sources of which have been determined. In 1959 H. de Vries and K. Oakley reported on the radiocarbon dating of the Piltdown skull and jaw, and their findings amply support earlier findings.

The following brief excerpts are quoted from the longer and detailed report. They are presented simply as highlights of the fuller data.

Further Evidence on Piltdown

K. P. Oakley

Experiments carried out in collaboration with Dr. A. A. Moss in the laboratory of the Mineral Department of the British Museum have shown that the color of the orange and yellowish or reddish-brown stained flints from Piltdown can be reproduced by dipping white-patinated flints in a solution of ferric chloride of various strengths and then treating the wet stain in ammonia fumes to produce ferric oxide. . . .

Thus it appears that the only flints found at Piltdown which Dawson and Woodward considered worthy of figuring as probable palaeolithic implements show features which are difficult to explain unless they were brought to the site from elsewhere and, having been suitably stained, planted in the gravel for the excavators to find. The fact that the pieces in question are crude and atypical (in the words of Ray Lankester "unlike any known or defined industry") suggests that they may have been chosen so that they could be compared with the poorly defined and altogether dubious artifacts which had then recently been found below the Red Crag of Suffolk (Moir, 1911). Whether in fact any artifacts occur *in* the Piltdown gravel is now doubtful. No humanly fractured flint was noted during recent excavations; all the artifacts previously reported were either surface finds or were introduced fraudulently. . . .

In conclusion, the Piltdown bone "implement" is a piece of the femur of a fossil elephant, obtained probably in two weathered pieces from a Middle Pleistocene brickearth or sandy formation. The ends were whittled with a steel knife, and the newly cut surfaces were stained with an iron solution. . . .

Between 1911 and 1914 eighteen fossil mammalian bones and teeth were found at, or in the immediate vicinity of, the Piltdown skull site. Four were recorded as having been found *in situ* in or below the chocolate-colored basal gravel, two on the surface of the adjoining field and the remainder on the spoil heaps at the edge of the small pit. Considering the thinness of the gravel (average thickness 18 in.), the small size of the pit

Further Contributions to the Solution of the Piltdown Problem, K. P. Oakley. *Bulletin of the British Museum (Natural History), Geology*, Vol. 2, No. 6, pp. 244, 245-248, 253, 256-257 (London, 1955). Reprinted by permission of the Trustees of the British Museum and Dr. K. P. Oakley.

(less than 50 x 10 yards in area), and the extreme rarity of fossils in the Pleistocene river gravels of Sussex, this was a remarkable yield. . . .

Some of the Piltdown fossils ("*Stegodon*," *Mastodon arvernesis* and *Rhinoceros* cf. *etruscus*) are undoubtedly Villafranchian ("Upper Pliocene" of earlier authors, but now classed as Lower Pleistocene; but others are not older than Middle or Upper Pleistocene. When they were first described there was some question as to whether gravels of two ages were present. Dawson concluded: "It is clear [wrote Dawson and Woodward in 1913] that this stratified gravel at Piltdown is of Pleistocene age, but that it contains in its lower stratum, animal remains derived from some destroyed Pliocene deposit probably situated not far away, and consisting of worn and broken fragments." In a later paper he wrote: "We cannot resist the conclusion that the third or dark bed is in the main composed of Pliocene drift. . . ."

With the increase of knowledge, the presence of "Pliocene" (Villafranchian) mammalian remains at Piltdown became increasingly difficult to explain, for, with one significant exception (see Table II footnote), none has been found elsewhere in southern England. If they were to be found *in situ* in Sussex, they would be expected in terrace or plateau deposits not less than 200 ft. above the level of the Ouse, but Edmunds (1926:68) demonstrated that the Piltdown gravel is part of a terrace 50 ft. above the Ouse. Thus it seemed that they could only have come from a block of indurated fossiliferous sand which worked its way down from a higher level and disintegrated on the Ouse flood-plain in 50 ft. terrace times.

When it had been established that the Piltdown mandible was a forgery it became probable that the Villafranchian fossils were also introduced in order to suggest that "Piltdown Man" dated from Pliocene times.

Any remaining doubt that these pieces of "planifrons" molars were of foreign origin was dispelled by their radioactivity. In the hope of tracing the origin of these pieces a series of mammalian teeth from the main Villafranchian localities was included among the fossils selected for the tests. The results obtained reinforce the conclusion that the Piltdown specimens were not obtained from an English deposit. The uranium content of fossil teeth, while increasing with geological age, is subject (as fluorine is) to considerable fluctuation from place to place. Nevertheless it appears that within relatively uniform strata of limited extent the ratio of the extremes of the variation in comparable material does not generally exceed the value of three. . . .

Fossils from nearly a dozen Villafranchian localities in Europe and Asia were tested, but none showed radioactivity in excess of 28 c.p.m. Professor C. Arambourg enabled us to extend the range of comparison by generously providing specimens from North African localities. A molar tooth originally recorded as *Elephas* cf. *planifrons,* from Garaet Ichkeul in Tunisia, has proved to have a radioactivity closely comparable with the Piltdown specimens. Not only is the count rate in the Ichkeul specimen and E.586 from Piltdown almost identical, but the difference between the activity of the enamel and of the cementum is unusually small in both. There is also close agreement in the fluorine content of these specimens. . . .

Of the eighteen specimens of fossil mammals recorded from the Piltdown gravel by Dawson and Woodward, ten are unquestionably frauds, and there are strong grounds for believing that this is also true of the remainder. Since the gravel is decalcified (pH 6.5) it is probably unfossiliferous. . . .

The mandible shows practically no radioactivity which is a further confirmation of its modernity.

The fluorine content of the canine and of the molars in the mandibular ramus was estimated in 1949 as $<0.1\%$, but as the mandibular bone itself appeared to contain c. 0.2%, and as the probable experimental error on samples of the small size then tested was known to be about $\pm.2\%$, there seemed no reason to regard the canine or the mandible as more recent than the human cranium, with fluorine content estimated to vary from 0.1 to 0.4%. In 1953, new samples of the teeth and of the skull bones were submitted to the Department of the Government Chemist, where Mr. C. F. M. Fryd had devised a technique for estimating smaller amounts of fluorine than could be measured in 1949. The experimental error in the determination of fluorine obviously depends on the size of the sample and the amount of fluorine it contains. The fluorine content of the Piltdown skull bones was determined in 1953 as 0.14 to 0.18%, and the limits of error as $\pm0.02\%$. Where the amount measured was exceptionally small, the fluorine content was recorded as less than $o.ox\%$, the true figure lying between $o.ox$ and zero. In 1953 all the determinations of the fluorine content of the Piltdown mandible and teeth proved to lie between 0.04% and zero. These results indicated that whereas the skull bones were probably prehistoric, the canine tooth, the mandible and the isolated molar were modern. This conclusion was reinforced by comparing the nitrogen content of the Piltdown bones and teeth (dentine) with that of modern and fossil specimens. . . .

As the fluorine and nitrogen content of the cranial bones were consistent with their being fairly ancient, it seemed at first that the hoax had been based on a genuine discovery of portions of a skull in the gravel, and that the animal remains and implement had been subsequently "planted" to suggest that it was Pliocene or Early Pleistocene in age. As the investigations proceeded the skull too became suspect. Dr. G. F. Claringbull carried out an X-ray crystallographic analysis of these bones and found that their main mineral constituent, hydroxy-apatite, had been partly replaced by gypsum. Studies of the chemical conditions in the Piltdown sub-soil and ground-water showed that such an unusual alteration could not have taken place naturally in the Piltdown gravel. Dr. M. H. Hey then demonstrated that when subfossil bones are artificially ironstained by soaking them in strong iron sulphate solutions this alteration does occur. Thus it is now clear that the cranial bones had been artificially stained to match the gravel, and "planted" at the site with all the other finds. The presence of chromium in some of the bones is now more readily explicable, for a dichromatic solution might have served to aid the oxidation of iron salts used in staining the bones. . . .

❋ ❋ ❋

Another technique for determining relative chronology is the arranging of a series of objects of the same class (for example, arrowpoints, decorated pottery vessels, coins, Bronze Age safety pins or axes, or ornaments) and determining how their form (or some other attribute such as decoration) may have changed over the course of time. This procedure is clearly illustrated by Sir John Evans' early study of British gold coins in which the changes in the designs on both faces are followed from the original naturalistic forms of the head of Philip II of Macedon and a charioteer driving two horses to unrecognizable dots and strokes.

Other examples of the application of typological seriation are the "sequence date" series devised by W. M. F. Petrie, using the wavy handled feature of predynastic Egyptian pottery (Petrie, 1901); the ordering of copper and bronze axes (Fox, 1870:531-539); sequential changes in Bronze and Iron Age fibulae (Viollier, 1901; Montelius, 1895, Part I, Pls. 1-21); and the sequence of changes in megalithic tomb constructions (Peake, 1940:131).

Rowe (1961) has provided an important paper on the relative reliability of chronologies (especially of pottery) secured from stratigraphy and seriational analysis.

Typological Changes in British Coins

John Evans

I am well aware that the question concerning the origin of a coinage in Britain, has already attracted the notice and investigation of many eminent men, whose judicious and erudite labors have so far exhausted

"On the Date of British Coins," by John Evans. *The Numismatic Chronicle and Journal of the Numismatic Society,* (London, 1850) Vol. XII, April, 1949—January, 1950, pp. 127-137.

the subject, as to leave little hope for any future gleaner in the same field. Nevertheless, I cannot suppress my conviction, that, in the attempts hitherto made to determine this question, hardly sufficient attention has been paid, either to the direct testimony of ancient authors, with the exception of Caesar; or to what may be deduced from the history of the early commerce of this country; or to what may be termed the pedigree of those British coins whose dates may, with comparative certainty, be determined.

I shall, in the present paper, endeavor to prove from these sources, that a currency of coined money must, of necessity, have existed in some parts of this island before the time of Caesar's invasion.

The main grounds for an opposite opinion, are no less than what are usually considered the words of Caesar himself (Bell. Gall. v. 12.)— "Utuntur aut nummo aereo aut annulis ferreis ad certum pondus examinatis pro nummis"—backed by two passages in Cicero's Epistles (Ep. ad. Fam. vii. 7.)—"In Britannia nihil esse audio neque auri, neque argenti"— and again, (Ep. ad. Att. iv. 16.) "Neque argenti scrupulum esse ullum in illa insula." From these authorities, it has been concluded by some that the Britons, at the time of Caesar's arrival among them, had no coinage of their own, and were wholly destitute both of gold and silver. But on close examination, it will, I think, appear, that this conclusion is incorrect, for both the epistles above quoted are written in a very jocose style; and the "nihil," and "neque scrupulum," must be regarded as hyperbolical; indeed, Cicero himself, with an "id si ita est," expresses his doubt of the truth of his assertion. So that the only inference that can fairly be drawn from these two passages is, that gold and silver were far scarcer in Britain than the amount of these metals acquired by the Romans in their conquest of Gaul had led them to expect.

The passage in Caesar has already been attacked, and to my mind successfully, by Mr. Hawkins, (Num. Chron. i. 13, *et seq.;* Eng. Silver Coins, p. 18, *et seq.*) who shows, on the authority of some of the best ancient MMS., that the use of gold is expressly mentioned by him. But under any circumstances, this passage can only be a negative argument against the hypothesis of gold and silver having been current in Britain at that time, as it does not directly deny that such was the case; and, at all events, Caesar's assertion cannot in any way apply to that part of the country which he never visited, and with which he was totally unacquainted, (Bell. Gall. iv. 20.).

If, however, the vanquished Britons were devoid of money worthy the name, what could have induced Caesar to lay a yearly tribute upon them, and to settle "quid in annos singulos vectigalis P. R. Britannia penderet"? (Bell. Gall. v. 22.; Conf. Dion. Cass. lib. xi.; et Eutrop. Brev. vi. 17). That a money payment was here intended, appears from the word "vectigal" being employed, a word, I believe, that is never used thus absolutely, except as having a reference to money. Suetonius, indeed, distinctly affirms that he demanded money—"pecunias et obsides imperavit": (In Vit. Jul. Caes. xxv.) and Cicero, writing on the same subject at the very time of its occurrence, uses the words "imperata pecunia." (Ep. ad. Att. iv. 17.). That this money was actually paid, we may gather from Diodorus, (Lib. vi.) though it appears soon afterwards to have been commuted for duties levied on the commerce between Gaul and Britain (Strabo. lib. ii. p. 116, ed. 1620; lib. iv. p. 200.).

Now, although some have imagined that the Britons commenced coining money on purpose to pay this tribute, an imagination not worth refuting, the passages cited cannot but induce us to suppose that they possessed the wherewithal to pay a money-tax, at the time such a tax was imposed on them by Caesar.

But what say the ancient historians as to the presence of gold and silver in this country? "Fert Britannia aurum et argentum pretium victoriae," says Tacitus (Agricol. xii.); says Strabo (Lib. iv. p. 199); and Solinus (Cap. xxxi. *sec. alios.* xxxv.) speaks of the "metallorum largam variamque copiam, quibus Britanniae solum undique generum pollet." He also instances the Silures as not employing money, but simply barter, which implies, that in this respect they differed from the inhabitants of some other parts of this country. Mela likewise mentions (Lib. iii. c. 3.) the inhabitants of the interior as becoming more ignorant of other riches than flocks and territory, as they receded farther from the continent, from which we must infer, that "other riches" were known to the inhabitants of the southern coast. It may, indeed, be urged, that these writers are all of them later than Caesar; yet it is to be observed, that the information upon which some of them wrote was derived from earlier sources, and that not one of them treats the presence of gold and silver in the island as of recent date, or appears to have had the remotest conception, that in Caesar's time it was destitute of them.

Let us now see what view of the subject the history of the early commerce of this country would naturally lead us to take. About the year 600 B.C., the Phoenicians of Carthage, and her colonies in Spain, commenced their commerce with the Cassiterides, and probably with Britain, and carried it on exclusively by barter. The commerce of the Greeks of Marseilles with these islands dates some 300 years later, and seems to have been carried on for some time in the same manner. About 200 B.C., the second Punic War, and the consequent abandonment of their colonies in Spain by the Carthaginians, appears to have put an end to their trade with Britain, and to have left its commerce in the hands of their Greek competitors. It was, perhaps, a consequence of the uncertainty entailed upon the navigation of the Mediterranean by these wars, that the merchants of Marseilles, about this time, gave up their direct intercourse with Britain by sea, and thenceforward carried on their trade overland through Gaul. This system diverted the commerce of Britain eastward from its first seat on the coast of Cornwall; the tin being now brought to the Isle of Wight (Diodorus Siculus, lib. v.), and thence transported to the coast of Gaul; whence, by a thirty days' journey, it was borne on horses to the mouth of the Rhone. The result was, that, by degrees, nearly the whole of the trade fell into the hands of Gaulish merchants, who, for various reasons, were better adapted than the Greeks for carrying on a traffic of this kind through their own country, and who thus formed a connecting link between the rude inhabitants of Britain and the flourishing cities of Marseilles and Narbonne.

Now, while this commerce was confined to the Phoenicians and Greeks, it was, no doubt, as easy as it was politic for them to keep the Britons, a barbarous people, with whom they had nothing in common, in ignorance of the use of money, and to obtain their valuable commodities in exchange for trumpery wares. But with the Gauls and Britons it was far otherwise: of kindred race—speaking the same language—with the same institutions, manners, and religion—the advances in knowledge and civilization, made by the one people, must speedily have been communicated to the other. And this becomes the more apparent, when we consider, that in addition to the intercourse of trade, a connection of a far closer kind existed between the two nations, Britain being regarded by the Gauls as the birthplace of their religion, (Caesar, Bell. Gall. vi. 13.) whither, even in far later times, their more learned Druids resorted for the completion of their education.

But the Gauls, at the time of their maintaining this commerce with the Britons, were acquainted with the use of money, which they had probably learned from the Greeks of Marseilles, whose coins, and especially the Philippi in circulation among them, they rudely imitated. We have, therefore, every reason to believe, that they must have communicated this knowledge to the Britons; and if this were actually the case, it is to that part of this country whither they principally traded (that is to say, to the counties adjoining the Isle of Wight) that we must look for the discovery of the earliest specimens of British coins; which should also, on this hypothesis, be struck on a Gaulish or Grecian model. If, on the contrary, it was not till after Caesar's invasion that money was struck in this island, it would most probably be in Kent—according to his account the most civilized part of the country, and that most subject to Roman influence— that they would be found; and if so, we should expect them to show traces of a Roman origin.

There are, however, but few British coins on which evidences of a Roman descent are apparent, and these are principally of the time of Cunobeline. We have, on the contrary, a large variety, I might almost say a majority of British types which, on careful examination, may be traced to one common origin, and whose prototype is evidently a rude imitation of the Greek, or more probably, Gaulish Philippus, (Ruding, pl. i. 17-21.). This prototype has, on the obverse, a rude laureated head; and, on the reverse, a horse, not infrequently with eight legs, and generally with the remains of a Victory and chariot behind it. It is, I believe, most frequently found in the counties adjoining the Isle of Wight, though occasionally occurring in Kent and Surrey. It is, at any rate, certain that some of the closest imitations of it are commonly discovered in Dorsetshire and Sussex. Coins of this type in gold generally weigh from 115 to 117 grains; and we find this weight being gradually decreased in its descendants, till, in the time of Cunobeline, it is reduced to from 82 to 84 grains. So that the weight alone would be nearly sufficient to prove its superior antiquity to any other type; it being almost universally the case, that the earlier coins of any country are heavier than those of more recent date, though of the same denomination.

I will now proceed to show how, from this prototype, by means of successive imitations of imitations, a number of new and totally distinct types arose, until their original was quite lost sight of. In doing this, however, I cannot present you with the exact numismatic succession of the types, but can only exhibit such specimens of the coins as have come down to our times as may enable you, without much difficulty, to trace the transition. It will be found of service to remember that these apparent changes are partly owing to the dies having increased in size through successive copying, while the flan having rather diminished than otherwise, a part only of the impression of the die is to be found upon the coins; as is the case with some of the Indian rupees, on which not above one-third of the inscription on the die appears. No. 2 on the accompanying sketch is an apparently rather late variety of the prototype, its weight being only 103½ grains, and its size considerably smaller than that of heavier specimens. From this to No. 3 the transition is easy; but the weight is diminished to 91½ grains. On No. 4, the leaves of the wreath proceed in opposite directions from the centre, and the type shows a tendency to assume cruciform appearance: the weight is again diminished to 87¼ grains. Some of the coins lately discovered on Whaddon Chase are very similar to this, but the remains of the clothing of the neck are more apparent, and some of the crescent-shaped figures representing the front hair are to be seen in the quarter shaded in the sketch. Their weight is from 88 to 90 grains. On No. 5, we have the wreath crossed by another, at right angles; but, to mark its descent, it still retains two locks of its prototype's back hair in one of the compartments formed by the cross, while in another we may observe the clothing of the neck, and in a third one of the crescent-shaped representatives of the front hair. On No. 6, the origin of the type is still apparent, there being locks of hair in each of the compartments. No. 7 is a somewhat similar type, evidently derived from the same origin, the wreath showing the outline of the jaw, being slightly curved, the dress of the neck being represented by a Y-shaped figure, and one of the crescent-shaped ornaments apparently doing duty as an eye, as vestiges of an outline of a nose and forehead may be perceived. The reverse of this coin is also remarkable, as showing traces of

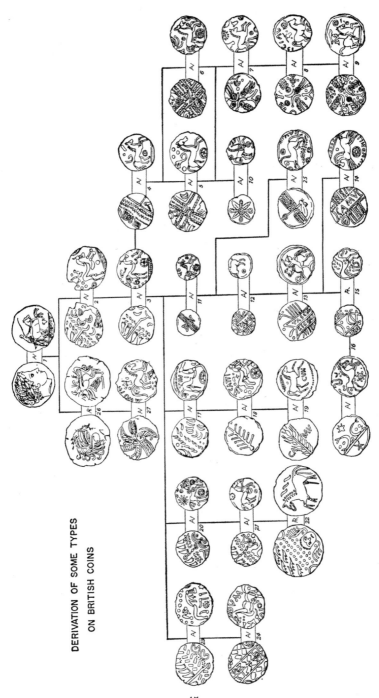

DERIVATION OF SOME TYPES
ON BRITISH COINS

both the head and hind-legs of the second horse of the biga. Its weight is
85½ grains. On No. 8 the laureated head is reduced to a regular cruciform
pattern, and on the reverse is the legend TASCIAV; and from this we
arrive at No. 9, which is the perfect Verulam type of Tasciovanus, with
the four converging branches, and the letters VER between them. The
weight of this specimen is 84 grains, about which point it appears to have
become fixed.

We have here then some sort of date from which, although it cannot
itself be accurately ascertained, we may argue back as to the probable age
of the prototype. Although we cannot exactly fix the year of Cunobeline's
death, or the length of his reign, it is certain that he was a contemporary
of Augustus, whom he probably did not survive many years, and that the
multitude and variety of his coins will justify us in assigning him a length-
ened reign. We cannot, therefore, greatly err in assuming Holinshed's
assertion, that it commenced in the nineteenth year of Augustus, that is to
say, B.C. 13, or forty-one years after Caesar's second invasion, as correct.
Now if, according to Mr. Birch's theory, the coins bearing TAXCIA,
TASCIAV, etc., as their only legend, are to be assigned to Tasciovanus,
the father of Cunobeline, it is probable that they were struck previously
to this date. But the reign of Tasciovanus, to judge by his coins, must,
like that of Cunobeline, have extended over no small number of years,
and may not unfairly be considered to have commenced from ten to
fifteen years after Caesar's invasion. On No. 8, as well as Nos. 12 and 13,
of the sketch, we have the name of this prince; and of these No. 8, at all
events, from the number of intervening varieties between it and No. 9,
must have been struck towards the commencement of his reign. I
will, therefore, appeal to the reason of any one, whether it is possible
for the utter change of type, weight, and workmanship, from No. 2 to
Nos. 8, 12, and 13, to have taken place in so short a time as that between
Caesar's invasion and the accession of Tasciovanus, or even of Cunobeline;
and that, too, in defiance of the efforts of each successive moneyer to
imitate the coins already in circulation. It must, on the contrary, be evident, that a considerable length of time must have elapsed to have produced such strange metamorphoses; so that I think we shall be fully
justified in assuming, that the prototype from which they were derived
was introduced into Britain at that period to which history would seem
to point, viz., soon after the commencement of the Graeco-Gaulish commerce with this country, or, at a rough estimate, B.C. 150.

I will not occupy your time by tracing the pedigrees of the other types
given in the sketch, as I trust they are sufficiently obvious. I think, however, that they will prove of some assistance towards classifying and
arranging the uninscribed varieties of British coins.

It is much to be regretted, that we have not, at present, sufficient facts
at our command as to the localities where coins of any particular type
are principally found, to trace the progress of the art of coining through

the country, or to observe what influence the invasion of the **Belgae** may have had upon it. Much, however, may be done by carefully observing and recording any fresh discoveries of British coins; and I have but little doubt, that if this be properly done, we shall, before many years are over, be able to attain a much clearer insight into the subject.

Thus far I may observe at present, that the coins generally recede farther from the prototype as the places of their discovery recede from the southern coast—as, for instance, the Yorkshire and Norfolk types, Nos. 24 and 16; and that in the southwestern counties the workmanship of the coins appears continually to have deteriorated; while in the southeastern and eastern, after declining for a time, it again improves, probably through the introduction of foreign artists, till, under Cunobeline, it attains its highest perfection.

❋ ❋ ❋

The modern application of counting tree rings, using wood found in an archaeological context, was developed by the astronomer Andrew E. Douglass who first got the idea about 1904, realized its significance about 1911, and developed the method about 1913. The history of Douglass' work in this field has been recounted elsewhere (Douglass, 1921; 1935; Stallings, 1939; Giddings, 1962.). Working in the American Southwest, Douglass brought the available data together in an important article published in 1929 (Douglass, 1929), which was amplified a few years later (Douglass, 1935).

That the age of a tree could be determined by counting the rings was known before Douglass' time. Leonardo da Vinci records it in his notebooks, and Americans as early as 1788 counted the rings of trees growing on archaeological sites to determine their minimum age. (Lyell, 1863:41; Griffin, 1959). Charles Babbage, a mathematician, was the first to foresee clearly the value of matching, by seasonal variation, the ring patterns of preserved dead trees that were of different but overlapping ages in order to achieve an extended count. (Morrison, 1952). In his article of 1838, he says, "The application of these principles to ascertaining the age of submerged forests, or to that of peat mosses, may possibly connect them ultimately with the chronology of man." Babbage's article, reprinted here, has been accurately characterized by Zeuner (1958:400) as a "remarkable case of vision in science."

Time Reckoning by Tree Ring Counts
Charles Babbage

ON THE AGE OF STRATA, AS INFERRED FROM THE RINGS OF TREES EMBEDDED IN THEM

The indelible records of past events which are preserved within the solid substance of our globe, may be in some measure understood without the aid of that refined analysis on which a complete acquaintance with them depends. The remains of vegetation, and of animal life, embedded in their coeval rocks, attest the existence of far distant times; and as science and the arts advance, we shall be enabled to read the minuter details of their living history. The object of the present note is to suggest to the reader a line of inquiry, by which we may still trace some small portion of the history of the past in the fossil woods which occur in so many of our strata.

It is well known that dicotyledonous trees increase in size by the deposition of an additional layer annually between the wood and the bark, and that a transverse section of such trees presents a series of nearly concentric though irregular rings, the number of which indicates the age of the tree. The relative thickness of these rings depends on the more or less flourishing state of the plant during the years in which they were formed. Each ring, may, in some trees, be observed to be subdivided into others, thus indicating successive periods of the same year during which its vegetation was advanced or checked. These rings are disturbed in certain parts by irregularities resulting from branches; and the year in which each branch first sprung from the parent stock may be ascertained by proper sections.

It has been found by experiment, that even the motion imparted to a tree by the winds has an influence on its growth. Two young trees of equal size and vigour were selected and planted in similar circumstances, except that one was restrained from having any motion in the direction of the meridian, by two strong ropes fixed to it, and connecting it to the ground, at some distance towards the north and south. The other tree was by similar means prevented from having any motion in the direction of east and west. After several years, both trees were cut down, and the sections of their stems were found to be oval; but the longer axis of the

The Ninth Bridge-Water Treatise, a Fragment, John Murray, (London, 1838). Second edition (Note M: C. Babbage, "On the Age of Strata, as Inferred from the Rings of Trees Embedded in Them," pp. 256-264).

oval of each was in the direction in which it had been capable of being moved by the winds.

These prominent effects are obvious to our senses; but every shower that falls, every change of temperature that occurs, and every wind that blows, leaves on the vegetable world the traces of its passage; slight, indeed, and imperceptible, perhaps, to us, but not the less permanently recorded in the depths of those woody fabrics. All these indications of the growth of the living tree are preserved in the fossil trunk, and with them also frequently the history of its partial decay.

Let us now inquire into the use we may make of these details relative to individual trees, when examining forests submerged by seas, embedded in peat mosses, or transformed, as in some of the older strata, into stone. Let us imagine, that we possessed sections of the trunks of a considerable number of trees, such as those occurring in the bed called the *Dirt-bed*, in the island of Portland. If we were to select a number of trees of about the same size, we should probably find many of them to have been contemporaries. This fact would be rendered probable if we observed, as we doubtless should do, on examining the annual rings, that some of them conspicuous for their size occurred at the same distances of years in several trees. If, for example, we found on several trees a remarkably large annual ring, followed at the distance of seven years by a remarkably thin ring, and this again, after two years, followed by another large ring, we should reasonably infer that seven years after a season highly favourable to the growth of these trees, there has occurred a season peculiarly unfavourable to them; that after two more years another very favourable season has happened, and that all the trees so observed had existed at the same period of time. The nature of the season, whether hot or cold, wet or dry, might be conjectured with some degree of probability, from the class of tree under consideration. This kind of evidence, though slight at first, receives additional and great confirmation by the discovery of every new ring which supports it; and, by an extensive concurrence of such observations, the succession of seasons might be in some measure ascertained at remote geological periods.

On examining the shape of the sections of such trees, we might perceive some general tendency towards a uniform inequality in their diameters; and we should perhaps find that the longer axes of the sections most frequently pointed in one direction. If we knew from the species of tree that it possessed no natural tendency to such an inequality, then we might infer that, during the growth of these trees, they were bent most frequently in one direction; and hence derive an indication of the prevailing winds at that time. In order to determine from which of the two opposite quarters these winds came, we might observe the centers of these sections; and we should *generally* find that the rings on one side were close and more compressed than those on the opposite side. From this we might infer the most exposed side, or that from which the wind most frequently blew. Doubtless there would be many exceptions arising from local circumstances—some trees might have been sheltered from the direct course of the wind, and have only been acted upon by an eddy. Some might have been protected by adjacent large trees, sufficiently near to shelter them from the ruder gales, but not close enough to obstruct the light and air by which they were nourished. Such a tree might have a series of large and rather uniform rings, during the period of its protections by its neighbor; and these might be followed by the destruction of its protector. The same storm might have mutilated some trees, and half uprooted others; these latter might strive to support themselves for years, making but little addition, by stinted layers, to the thickness of their stems; and then, having thrown out new roots, they might regain their former rate of growth, until a new tempest again shook them from their places. Similar effects might result from floods and the action of rivers on the trees adjacent to their banks. But the effect of all these local and peculiar circumstances would disappear, if a sufficient number of sections could be procured from fossil trees, spread over a considerable extent of country.

The annual rings might however furnish other intimations of the successive existence of these trees.

On examining some rings remarkable for their size and position, let us suppose that we find, in one section, two remarkably large rings, separated from another large ring, by one very stinted ring, and this followed, after three ordinary rings, by two very small and two very large ones. Such a group might be indicated by the letters

oLLsLooossLLo

where *o* denotes an ordinary year or ring, *L* a large one, *s* a small or stinted ring. If such a group occurred in the sections of several different trees, it might fairly be attributed to general causes.

Let us now suppose such a group to be found near the center of one tree, and towards the external edge or bark of another; we should certainly conclude that the tree near whose bark it occurred was the more ancient tree; that it had been advanced in age when *that* group of seasons occurred which had left their mark near the pith of more recent tree, which was young at the time those seasons happened. If, on counting the rings of this younger tree, we found that there were, counting inward from the bark to this remarkable group, three hundred and fifty rings, we should justly conclude that, three hundred and fifty years before the death of this tree, which we will call A, the other, which we will call B, and whose section we possess, had been an old tree. If we now search towards the center of the second tree B, for another remarkable group of rings; and if we also find a similar group near the bark of a third tree, which we will call C; and if, on counting the distance of the second group from the first in B, we find an interval of 420 rings, then we draw the inference that the tree A, 350 years before its destruction, was influenced in its growth by a succession of ten remarkable seasons, which also had their effect on a neighboring tree B, which was at that time of considerable age. We conclude further, that the tree B was influenced in its youth, or 420 years before the group of the ten seasons, by another remarkable succession of seasons, which also acted on a third tree C in its old age, at a period of 770 years antecedent. If we could discover other trees having other cycles of seasons, capable of identification, we might trace back the history of the ancient forest, and possibly find in it some indications for conjecturing the time occupied in forming the stratum in which it is embedded.

The application of these principles to ascertaining the age of submerged forests, or to that of peat mosses, may possibly connect them ultimately with the chronology of man. Already we have an instance of a wooden hut with a stone hearth before it, and burnt wood on it, and a gate leading to a pile of wood, discovered at a depth of fifteen feet below the surface of a bog in Ireland: and it was found that this hut had probably been built when the bog had only reached half its present thickness, since there were still fifteen feet of turf below it.

The realization of the views here thrown out would require the united exertions of many individuals patiently exerted through a series of years. The first step must be to study full the relations of the annual rings in every part of an individual tree. The effect of a favourable or unfavourable season on a section near the root must be compared with the influence of the same circumstances on its growth towards the top of the tree. Vertical sections also must be examined in order to register the annual additions to its height, and to compare them with its increase of thickness. Every branch must be traced to its origin, and its sections be registered. The means of identifying the influence of different seasons in various sections of the same individual tree and its branches being thus attained, the conclusions arrived at must be applied to several trees under similar circumstances, and such modifications must be applied to them as the case may be; and before any general conclusions can be reached respecting a tract of country once occupied by a forest, it will be necessary to have a considerable number of sections of trees scattered over various parts of it.

One of the earliest examples in the archaeological literature of a "synchronism" is provided by the famous Layard who was able, through Assyrian and Egyptian seal-impressions of rulers occurring on the same piece of clay, to assign a date to the Assyrian dynasty because the Egyptian ruler's reign was firmly dated.

Clark (1957:163-168) and Heizer (1959, Chap. 10) have cited a number of examples of chronological coordination through synchronisms, several of which concern the extension of historical dates to prehistoric (i.e. nonliterate) communities.

Assyrian-Egyptian Cross-Dating

Austen Layard

Other corroborative evidence as to the identity of the king who built the palace of Kouyunjik with Sennacherib, is scarcely less remarkable. In a chamber, or passage, in the south-west corner of this edifice were found a large number of pieces of fine clay bearing the impressions of seals which, there is no doubt, had been affixed, like modern official seals of wax, to documents, written on leather, papyrus, or parchment. Such documents, with seals in clay still attached, have been discovered in Egypt, and specimens are preserved in the British Museum. The writings themselves had been consumed by the fire which destroyed the building or had perished from decay. In the stamped clay, however, may still be seen the holes for the string, or strips of skin, by which the seal was fastened; in some instances the ashes of the string itself remain, with the marks of the fingers and thumb.

The greater part of these seals are Assyrian, but with them are others bearing Egyptian, Phoenician, and doubtful symbols and characters. Sometimes the same seal is impressed more than once on the same piece of clay. The Assyrian devices are of various kinds; the most common is that of a king plunging a dagger into the body of a rampant lion. This appears to have been the royal, and indeed, the national, seal or signet. It is frequently encircled by a short inscription, which has not yet been deciphered, or by a simple guilloche border. The same group, emblematic of the superior power and wisdom of the king, as well of his sacred character, is found on Assyrian cylinders, gems, and monuments. From the Assyrians it was adopted by the Persians, and appears upon the walls of Persepolis and on the coins of Darius.

Other devices found among these impressions of seals are: 1. A king, attended by a priest, in act of adoration before a deity standing on a lion,

Discoveries in the Ruins of Nineveh and Babylon; with Travels in Armenia, Kurdistan and the Desert, by Austen H. Layard. New York: G. P. Putnam & Co., 1853. (Excerpt here taken from pp. 153-160).

and surrounded by seven stars: above the god's head, on one seal, is a scorpion. 2. The king, followed by an attendant bearing a parasol, and preceded by a rampant horse. 3. A god, or the king, probably the former, rising from a crescent. There appears to be a fish in front of the figure. 4. The king, with a eunuch or priest before him; a flower, or ornamented staff, between them. 5. A scorpion, surrounded by a guilloche border (a device of very frequent occurrence, and probably astronomical). 6. A priest worshipping before a god, encircled by stars. 7. A priest worshipping before a god. Behind him are a bull, and the sacred astronomical emblems. 8. An ear of corn, surrounded by a fancy border. 9. An object resembling a dagger, with flowers attached to the handle; perhaps a sacrificial knife. 10. The head of a bull and a trident, two sacred symbols of frequent occurrence on Assyrian monuments. 11. A crescent in the midst of a many-rayed star. 12. Several rudely cut seals, representing priests and various sacred animals, stars, &c.

The seals most remarkable for beauty of design and skillful execution represent horsemen, one at full speed raising a spear, the other hunting a stag. The impressions show that they were little inferior to Greek intaglios. No Assyrian or Babylonian relics yet discovered, equal them in delicacy of workmanship, and the best examples of the art of engraving on gems—an art which appears to have reached great perfection amongst the Assyrians—are unknown to us, except through these impressions.

There are three seals apparently Phoenician; two of them bearing Phoenician characters, for which I cannot suggest any interpretation. It is, however, possible that these characters may belong to some other Semitic nation, as a cursive alphabet, having a close resemblance to the Phoenician, was used from Tadmor to Babylon. A few have doubtful symbols upon them, which I will not attempt to explain; perhaps hieroglyphical signs.

Of the purely Egyptian seals there are four. One has two cartouches placed on the symbol of gold, and each surmounted by a tall plume; they probably contained the praenomen and name of a king, but not the slightest trace remains of the hieroglyphs. The impression is concave, having been made from a convex surface: the back of some of the Egyptian ovals, the rudest form of the scarabaeus, are of this shape. On the second seal is the figure of the Egyptian god Harpocrates, seated on a lotus flower, with his finger placed upon his mouth; an attitude in which he is represented on an ivory from Nimroud. The hieroglyph before him does not appear to be Egyptian.

But the most remarkable and important of the Egyptian seals are two impressions of a royal signet, which though imperfect, retain the cartouche, with the name of the king, so as to be perfectly legible. It is well known to Egyptian scholars, as that of the second Sabaco the Ethiopian, of the twenty-fifth dynasty. On the same piece of clay is impressed an

Assyrian seal, with a device representing a priest ministering before the king, probably a royal signet.

There can be no doubt whatever as to the identity of the cartouche.[1]

[1] I am endebted to Mr. Birch for the following remarks upon this seal:—"The most important of the numerous seals discovered at Kouyunjik is one which has received two impressions—an Assyrian, representing a personage in adoration before a deity; and a second, with the representation and name of the Egyptian monarch, Sabaco, of the twenty-fifth dynasty of Ethiopians, and evidently impressed from a royal Egyptian

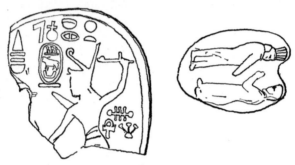

Fig. 4

Impressions of royal Assyrian (right) and Egyptian (left) signets on a clay document seal. After Layard (1853:156).

seal. [Fig. 4.] Similar impressions are by no means unknown, and a few examples have reached the present time. Not to instance the clay seals found attached to the rolls of papyrus containing letters written in the time of the Ptolemies and Romans, there are in the British Museum seals bearing the name of Shashank or Shishak (No. 5585.) of Amasis II of the twenty-sixth dynasty (No. 5584.) and of Nafuarut or Nepherophis, of the twenty-ninth dynasty (No. 5585). Such seals were, therefore, affixed by the Egyptians to public documents, and it was in accordance with this principle, common to the two monarchies, that the seal of the Egyptian king has been found in Assyria. It appears to have been impressed from an oval, in all probability the Bezel of a metallic finger ring, like the celebrated seal of Cheops; in this case an oval, two inches in length by one inch wide. The king Sabaco is represented upon the left in an action very commonly seen in the historical monuments of Egypt, wearing the red cap *teshr*. He bends down, seizing with his left hand the hair of the head of an enemy, whom he is about to smite with a kind of mace or axe in his right, having slung his bow at his side. Above and before him are hieroglyphs, expressing *Netr nfr nb ar cht Shabaka*, 'the perfect God, the Lord who produces things, Shabaka or Sabaco).' Behind is an expression of constant occurrence in Egyptian texts: *sha(s)anch-haf*, 'life follows his head.' Although no figure of any deity is seen, the hieroglyphs at the left edge show that the king was performing this action before one—*ma, na nak*, 'I have given to thee,' which must have been followed by some such expression as 'a perfect life,' 'all enemies or countries under thy sandals.' It is impossible to determine which god of the Pantheon was there, probably Amon-Ra, or the Theban Jupiter. These seals, therefore, assume a most important character as to the synchronism of the two monarchies. There can, indeed, be no doubt that the Shabak found upon them is the usual king of the inscriptions; and it is owing alone to the confusion of Herodotus and Diodorus that the difficulty of identifying the true chronological position has occurred. The twenty-fifth dynasty of Manetho, according to all three versions, con-

Sabaco reigned in Egypt at the end of the seventh century before Christ, the exact time at which Sennacherib came to the throne. He is probably the So mentioned in the second book of Kings (xvii. 4.) as having received ambassadors from Hoshea, the king of Israel, who, by entering into a league with the Egyptians, called down the vengeance of Shalmaneser, whose tributary he was, which led to the first great captivity of the people of Samaria. Shalmaneser we know to have been an immediate predecessor of Sennacherib, and Tirakhah, the Egyptian king, who was defeated by the Assyrians near Lachish, was the immediate successor of Sabaco II.

It would seem that a peace having been concluded between the Egyptians and one of the Assyrian monarchs, probably Sennacherib, the royal signets of the two kings, thus found together, were attached to the treaty, which was deposited amongst the archives of the kingdom. Whilst the document itself, written upon parchment or papyrus, has completely perished, this singular proof of the alliance, if not actual meeting, of the two monarchs is still preserved amidst the remains of the state papers of the Assyrian empire; furnishing one of the most remarkable instances of confirmatory evidence on record, whether we regard it as verifying the correctness of the interpretation of the cuneiform character, or as an illustration of Scripture history.

Little doubt, I trust, can now exist in the minds of my readers as to the identification of the builder of the palace of Kouyunjik, with the Sennacherib of Scripture. Had the name stood alone, we might reasonably have questioned the correctness of the reading, especially as the signs or monograms, with which it is written, are admitted to have no phonetic power. But when characters, whose alphabetic values have been determined from a perfectly distinct source, such as the Babylonian column of the trilingual inscriptions, furnish us with names in the records attributed to Sennacherib, written almost identically as in the Hebrew version of the Bible, such as Hezekiah, Jerusalem, Judah, Sidon, and others, and all occurring in one and the same paragraph, their reading, moreover, confirmed by synchronisms, and illustrated by sculptured representations of the events, the identification must be admitted to be complete.

The palace of Khorsabad, as I have already observed, was built by the father of Sennacherib. The edifice in the south-west corner of Nimroud was raised by the son, as we learn from the inscription on the back of the bulls discovered in that building. The name of the king is admitted

---

sisted of three Ethiopic kings, the seat of whose empire was originally at Gebel Barkal, or Napata, and who subsequently conquered the whole of Egypt. The first monarch of this line was called Sabaco by the Greek writers; the second, Sebechos, or Suechos, his son; the third was Tarkos or Taracus . . .

The great interest attached to the Kouyunjik seals depends upon having the precise date of this king, as they were probably affixed to a treaty with Assyria, or some neighboring nation. There can be no doubt as to the name of Sabaco . . . It is indeed highly probable, that this is the monarch mentioned in the Book of Kings as Sua or So, and that his seal was affixed to some treaty between Assyria and Egypt."

to be Essarhaddon, and there are events, as it will hereafter be seen, mentioned in his records, which further tend to identify him with the Essarhaddon of Scripture, who, after the murder of his father Sennacherib, succeeded to the throne.

※ ※ ※

The recently developed radiocarbon or Carbon-14 technique of archaeological dating was largely conceived and perfected by Willard F. Libby who was given the Nobel Award in 1960 in recognition for this achievement. The article reprinted here is the first substantive report of accomplished ancient datings and is therefore of considerable historical interest. In 1947 Libby and five of his associates published the following statement (The Physical Review, Vol. 72, p. 936), *which may be taken as the first precise realization of the potential use of radioactive carbon for dating purposes: "Since the radiocarbon originates in the top layers of the atmosphere, thereby entering the life cycle and all living matter, and since the neutron intensity at sea level is negligible, we are led to the prediction that the intake of radiocarbon by living bodies will cease when they die, and that the period of time elapsed since death will be measurable by direct comparison of the specific activity of the specimen with that of living matter in general. In other words, if we can assume that the specific activity of living matter has remained constant over the time interval being measured, a specimen 5000 years buried will have 5.3 counts per minute per gram of carbon rather than the original 10.5. By invoking isotopic enrichment it should be possible to measure samples as old as 40,000 years. Of course, the limit could be extended by further enrichment, though the effort required would probably be prohibitive in most cases. It is planned to measure certain dated samples as a check on these conclusions."*

For further reading on the theory and application of the radiocarbon method see Libby (1955) and Aitken (1961, chap. 6). Lists of radiocarbon dates are now published annually under the title Radiocarbon Supplement *by the* American Journal of Science (*Vol. 1, 1959; Vol. 2, 1960; Vol. 3, 1961*) *under the editorship of R. F. Flint and W. S. Deevey, Jr.*

Radiocarbon Dating

W. F. Libby, E. C. Anderson, and J. R. Arnold

Some time ago the occurrence of radiocarbon in living matter and dissolved ocean carbonate was reported (see references 1, 2, 4, 5 on p. 60) as a result of researches on sewage methane gas from the City of Baltimore. The postulated origin (see reference 5)—cosmic ray neutrons reacting with atmospheric nitrogen to give radiocarbon at high altitudes—clearly predicted that all material in the life cycle and all material exchangeable with atmospheric carbon dioxide, such as carbonate dissolved in sea water, would be radioactive. The long half-life of radiocarbon, $5,720 \pm 47$ years (see reference 3), further seemed to ensure that the mixing processes would have ample time to distribute the radiocarbon uniformly throughout the world.

Since completing the first tests using isotopic enrichment with Dr. Grosse and his associates, an improvement in counting technique has enabled us to investigate materials without enrichment to about 5-10% error. The samples are counted in the form of elementary carbon in a screen wall counter (see reference 6). Six grams of carbon are spread uniformly over an area of 300 cm², to give an "infinitely thick" layer; about 5.9% of the disintegrations register in this arrangement. The background of the counter has been reduced from 150 cpm (when shielded by 2 inches of lead) to 10 cpm by means of anticoincidence shielding and the addition of a 4 inch iron liner inside the lead shield. The technique will be described in detail elsewhere. A world-wide assay has been completed, and the uniformity apparently established. The data are presented in Table 1.

The numbers quoted are intended to be absolute disintegration rates per gram of carbon. It must be said, however, that our absolute calibration of the counters used may have as much as 10% error. We hope to improve this in the near future. Since all the samples were measured with the same technique, the relative comparison does not involve this point. With the exception of the Antarctic seal sample, which has been run only once to date, the uniformity is well within experimental error. Since one expects the arctic samples if anything to be high, because the neutron intensity is lowest at the equator and rises towards the poles (see

"Age Determination by Radiocarbon Content: World-Wide Assay of Natural Radiocarbon," by W. F. Libby, E. C. Anderson and J. R. Arnold. *Science*, Vol. 109, No. 2827 March 4, 1949), pp. 227-228. Reprinted by permission of Professor W. F. Libby and the editor of *Science*.

TABLE 1

World-Wide Assay of Radiocarbon

Sample	Assay (cpm/gm of carbon)
Baltimore sewage methane (1, 2)	10.5 ± 1.0
Ironwood from Marshall Islands	11.5 ± 0.6
Ironwood from Marshall Islands	12.6 ± 1.0
Elmwood, Chicago Campus	12.7 ± 0.8
Elmwood, Chicago Campus	11.9 ± 0.7
Pine, Mt. Wilson, New Mexico (10,000' altitude)	12.5 ± 0.6
Bolivian wood	13.5 ± 0.6
Bolivian wood	11.3 ± 0.8
Ceylon wood	12.5 ± 0.7
Tierra del Fuego wood	12.8 ± 0.5
Panamanian wood	13.0 ± 0.5
Palestinian wood	12.4 ± 0.4
Swedish wood	12.6 ± 0.5
New South Wales wood	13.3 ± 0.4
North African wood	11.9 ± 0.4
Weighted average	12.5 ± 0.2
Sea shell, Florida west coast	13.3 ± 0.5
Sea shell, Florida west coast	14.9 ± 0.7
Sea shell, Florida west coast	14.6 ± 0.5
Weighted average	14.1 ± 0.3
Seal oil, Antarctic	10.4 ± 0.7

reference 9), and since the deviation of the seal oil from the mean is not much larger than the error of the measurement, it is believed that further measurements will show this sample to be normal also. The result on the sea shell sample is interesting. It has been shown (see references 7 and 8) that C^{13} occurs in higher abundance in carbonates than in organic material. The result we find for radiocarbon in sea shells versus wood and other organic material is in line with this earlier finding for C^{13}. It is true, however, that the difference may be somewhat larger in our case than that predicted from the earlier results, though the error of our measurement is so large at present as to well overlap the predicted value.

AGE DETERMINATION

Having established the world-wide uniformity of the radiocarbon assay at the present time, it seems a logical assumption that this would have been true in ancient times. Assuming this, and using the half-life of radiocarbon, $5,720 \pm 47$ years (see reference 2), one can calculate the specific activity to be expected after any given time interval elapsed since the removal of any carbonaceous material from equilibrium with the life cycle. For living materials this probably coincides with the time of death; for carbonates it would correspond to the time of crystallization (assuming no further interchange with the solution or atmospheric carbon dioxide to occur). On this basis we have undertaken examination of wood samples of well established age from the ancient Egyptian tombs. Two such samples were used, one from the tomb of Sneferu at Meydum (furnished by Froelich Rainey, of the University of Pennsylvania Museum, Philadelphia) which was 4,575 ± 75 years old; the other from the tomb of Zoser at Sakkara (furnished by Ambrose Lansing, of the Metropolitan Museum of New York) which was 4,650 ± 75 years old. The former sample is cypress wood; the latter is acacia. John Wilson, of the Oriental Institute of the University of Chicago, has given the dates quoted, at the behest of a committee of the American Anthropological Association, consisting of Frederick Johnson, chairman, Froelich Rainey, and Donald Collier. The expected assay for 4,600 year material is easily calculated to be 7.15 ± 0.15 cpm/gm of carbon on the basis of the present assay and the half-life. Table 2 presents the data obtained on these materials.

TABLE 2

Age Determination on the Ancient Egyptian Samples

Samples	Specific gravity found (cpm/gm of carbon)
Zoser	7.88 ± 0.74
Zoser	7.36 ± 0.53
Sneferu	6.95 ± 0.40
Sneferu	7.42 ± 0.38
Sneferu	6.26 ± 0.41
Weighted average (both samples)	7.04 ± 0.20
Expected value	7.15 ± 0.15

The data on both samples were averaged since the error in ages almost overlaps the difference, and the weighting was taken according to the error quoted in each run. The errors quoted here and in Table 1 also are standard deviations determined strictly from the statistical counting error, and since the data agree within these errors, we believe that no other appreciable error is involved in the measurement. It is gratifying that the mean of the determinations agrees with the expected value within 1 standard deviation unit. An error of 0.4 cpm/gm in the specific activity corresponds to an error of 450 years in a 4,600 year old sample.

On this basis we feel encouraged to proceed with further tests on younger samples of known age. This work is now in progress. It is hoped that certain unknowns can be measured in the near future. A large thermal diffusion column similar to the one used by Dr. Grosse and his associates has been installed in the laboratory and a considerable increase in accuracy should result, permitting the measurement of samples as old as 20,000 to 25,000 years.

References

1. Anderson, E. C., Libby, W. F., Weinhouse, S., Reid, A. F., Kirshenbaum, A. D., and Grosse, A. V. *Phys. Rev.*, 1947, 72, 931.
2. Anderson, E. C., Libby, W. F., Weinhouse, S., Reid, A. F., Kirshenbaum, A. D., and Grosse, A. V. *Science*, 1947, 105, 576.
3. Engelkemeir, A. G., Hamill, W. H., Ingraham, M. G., and Libby, W. F. (To be published.)
4. Grosse, A. V., and Libby, W. F. *Science*, 1947, 106, 88.
5. Libby, W. F. *Phys. Rev.*, 1946, 69, 671.
6. Libby, W. F., and Lee, D. D. *Phys. Rev.*, 1939, 55, 245.
7. Murphey, B. F., and Nier, A. O. *Phys. Rev.*, 1941, 59, 771.
8. Nier, A. O., and Gulbransen, E. A. *J. Amer. Chem. Soc.*, 1939, 61, 697.
9. Simpson, J. A., Jr. *Phys. Rev.*, 1948, 73, 1277.

✳ 2 ✳

ANCIENT IMPLEMENTS

Although the Greek and Roman writers were aware that some peoples made and used stone implements, this knowledge became quite lost during the Dark Ages after the fall of Rome and had to be rediscovered. After Mercatus' appreciation of the fact that stone implements were made by man, a number of observers made similar, and probably independent, statements (cf. Heizer, 1962). Once the true nature of ancient stone tools was established, it was only a matter of time and chance until some intelligent mind would recognize, in a deposit of obvious geological antiquity, stone implements which were inescapably of the same age as the deposit and the materials contained in it. A London pharmacist, Conyers, who found a chipped flint handaxe associated with elephant bones near Grays Inn Lane about 1690, made just this sort of discovery, but it was later explained as an ancient British weapon used to tip a spear which had served to kill one of the elephants used by the Roman army under Claudius. The time was not yet ripe, apparently, for the elephant to be recognized as dating from Pleistocene times. Still earlier the English antiquary William Dugdale in 1656 writes of finding what were probably Neolithic celts which he recognized as "made by the native Britains . . . for weapons, inasmuch as they had not then attained to the knowledge of working iron or brass to such uses" (Salzman, 1951). In 1790, just one hundred years after Conyers, John Frere found in Suffolk a number of Acheulian handaxes associated with the remains of extinct animals in a brickearth pit, and his account, reprinted here, shows that he was much more ready to grant the possibility of really ancient evidence of man. Studies of the features of the earth's surface by men like Steno, Buffon, Raspe, and Arduino led James Hutton (in his *Theory of the*

Earth, 1795) to formulate the principle of "uniformitarianism" which stated that geological features were understandable as having resulted from processes still occurring (i.e. vulcanism, erosion, deposition, uplift, etc.). When William Smith in 1816 published his *Strata Identified by Organized Fossils,* paleontology, and its handmaiden geology, were established as sciences with definite methods of study. For a thorough review of this development see Greene (1961). Charles Lyell, who published *Principles of Geology* in 1830, had once believed in the explanation of earth history called "catastrophism." Lyell altered his beliefs to uniformitarianism which he labeled the "theory of existing causes" (Haber, 1959c:215 ff.).

William Cowper poetically spoke for much of the contemporary opinion of the new geological chronology when he wrote just before 1800

> "Some drill and bore
> The solid earth, and from the strata there
> Extract a register, by which we learn
> That He who made it, and revealed its date
> To Moses, was mistaken in its age."

Thus, the development of stratigraphic paleontology began shortly after 1800 and was bolstered by repeated discoveries of human bones or man-made tools in association with the remains of extinct animals.

Michel Mercatus, physician to Pope Clement VIII, died in 1593. He left a manuscript which was edited by Lancisius and published in 1717. In this work Mercatus discusses ceraunia of two kinds: first, Neolithic polished stone axes (ceraunia cuneata), and second, chipped flint arrow and spear points (ceraunia vulgaris). The account is vague and rambling, but Mercatus dates ceraunia vulgaris before the use of iron (a hint of the Stone Age period) and also considers them to have been made by human hands. The famous Agricola in 1558 had expressed doubts about the heavenly origin of ceraunia (de Blasio, 1922:86), and there were specific proposals by Olaf Wurm, a Dane, in 1655; by William Dugdale in 1656; by R. Sibbald in 1684; and by Robert Plot in 1686 (Peake, 1940:117-118; Heizer, 1962) that chipped or polished stone tools were made by man in ancient times before the use of metals was known. Plot wrote that neither the Britains nor Romans made stone axes, and stated, "How they might be fastened to a helve may be seen in the Museum Ashmoleaneum where there are several Indian ones of like kind fitted up in the same order as when formerly used." Some people still objected to the idea that stone tools predated metal ones, as witness two articles in an Irish journal of 1857 where it is argued that stone axes are imitations of bronze or iron pieces (Trevelyan, 1857; O'Laverty, 1857). Among the earliest illustrations of prehistoric stone implements is that of a Neolithic celt by Dugdale in 1656; Neolithic celts by Mahudel in 1740 (reproduced by Laming, 1952, pl. 1); the biface handaxe found by Conyers in 1690 (reproduced by Laming, 1952, pl. 2); and neolithic celts ("lapis fulmineus") and flaked implements ("ceraunia") in the 1717 edition of Mercatus (reproduced by Boule and Vallois, 1946, fig. 1).

Jussieu, among others in the early eighteenth century saw that the stone implements found in Europe must be man-made tools rather than the result of lightning striking the earth. The discovery of the New World, and of the modern Stone Age peoples who dwelt there, provided the means for accurately identifying the Neolithic and Paleolithic tools that were found in Europe. Jussieu's account is so clear on this point that it is a good comparison piece to Mercatus' more tentative suggestion. Jussieu wrote elsewhere (p. 17) in the same volume from which the following article is taken, "If the other sculptured stones are monuments of material revolutions, these [prehistoric stone implements] are the monument of a great revolution which one can call *moral;* and the comparison of the New World with Old serves equally to prove both kinds of revolution."

On Ceraunia Cuneata

Michel Mercatus

There are three kinds of Cerauniae, differentiated by shape and color. Sotacus, our most ancient authority, has recorded two of these, the black and red. A third kind has been added which is quite rare, and sought by the Parthian Magi (Priests), green in color . . . It is thought that all kinds are hurled down from the sky by lightning bolts, and that the third kind is only found in a spot that has been struck by lightning. In our day they are known by scientists under a different name, probably from a translation of the Greek word. For they are called "Folgora (lightning)" by which name we commonly understand "fulmina." The Germans rightly distinguish them from other stones that fall from the sky by calling them "der glatte Donnerstein." Surprisingly, this is not true of more recent authorities, who have restored the old name "Cerauniae" to these well known stones. Our goldsmiths use them for polishing gold, a task for which ebony was employed in very ancient times. Nor did posterity neglect the ancient custom without good reason. For the Cerauniae give the same degree of smoothness to the material as the ebony

Extract here translated from the Latin reprint in "Materiaux pour l'histoire primitive et naturelle de l'homme." Vol. 10 (Second series, Vol. 6), pp. 49-57, 1875.

did; both are extremely hard, though the Cerauniae even more so, especially as their shape is so naturally suitable for polishing. In length and breadth this shape is completely that of an axe, with the ends of the corners blunted, usually a half-finger thick, and tapering toward the edge. It is inconceivable that the ancients did not appreciate the usefulness of this shape for polishing if Cerauniae were known then. It seems that cobblers once employed them for putting a high polish to ladies' footwear, and called them "Agerati (unaging)," according to Heras the Cappadocian doctor, who lived about the time of Domitian; their name fits in with this. For they were called "ageratoi (the Greek for unaging)" because of their hardness, since no amount of friction from leather has any eroding effect upon them. Regardless of color, some are a palm's width, others are smaller, some are broad, others extended lengthways, and some begin narrow and widen toward the edge, while others are almost the same width at both ends. The black ones are often square-shaped, but almost rounded at the corners which have been worn away: these antiquity called "Baetuli." Hesychius records that the stone which was substituted for Jupiter by Rhea, and which Saturn devoured in the myth, was a "baitulos" (meteoric stone), which the Barbarians solemnly called "Abadir" in their mystery rites. Since Jupiter owed both his life and his kingdom to it, they were convinced that the "Baetuli" were sent by Jupiter, and possessed the power of storming cities and fleets. I should add this, because not only the Baetuli but also their very name was of doubtful origin. The green stones generally have a palish color, while the red ones are tinged with dark brown, or sometimes yellow, which also darkens the paleness. The red and green are the hardest kinds, even more so than agate, though they look like flint: the black are found to be the softest of all. Inasmuch as Cerauniae have been found to turn up in various places in Italy, Germany, and the mountains of Spain, and by the side of rivers among flint-stones, one may suppose that they occur in other areas too.

Just as we have said that they are useful to goldsmiths, so also are they useful for smoothing silverware and for gilding metals. Some people carry them as a protection against lightning, and believe that this power derives from the fact that they are hurled down by the lightning. But it is the place *where* they fall that receives such immunity, and this is a matter of pure chance. When the people who carry them move to a different place, then they must expect a different outcome, unless the Cerauniae have made a plot against the sky, so that some notorious Typhon may hope to escape with impunity (Typhon: a monster who stole Jupiter's thunderbolts, but was eventually overcome by one). Galen recommends Ageratus for its moderate healing powers, although it cannot be tasted. For he says that it helps an uvula which is suffering from a slight inflammation; in the case of a more serious inflammation, it should be treated with oak-apple. To this end, the dust of the oak-apple should be applied to the uvula by means of a spoon. Someone in the pseudo-writings of Galen advises great caution here, since nature is not inferior to art in imitating things. Our suspicions are increased by the discovery of small pieces of Ceraunia unsuitable for sharp weapon-heads. Nothing can be said positively about the theory of lightning already mentioned, except that it is found here and there. Our verdict, then, is an open one, for each man to decide for himself.

CERAUNIA VULGARIS, AND SICILEX

Ceraunia is plentiful in Italy, where it is popularly called 'Sagitta' (arrow), since it is carved in the shape of a triangular weapon, made of flint, slender, and hard. Two opinions are held in regard to this. Most men believe that it is deposited by lightning. Those who study history think that before the use of iron it was beaten out of the hardest flints, to be used for the madness of war. For very early man used sections of flint as knives. Sephora, the wife of Moysus, is said in the Holy Book to have initiated her son to the Jewish rite with a very sharp stone; and when Joshua entered Palestine, he was ordered by God to prepare two stone knives for the same purpose, whence was established in Israel the custom of circumcision with a stone. In our age, in the absence of molten iron in western regions, ships, houses, and all mechanical tools have been constructed by cutting stones to a sharp point. Indeed 'Silex' (flint), as its name implies, seems like 'Sicilex' which has been selected for cutting. 'Sicilices' are those stones by which missiles and hunting spears are sharpened, as we find in that verse of Ennius recorded by Festus:

"The skirmishers, with broad cutting-spears
(Sicilicibus) advanced in a body."

This Ceraunia has the same shape, so that the opinion persists that before molten iron the ancients made 'Sicilices' from 'Silice' (flint), and that this Ceraunia is included among their number. From small beginnings, men's hatred grew to immense proportions, and Africans joined battle (using clubs which are called 'phalangae,' poles with the Egyptians; however, both Pliny and Pomponius Mela record that the Phoenicians had already considered war. Nor is Lucretius right when he says:

"Ancient weapons consisted of hands, claws, and teeth."

For since they are of little value to man, he used his reason; that very hand which advised instruments most fitted for making things was also put to use, so that instead of displaying cruelty after the fashion of wild beasts, he was able to fight more nobly. To begin with, reason showed him that he should collect stones and clubs, things all ready to hand, and fight his enemy from a distance. The first battles resulted from private quarrels, before peoples and nations contested in war. Then jealousy, avarice, and ambition, thirsting more greedily for human blood, discovered greater atrocities. They began using spears, and tipping every kind of weapon with points made of horn, bone, and flint, according to those who think that Ceraunia was made from them to pierce more highly protected breastplates. This is suggested by its shape, which is rough and blunted on the surface, with a jagged edge, since it has not been shaped by a saw or file, which did not exist then; but it was beaten by a stone to force it into a triangle either uniform, oblong, or pointed in shape, and a sharp piece was left where it was to be joined to the spear shaft; this was fixed into the shaft of the weapon. The substance shines, despite the rough surface, because of its considerable hardness; its color might be white, or yellowish, rich red-ochre, grassy-green, blackish, or sometimes variegated with spots. Thin metal strips are found of the same material, a palm's length long and half an inch wide, or smaller, worn at the corners, smoothed on the surface; this is level, then gradually tapers to an angle, bisecting the center. Those who think that the ancients made Ceraunia for sharpening weapons say that they covered their bows with these metal strips. But when was their use most prevalent, and at what time did the reign of iron, to which they yielded, invade the earth? The Holy Book asserts that iron was manufactured before the flood destroyed the human race, and that its creator was Tabalcais, who was seven generations removed from the first parent. Josephus writes that the same man bravely engaged in warlike activities in antiquity, so that one man seems to have been the creator both of iron and war, and to have united the hatreds of a few men, joined by affinity of blood, and to have discovered iron tools with which to effectuate their hatred; there were none more ancient than these. Although the production of iron was preserved after the universal destruction of living things which attended the flood, it must have been by the man who remembered its first creator and his work: yet when the nations had been restored, and again distributed throughout the world, the art of working iron was left with only a few. For it could not accompany people who emigrated to different areas, unless the metal itself went with them; they could have found it only by digging deep into the veins of the earth, which is also very difficult without iron tools. Intelligence alone is insufficient to deal with this substance; it is tamed only by a considerable amount of hard work. So, although iron was used to some extent from the earliest times, it could only have been in the hands of a very few; it started in Armenia, when the last of the flood had subsided, then in Cilicia and Syria: other races were prevented from developing that usage for themselves by their simple way of life, or by laziness, or by the unattractiveness of iron; or most of all by its uneven distribution, since it is not found everywhere. No iron mine existed in Palestine up to the reign of Saul; he alone, with his son Jonathan, had a lance and sword made of iron: the other iron implements were those of the farmers, and had to be repaired after use. The Israelites, who were mountain dwellers, brought them down to Philisthiis. Meanwhile, then, whenever, from the earliest days of trade, injuries provoked nations to war, cruelty was resorted to without iron; but each man tried the most savage means available to him. Western people used to point their arrows with fish bones, and considered this sufficiently sharp, since they themselves were naked. In Italy, and particularly in Latium, in whose fields this kind of Ceraunia is most frequently excavated; the aborigines of Sicily, if the theory is correct, used to make sharp pointed darts, to prevent leather breastplates from protecting some vulnerable area. All this was ended when iron was at last introduced by intertrading between nations. The usual result was that individual nations considered the inventors of iron to have been those peoples by whom they themselves were introduced to it; Pliny says that the Dactyli of Ida found it in Crete; Strabo thinks it was the Telchines; Clement says that it was Selmens in Cyprus; and so opinions differ. We, however, are satisfied if we have shown that Ceraunia of this kind could have been produced by the ancients. For this is shown by its material and shape, supported by its name, and confirmed, finally, by its use. If this could be proved for certain, then Ceraunia ought not to be included in the category of idiomorphic substances, since it would have been made artificially.

❋ ❋ ❋

Origin and Uses of the Thunderstone

Antoine de Jussieu

Nothing is as well known in the realm of science as the qualities which the ancients and we ourselves, in a tradition which is still preserved among us, have attributed to the thunderstone (*pierre de foudre*).

The explication of its name, ceraunia, indicates that they believed it to be descended from heaven in the moment when the thunder burst and struck somewhere on the earth.

This alleged origin caused it to be regarded with a degree of respect due to the majesty of God who, so they thought, had launched it. Pliny also listed it in the catalogue of precious stones.

But hardly anybody has made more of this than the people of the North [i.e., of Europe] with the superstitions which they attached to these

"De l'Origine et des usages de la pierre de foudre." *Mémoires de l'Académie Royale,* 1723, pp. 6-9. Paris.

stones. They had formerly adored an idol which they thought ruled over the thunder and whom they represented with a thunderbolt in hand in the form of a pointed, worked stone (*pierre taillées en coin*). These stones were kept as protection against thunder and lightning which they believed could be kept away from their houses if, at the first sound of thunder, they knocked with the stone three times at those places by which the lightning might have entered.

Helwing, the well known minister of Angerbourg in Prussia, who wrote a special treatise on the stones of his country, said that he had to use secular force to destroy this superstition in the area under his jurisdiction; a superstition which was more deeply rooted because it was maintained by continuous new finds of this kind of stone and the people could not help imagining that stones of this shape had something mysterious about them.

In that respect this nation [France] seems to agree with the Chinese, among whom Rumphius, who has illustrated the shapes and kinds of stones in his "Report on Shells," assures us there existed a similar idea based on observations made on the shapes, qualities, and colors of this kind of stone and on the sites at which they are found, which are often tree trunks believed to have been struck by lightning.

While somewhat removed from these ideas, we continue to believe that the ceraunia is a natural stone which is characterized by being shaped like wedges (*coin*) or arrowheads (*fer de flèche*), in the same way as the oval, cylindrical, prismatic, or round shapes are characteristic of the pebbles of Meudoc, the emerald, other crystals, and the "*échinites.*"

Mercator [Mercatus] enlightened as he was in the history of fossils, did not want to adhere so completely to the opinion that the stones were shaped in these forms that he would have renounced the opinion of those who admitted the natural possibility of a "*jeu de nature.*"

But today, with attention devoted to two or three of these stones which came, some from the American Islands and others from Canada, we will be able to correct our misinterpretation from the moment we learn that, without a doubt, the savages in these countries have different ways of using nearly similar stones which they have fashioned with infinite patience by rubbing them against other stones, lacking any tool of iron or steel.

The primary needs of the savages are to either cut or split wood, to make weapons to kill animals for their subsistence, or to defend themselves against their enemies.

The shapes of axe and wedge (*coin*) which they have given to some stones which we have received from them show clearly that they were made for the first of these uses; and the points which they have given to some flint stones, which are skilfully attached to the end of certain long and thin pieces of wood, make it reasonably certain that they were used as arrows.

I am displaying one original specimen of each of these tools: the first is in the form of an axe and comes from the Caribs; the second resembles a wedge deriving from Canada; the third are three arrows, each having as armature, instead of a steel point, a piece of triangular flint sharpened at the angle which serves as point, and with two cutting edges.

Looking at the shapes of these pieces which make up the collection, those which resemble any of the three forms and, mostly, those of wedge or arrowhead shape which until now have always been taken for thunderstones and for something mysterious, we scarcely could hesitate now to recognize as tools, like the steel tools to which they bear a resemblance, which have been fashioned either by the first inhabitants of the countries where they have been found or which were introduced by strangers who used them in a kind of commerce. One reason for this guess is that in most of the countries where these tools are found there are hardly any quarries or pebbles of the same kind which could have been used to make these tools locally, and consequently there is a great possibility that the inhabitants of a country where pebbles of the same fine grain and the same degree of hardness are found, came to exchange them for other commodities; and finally, to confirm this guess, the same practice still obtains among the savages where those who have more skill and patience make the tools and furnish them to others who perhaps know better how to use them.

The people of France, Germany, and other Northern countries who, but for the discovery of iron, would have much resemblance to the savages of today, had no less need than they—before using iron—to cut wood, to remove bark, to split branches, to kill wild animals, to hunt for their food, and to defend themselves against their enemies. This they could not possibly have done without these tools which, not being subject to rust, are found today in the ground intact and nearly with their original polish.

As it is common enough for two things of very different nature to have at times the same name, and as the name thunderstone, which should only be applied to the kind of stone I have described, is also used in French for a sort of vitriolic marcasite, either oblong or rounded, sometimes rough at the edges, sometimes smooth, and sometimes with facets, I strongly advise that the latter be not mistaken for the first kind, not only because they do not resemble each other but are even different in the respect that the latter has the quality of fusing and of changing into vitriol when exposed to air, while the one about which I am speaking is a true and very hard stone, so finely grained that it is used as touchstone for metals and for polishing different things.

✻ ✻ ✻

John Frere's account of finding in 1790 Acheulean handaxes associated with the large bones of unknown animals (actually elephants) is the first clear presentation of the association in an open site of man-made tools and extinct animals. This account was ignored until J. Flower called attention to it sixty years later. Prestwich (see his account further on in this chapter) and Lyell (1863:166-169) visited the Hoxne pit and described the geology, and interest in the locality is still active (West, 1956).

The Beginning of Paleolithic Archaeology

John Frere

LETTER TO THE REV. JOHN BRAND, SECRETARY, READ JUNE 22, 1797

Sir:

I take the liberty to request you to lay before the Society some flints found in the parish of Hoxne, in the county of Suffolk, which, if not particularly objects of curiosity in themselves, must, I think, be considered in that light from the situation in which they were found.

They are, I think, evident weapons of war, fabricated and used by a people who had not the use of metals. They lay in great numbers at the depth of about twelve feet, in a stratified soil, which was dug into for the purpose of raising clay for bricks.

The strata are as follows:

1. Vegetable earth 1½ feet.
2. Argill 7½ feet.
3. Sand mixed with shells and other marine substances 1 foot.
4. A gravelly soil, in which the flints are found, generally at the rate of five or six in a square yard, 2 feet.

In the same stratum are frequently found small fragments of wood, very perfect when first dug up, but which soon decompose on being exposed to the air; and in the stratum of sand (No. 3), were found some extraor-

John Frere, "Account of Flint Weapons Discovered at Hoxne in Suffolk," *Archaeologia*, 1800, vol. 13, pp. 204-205.

dinary bones, particularly a jaw-bone of enormous size, of some un-known animal, with the teeth remaining in it. I was very eager to obtain a sight of this; and finding it had been carried to a neighboring gentleman, I inquired of him, but learned that he had presented it, together with a huge thigh-bone, found in the same place, to Sir Ashton Lever, and it therefore is probably now in Parkinson's Museum.

The situation in which these weapons were found may tempt us to refer them to a very remote period indeed; even beyond that of the present world; but, whatever our conjectures on that head may be, it will be difficult to account for the stratum in which they lie being covered with another stratum, which, on that supposition, may be conjectured to have been once the bottom, or at least the shore, of the sea. The manner in which they lie would lead to the persuasion that it was a place of their manufacture and not of their accidental deposit; and the numbers of them were so great that the man who carried on the brick-work told me that before he was aware of their being objects of curiosity, he had emptied baskets full of them into the ruts of the adjoining road. It may be conjectured that the different strata were formed by inundations happen-ing at distant periods, and bringing down in succession the different materials of which they consist; to which I can only say that the ground in question does not lie at the foot of any higher ground, but does itself overhang a track of boggy earth, which extends under the fourth stratum; so that it should rather seem that torrents had washed away the incum-bent strata and left the bog-earth bare, than that the bog-earth was covered by them, especially as the strata appear to be disposed horizon-tally, and present their edges to the abrupt termination of the high ground.

If you think the above worthy the notice of the Society you will please to lay it before them.

> I am, Sir,
> with great respect,
> Your faithful humble Servant,
> John Frere

* * *

Tournal was one of several workers who excavated in European caves between 1800 and 1850. Such cave explorations were being done in Eng-land, France, Belgium, Germany, and Italy. The names of Christol, Schmerling, MacEnery, Buckland, de Saussure, Dumas, Bové, and de Serres are all known in this connection. Information on their activities and discoveries can be found in Lyell (1863:59-74) and Daniel (1950:

33-38). Tournal's paper ranks as one of the earliest published accounts of cave deposit investigations which produced evidence of the contemporaneity of man and extinct animals, but as with other evidence of this sort, the world was unprepared to admit it as true at the time. For one instance of a discovery which we may suppose was of considerable importance, but which was lost because of lack of interest, see Lyell's (1863:510-512) account of the discovery of human remains near Strasbourg in 1823. Nougier (1955) has told the story of the discovery of the European caves which contained paintings of the Paleolithic period. The earliest such recognition was that of Altamira cave in Spain in 1879.

General Considerations on The Phenomenon of Bone Caverns

M. Tournal

Many observations have been published concerning caverns with evidences of osseous faunal remains in them. This phenomenon, at first thought so simple, now appears to be very complicated, if one considers the observations and discussions that have taken place in the matter. The circle of interested persons in which the questions were originally discussed has become so vast that it seems useless here generally to review the principal questions involved today in this field.

I have thought that I was, in a manner of speaking, authorized to take charge of this work, because the attention of naturalists has again been fixed on these matters since I have published [1828] on the fossil human bone of the Bize Cavern, near Narbonne, and since the publication of Messrs. de Serres and Jules de Christol on several other caverns in the south of France.

I should like first of all to pay signal recognition to the works of Messrs. Buckland, Bertrand Jeslin, and Constant Prévost, who were the first to have thrown light on the curious phenomenon of caverns which contain faunal skeletal remains. The work of Mr. Buckland (*Reliquiae Diluvianae*), to which one cannot take any exception save perhaps with the title, will always be an admirable model of description and an immense collection of carefully observed facts. It is annoying that we do not have a French edition.

The caverns or grottoes which one encounters so commonly in moun-

Annales de Chimie et de Physique, Vol. 25:161-181, 1833. Trans. by A. B. Elsasser and reprinted from Krober Anthropological Society Papers No. 21, pp. 6-16, 1959.

tainous limestone formations have always caught the attention of the curious by the odd disposition of passages and rooms which are seen in them, by the impressiveness of the vaults and pillars and by the rocky deposits, called stalactites and stalagmites, which decorate the caverns' interiors in such a bizarre and capricious fashion. Several more or less ingenious theories have successively been set forth to explain the origin of these caves. Thus it has been suggested that they have been the result of the issue of springs charged with carbonic acid, by the dissolving action of water upon mineral materials which are often found in irregular agglomerations, like gypsum, marl, and so on, within calcareous soil. It seems to me that one might better attribute the origin of these caves to numerous disturbances which the soil has undergone, disturbances which must have, in displacing originally horizontal calcareous strata, produced these irregular hollows which underground water has then eroded and enlarged. This theory seems justified by the observation of upthrusting of earth strata in the area in which the caves occur, and also of the interior walls of these caves, where angular projections are rarely seen: on the contrary, the surfaces are smooth, with rounded contours. However, I do not pretend to be certain that all the caves have been formed in this manner. I wish only to indicate what must have been the most probable general cause.

If the phenomena of the caves were limited to the simple observations that I have just made, and to the theories that have been conceived to explain them, they would not be worthy of attracting the attention of naturalists. But the whole matter is much more vast, interesting, and complicated than might first be imagined. Indeed, in examining closely several of the caverns, it is discovered that a vault sometimes contains bones, pebbles, and silt, all adhering together as a result of the calculous infiltration; that the soil is covered with an ordinarily reddish, silty deposit which also contains bone and pebbles; that the silt or mud, sometimes hardened, fills vertical fissures and more or less extended galleries. In breaking the often quite thick stalagmitic crust which one walks upon, almost always silt is found below it, and with it, bones and other material transported by streams. It is for caverns which present this phenomenon that the name "bone cavern" has been specially reserved.

This observation once recognized, a multitude of questions will present themselves; one asks first of all why certain caverns contain no bones whatever? To what species of animal do the remains buried in the silt belong? Were they (the animals) the same throughout, or did they vary from one location to another? One asks oneself finally how and since when they had been introduced into the caverns?

When these general questions were resolved, new ones presented themselves; these arose as a result of the solutions themselves of the preceding questions. We are going to try to set forth briefly some of the opinions which have been educed on these questions, and their most probable solutions. We shall say here a word about the most recent discussions which have produced several partisan and even opposing camps.

All the caverns, as we have indicated above, do not include bones; some contain only mud or silt and pebbles. In others, absolutely nothing is found except calculous infiltrations or prodigious quantities of guano from recent bats and birds of prey. It is again difficult to tell what the causes of the difference are, or at least to establish, as we have tried to do, a general rule in this regard. Actually, bone caverns are observed at all altitudes, in calcareous formations of very different ages, and at levels which are well above those of valleys of the present time. A point that one might be allowed to hazard is that generally the caves which animals could get into only with difficulty, which for example are located in the centers of high mountain regions, or too distant from water courses, or which must, because of their geographic position, have been out of the range of the animals, do not contain bones. It seems likewise that their presence depends on the age of the caves or upon the time of formation of the openings leading into them. One might easily conceive that the caverns which have remained entirely closed since the time of their formation, and which have been open only occasionally since, this caused by the slow and successive disintegration of mountains, could only have been filled up in quite recent times.

What we have just said naturally leads us to the examination of whether or not the different species of animals buried in the silt and gravel of the caves vary from one locality to another, and to the question of the cause of any such variation. Upon the latter point all the observers are in accord. To be sure, in the deposits of certain caves are encountered almost nothing but bones of a bear species of great size (*Ursus speleus*); very often the bones are still in articulation (Mr. Pitorre has observed about 15 vertebrae in articulation.), and in perfect preservation. (Several species of bear have been found in the caves; the most common is one with a convex forehead. Mr. de Serres has observed in the caverns of Minerva (Hérault) a new species which must have equalled the size of a large horse. Those of Bize, near Narbonne, include remains of a small species which is distinguished only with difficulty from the brown bear of the Pyrenees.) In other caverns a considerable accumulation of partially gnawed bones may be observed. The bones belong to different species of animals, among which is noted a large number of hyenas and some perfectly preserved coprolites of these animals. Sometimes vertical crevices (Under the name of "bony breccia" are distinguished rock crevices filled with hardened alluvium, including bones and pebbles. The phenomena of bony breccia, being quite similar to those of the bone caverns, are accordingly found occurring together in the same locality. I believe I can dispense with further talk on the subject; this little note seems to me more than adequate.) contain nothing but the bones of small rodents, birds and small carnivores; but besides the differences which we have just pointed out, one very great one is yet noted in the distribution of the species, and this difference is in agreement with the geographical position of the caves and their situation, which could be in large forests, or better, on the edge of large plains.

It is easy, after what I have just said, to explain how the bones have been introduced into the caves, and one can easily see that the explanation must vary infinitely according to the locality under observation. In fact, in those (localities) where nothing but bear bones are encountered, it is evident that these animals must have lived peaceably in these deep retreats, and during a long period of time. Mr. Buckland has noted in England very narrow corridors, worn and polished by the friction brought about by the continual passage of these animals. After the death of the animals, when their cartilaginous tissue was entirely decomposed, the ground waters must have dispersed their bones and carried them even into narrow crannies.

The manner in which the broken and gnawed bones of different species are accumulated is equally easy to conceive. One has, so to speak, surprised nature in the act, when one has observed in our time the charnel houses of hyenas and other carnivorous animals which carry their prey into grottoes in order to eat them, and which at length accumulate immense quantities of gnawed bones, belonging to all sorts of animals. Now, in the case which concerns us, the identity is perfect, since with the hyenas are found the bones which they have gnawed, and even their coprolites. At the same time it has been observed that in the caverns the bones accumulate in the most remote passages. (It is well-known that carnivorous animals have the habit of devouring their prey in dim, remote, spots. The house cat, although for a very long time living in domesticity, has not at all yet lost this habit.) What has just been said for the hyena bone caverns applies equally to caverns which contain less ferocious or smaller-sized carnivores. In the cavern of Bize, near Narbonne, one crevice contains rat and rabbit bones exclusively; it is quite evident in this case that it must have served as the particular habitat of these small animals.

These examples, to which I could add several others, will suffice to prove that the bones of animals have not been introduced everywhere in the same manner, that the explanation must then vary necessarily according to the locality which one is observing, and that several circumstances could even have concurred to complicate this phenomenon.

It now remains for me to treat a very grave question, one which has given place to several explanations and has excited very animated discussions. I wish to speak of the introduction into the caverns of silty deposits and rolled pebbles in the midst of which the bones were buried.

Mr. Buckland and several other geologists had first of all thought that the cause which brought about transport of these materials into the caverns had been sudden, short-lived, and universal; they attribute it to one of the last upheavals of the earth, to a cataclysm, a general inundation to a *deluge,* in short, making thus allusion to the Deluge of Moses, which they were trying to support, besides, by other proofs; they had named the soil which they supposed deposited during that tempestuous epoch, and of which the silt of the bone caves made up part, *flood soil.* (I would have liked to avoid speaking of the Deluge of Genesis because it has always seemed to me that one should avoid calling in the authority of religious traditions in scientific discussion. However, since some have wished to pass over the wall of separation, and to place the question on this ground, we must be permitted to pursue in all freedom the thread of our observations and inductions. I shall point out then that the naturalists who have needed the tradition of Moses to support their observations have all committed grave heresies in wanting to remain orthodox. I shall indicate but one: They say that one does not find human bones in the flood deposits. Yet the flood having occurred, according to Genesis, in order to destroy the whole human species, one should of necessity find, in the deposits that are said to have been laid down during that epoch, the remains of individuals who were its victims.) Proceeding with this notion, they divided the organic whole which is found buried in the late deposits which were laid down on the surface of the earth into "pre-" and "post-" flood deposits. (The strongest proof that was brought to bear in favor of the existence of "flood soil," which is designated also under the name "diluvium," was its composition and its wide distribution.)

Some naturalists still think that the diluvial cataclysm was occasioned by an alteration brought about in the axis and poles of the earth, by the collision of a star, or even by the sudden shift in a chain of mountains. They do not fail to cite in support of this opinion the vague traditions of great inundation, which have been handed down by groups of different people, e.g., the submersion of Samothrace, or the floods of Deucalion and Ogyges.

But it will suffice, to upset all these fictions about the shift of the axis of the globe, to put in opposition to them the opinion of Arago, Fourrier, and La Place. Besides, a thorough examination of the terrain designated under the name "diluvium" proves in the most evident manner that, far from being the result of a single violent, general, and short-lived inundation, there have been on the contrary deposits laid down during an extremely long period of time, and that they are the result of a multitude of local phenomena, generally slow but sometimes also sudden and transitory. Actually, to speak only of the silty deposit of the caves, it has been observed in certain localities that the silt alternated with very thick strata of stalagmitic deposit, and that consequently a long time must have elapsed in the formation of the entire deposit. One observes in other localities that this same silt shows several quite distinct layers, and that sometimes it is divided into laminae representing a number of small successive deposits.

I have said above, and I believe it necessary to recall again, that it was not accurate to say that the characteristics of the flood terrain might be everywhere the same. The color, which is in general reddish, depends on the composition of the different calcareous formations, all of which, under the prolonged influence of atmospheric agents, made up a silt colored red by the superoxidation of iron. It is this silt that must have been transported by the waters of rivers, streams, and springs into the caves or crevices where we still observe it today. What I have just said for the silt can partly be applied to the pebbles which it contains. Generally their composition is local, that is to say that they have been transported from adjacent mountains.

Almost always this silt and these pebbles must have been brought into the caverns from top to bottom, through the vertical crevices and not through the present openings to cuts in the horizontal plane, which did not exist at the time of the filling of the caverns. (I think, however, contrary to the generally credited opinion, that the streams which now flow in a generally horizontal plane, i.e., in "valleys," far from having filled up the caverns, very often served only to clear them out). The surface relief must have undergone considerable changes in several places, such that the rivers which today flow in the valleys at that time might have had their courses on or near the summits of the mountains. These changes of relief must be attributed to the breaking down of soil, produced by internal agents, breaking down which was followed no doubt by a lowering of sea-level.

After having proved thus that the bone caverns varied from one place to another, and that they had been filled during a very long period and under the influence of very varied circumstances, it remains for me to speak of new questions which offer a large interest.

The most important is to know if the silty deposit of the caverns includes pottery and human bones, and, in the affirmative, if these objects are of the same date. In a word, the question is whether man has been contemporaneous with extinct animal species that are found buried in the caves, animals which have been considered by all the naturalists as fossils, and if consequently there are *human fossil bones*.

In the terrain considered as "diluvial" and in the silt of the caverns there had been observed for a long time remains of man's industry and some fragments of human bones, but these objects had not caught anyone's attention because it was supposed that the jumble was later, and accidental. The important men of science wanted it thus and their opinion had the value of a thing already judged. Nevertheless the discovery of the caves of Aude, Hérault, and Gard offered for observation a mass of human bone debris and remains of antique pottery, buried in the same deposit with bones of hyenas, lions, tigers, and deer, and a multitude of other animals belonging to extinct species. Attention was then fixed anew on these materials, and Messrs. de Serres, Jules de Christol, and myself, after a close and conscientious examination, thought that all of the objects were of the same date, from which we drew the conclusion that man had been contemporaneous with animal species disappeared today from the surface of the earth and considered as fossils by all the naturalists.

Our observation was based principally on the equal amount of alteration of the bones, and upon their manner of occurrence in the cave. To these proofs have been added others, such as the variety of species which could not have been produced except through domestication; also, the discovery of bones of extinct species, carrying the imprint of cutting implements presumably man-made and so on.

The problem being thus resolved, the secondary question of the existence of man in the fossil state was deduced, as it were, automatically, and became almost a question of terminology, since it was evident that the contemporaries of fossil animals would have to receive the same designation. (In a work published two years ago, and which has received wide publicity, I applied myself to demonstrating that the generally accepted definition of the word "fossil" (organic body buried in the successive strata of the earth) did not suffice when one wished to apply it to organic bodies buried in the last strata which were laid down on the surface of the earth, because it was impossible to say *where the successive strata were terminated.* I must point out again that the physical and chemical characters are hardly helpful in indicating that an organic body is fossil, since the name is given to everything which calls to mind the existence of an organized body. It is thus that one considers as fossils the molds, imprints, and the petrifications of every nature, in a word, the debris of all that has lived, or even everything that recalls a positive existence. Mr. Deshayes has developed this idea well in his work on the description of characteristics of land mollusks.) Also we did not hesitate, with Mr. Jules de Christol, and despite the objections which our observation must raise, we did not hesitate, I say, to proclaim, and we support the idea even today, that *man exists in the fossil state.* Geologists do not confuse, I hope, our observation with the mystification of the shapeless block of sandstone found at Fontainebleau, and other absurdities.

After what I said in the note above it stands well-established that the *situation* of an organic body is the sole characteristic to refer to in order to determine if a body is in reality *fossil.* But as the evidently successive strata are confused and vary but slightly from those which are still being deposited in our times, and as it is impossible to say where some begin and others end, it is equally impossible to say where the organic fossil bodies can be identified as such.

Several geologists, well aware of this difficulty, have admitted the existence of "subfossils" or "demifossils"; but the difficulty always remains the same, notwithstanding their efforts. Mr. de Serres has likewise attempted to avoid this difficulty by calling the organic bodies buried since the last retreat of the oceans "humatiles" (from *humatus,* buried body), reserving that of *fossils* for all those buried during the preceding period. But outside of the inconvenience of a new word given to these quasi-fossils, to these fossils which are not fossils, this new designation offers the disadvantage of depending upon an *event* which is not yet well fixed in geological chronology, and which, by its very etymology, can be applied to *all* the buried, organic bodies in the successive strata of the earth. (Moreover, if we adopt only the sense which Mr. de Serres attaches to the word *humatiles,* man would always exist in the fossil state, as it seems proved that since his existence the level of the oceans has risen from 100 to 150 feet above its present level, and that many caverns have been filled since that epoch. This is what would explain the presence of certain marine shells in the deposits of some caverns, and of some bony breccia. It is desirable then to leave things so that general terms may be adopted, to agree that no limitations be imposed, not to try to establish a division where it is yet impossible to make one, and to agree frankly that since man is contemporaneous with animal species regarded by all the naturalists as fossils, the existence of fossil man cannot be called in question.

The only division that should be adopted, and which has been, I believe, already proposed, is the following:

Ancient Geological Period

This includes (1) the immense stretch of time which preceded the appearance of man on the surface of the globe, during which an infinity of generations have succeeded each other, and (2) the modern geological period or "Age of Man." This period perhaps divided into:

Prehistoric Period

This started with the appearance of man on the surface of the globe, and extends to the beginning of the most ancient traditions. It is probable that during this period sea level rose to 150 feet above its present level. Mr. Reboul is to publish on this subject a very important work, which will remove doubts and will settle many irresolutions.

Historic Period

This hardly dates beyond seven thousand years ago, i.e., to the epoch of the construction of Thebes, during the nineteenth Egyptian Dynasty (Josephus cites the kings of this dynasty month by month and day by day.)

This period could be extended farther back, following new historic observations.

This division offers, as one can see, the advantage of being based only on positive observations and of setting aside the solution of the question relative to the limitation of fossils, a question which, as I have already said, does not seem to be able to be solved in the present state of science.

Before finishing the discussion relative to fossil human bones, I should state that Mr. Desnoyers thinks that these bones are quite recent, and that they belonged to the first inhabitants of Gaul who established their abode in the caves. This opinion, which seems probable for the cave of Fort near Miallet, in which Mr. Tessier has observed figurines, fragments of jars, bracelets and other antique objects, cannot by any means be applied to the localities which we have described with the Messrs. Marcel de Serres and Jules de Christol, and above all to the cavern visited and described with such art by the latter. (It does not much matter, after what we have just said, that the Aquitanians had retired into the caverns, and that Caesar had ordered that they be shut up there. Even the judgment of Florius in these affairs does not matter. To want thus to generalize all these examples, and to say that wheresoever one observes a melange of bones of human beings and extinct animal species, this mixture has taken place at a later time, is to present a conclusion of nonacceptance and to declare the problem a priori insoluble. But yet again, and notwithstanding what I have just said, I recognize that the observations of the Messrs. Desnoyers and Tessier are true and offer something of importance; only they do not seem to me amenable to general application.)

I now come to another order of considerations which, although not resting on such positive data as the preceding, nevertheless offer a great interest. I have already said that probably since the appearance of man on the surface of the earth, sea level had risen about 150 feet above the present level. The breccias of Cagliarai, Nice, Gibraltar, and Tripoli would be proof of this, since they include marine shells. It would be the same with a deposit of shell, including pottery, observed by Mr. de la Marmora at Cape Saint Hospice, near Nice. This same phenomenon is presented also in the bony breccia of Dalmatia and of Syria, which include likewise human bones, and, according to Count Rasoumovski, in the ossiferous gravels of Bades, near Vienna.

Mr. Boué has called to our attention that these occurrences had been noted in too many places to be able to fit the more or less ingenious explanations by which one has human bones introduced in these deposits since historic times.

Conceding then that these different observations are accurate; that the sea-level has diminished by fits and starts; that this diminution has been occasioned by shocks imparted to the soil and the sudden reëlevation of great mountain chains, and that the last retreat of the sea took place whilst man already existed on the surface of the globe, we shall have a new proof that all the bone caverns are not of the same epoch, that a great number were under water during the Tertiary Period, and that certain of these whose level is very little elevated, may well have been submerged during the prehistoric period. According to this viewpoint, the caverns would have been filled only in proportion to their immersion.

If it were permitted to set forth an opinion about the remains of our species, of which I have spoken above, and which are found buried in the caverns and bony breccias in several locations in Europe, I would have ranged myself on the side of the naturalists who think that our regions could have been successively inhabited by different races of men. The form of the heads found at Vienna approaches that of the African or Negro race. Those found in the fluviatile mud on the banks of the Rhine and the Danube show great resemblance to the heads of the Caribs or those of the ancient inhabitants of Peru and Chile. I would be able thus to multiply examples, but these that I have cited will, I think, suffice.

It is true that, in attributing to our species such remote antiquity, one has the right to be surprised at not finding even in man's unwritten history the tradition of violent upheavals which the earth has undergone and following which mountains were suddenly uplifted, rivers have changed their courses, barriers which held back immense quantities of water have been broken down, and the shore lines of the sea were extended. If history remains silent on all of these events, or if we have only extremely vague or fragmentary reminders of them, this is because traditions diminish as sources of information in proportion as they are removed from their points of origin. It is not, then, in examining the old chronicles or even in studying the mysterious writings of the most ancient peoples that we shall be able to hope to discover the early history of the human species. Geology alone can reconstruct the time sequence; but this science is still brand new—it offers an immense field of observation and promises the furnishing of a supplement to our short records. It is necessary here more than elsewhere to apply philosophic doubt, to adopt nothing lightly, nor to reject anything except after severe and impartial examination.

I shall at this point terminate these observations, already quite lengthy, although I have tried to shorten them as much as possible. I think it necessary to review in a few sentences the principal points of this work, which is nothing, so to speak, but a summary of the present state of our knowledge upon one of the newest and most curious questions of geology.

1. The bones buried in caverns have been introduced there in several different ways.

2. The buried species vary from one locality to another, and this difference depends either on the time of filling or on the geographic situation of the cavern.

3. Man has been contemporaneous with extinct animal species which

are encountered buried in the alluvial deposits of caverns, animals which are regarded by all the naturalists as fossils; man exists, then, in the fossil state.

4. The silt and the pebbles which are found in the bone caverns have not been introduced into these cavities by a sudden and short-lived cause, but on the contrary have been introduced almost always slowly and in several different ways.

5. The close examination of pebbles included in the silty deposit proves that they obviously have been carried from neighboring localities, and consequently that the agency which transported them was entirely local.

6. The period during which the bone caverns have been filled has been a long one.

7. In certain caverns, the silty deposit, the bones, and the pebbles have been introduced simultaneously; in others, on the contrary, the silt has been introduced later, and has thus moved in, as it were, on the bones.

List of Animal Species Found in the Caverns of the South of France

Elephant	Lion	Marten (Christol)
Rhinoceros	Leopard	Hare
Wild Boar	Lynx	Rabbit
Horse	Fossil Hyena	Lagomis
Oxen, two species	Striped Hyena	Field Mouse
Deer, five species	(Christol)	Several species of bird
Antelope, of a very large size	Brown Hyena	Terrestrial tortoise
	(Christol)	Lizard
Chamois	Dog, two species	Snake, of the size of the
Goat	Wolf	*Coluber nutrix*
Sheep	Fox	Badger
Bear, at least two species	Polecat (Christol)	Tiger

The sole difference which exists between the caverns of England and Germany, compared with those of the south of France, is that in England is found the hippopotamus, and at Sandwik in Westphalia, the glutton [*Gulo gulo*].

M. C. Prévost likewise has just observed bones of the hippopotamus in the caverns of Syracuse.

❋ ❋ ❋

Jacques Boucher Crevecoeur de Perthes was a French customs official with a post at Amiens. Here, and at Abbeville, he began to collect bones and chipped implements in the brickearth and sand pits as early as 1837.

*He saw these tools as ancient remains of man's handiwork, and in 1838
began persistently to present this view in scientific meetings. Between 1838
and 1841 he published a five volume work,* De la Création: essai sur l'origine et la progression des êtres, *at Abbeville. His views were received with
skepticism and often derision, but he remained convinced of the correctness of his observations and in 1847 published the first volume of his*
Antiquités Celtiques et Antédiluviennes. *The second volume was published in 1858 and the third in 1865.*

*The vindication in 1859 of his observations and the honor accorded
him as a result must have pleased him greatly. In 1860 in a published
work (of which an extract is given here) he holds no rancor for the refusal
of his colleagues to agree with him over the preceding twenty years, and
says simply of the visits of the British geologists, "The results were what
they had to be." In the third volume of his* Antiquités Celtiques *(1865:-
525-644), as well as in the earlier* De l'Homme Antédiluvien et de ses
oeuvres *(1860:38-54), he carefully reviews the history of the independent
verification of his findings (see also Hamy, 1870:34-37).*

*Where John Frere may be said to have barely opened the door to Pale-
olithic archaeology, Boucher de Perthes flung it open wide with a mighty
crash.*

On Antediluvian Man and His Works

Boucher de Perthes

Gentlemen,

Nearly a quarter of a century has gone by since I addressed you here
on the antiquity of man and his probable contemporaneity with the giant
mammals, which species, destroyed in the great diluvial catastrophe, have
not reappeared on earth.

This theory (*système*) which I submitted for your consideration was
new: that man who prior to the flood lived among the giants who were
his predecessors in creation was never given recognition by science.

Rejected by science, this theory was also rejected by opinion; one
century before, this view, which accepted the human giants without
question, did not want to believe in the giant animals, and in each
elephant bone science saw the bone of a human.

Today science believes in the elephants but no longer believes in the
giants. In this respect science is right, but its skepticism was too far afield

Boucher de Perthes. *De l'Homme Antédiluvien et de ses oeuvres.* (Paris: Jung-
Treuttel, 1860). The present passage is taken from pp. 1-18. I am indebted to my son,
Stephen, for the translation.

when it denied that man had lived during the period which preceded the diluvian formation or the cataclysm which gave the terrestrial surface its present configuration. It is this lacuna in our history, this ignorance of ours of the first steps of man on earth, to which I draw your attention; it is on these primitive peoples, their customs, their habits, their monuments, or the vestiges they must have left, that I desire to shed some light.

Your advice has not failed me; I had used it amply when in our meetings of 1836 to 1840 I brought out this theory as a complement to my book *De la Création*,[1] adding that this fossil man or his artifacts should be found in the diluvium or the deposits called tertiary. If you did not follow all my ideas, you did not deny them either; you heard them, not with the intention of condemning them but with that of judging them; you agreed with the principle but you wished proof.

Alas! I had none to give you; I was still dealing with probabilities and theories. In a word, my science was nothing but an anticipation. But this anticipation of mine had become certitude; though I had not analyzed a single stratum, I believed my discovery to be fact.

I was quite young when this thought first engrossed me. In 1805, when I was in Marseilles at the home of M. Brack, brother-in-law of Georges Cuvier and a friend of my father, I went to see a grotto, called the Grotto of Roland, in the vicinity. My main purpose was to look there for the bones about which I had often heard Cuvier speak. I collected several specimens. Were they fossils? I did not dare say.

Later, in 1810, I visited another grotto, that of Palo (États-Romains). This time I was with M. Dubois-Aymé, former member of the Institute. They claimed to have found there some human skeletons. It was possible, but we did not see any. We collected, as I did at Marseilles, animal bones, and I collected several stones which seemed to me to be worked. I showed them to M. Dubois, telling him my theories; he promised to make a note of it, which he would send to the Institute.

When in 1836 I spoke to you on worked stones of the diluvial age, stones which had yet to be discovered, I had formed a collection of these from grottos, tombs, peat bogs, and similar areas. While collecting these stones which evidently were no longer in their primitive deposits, the idea came to me that I should find out what could have been their origin or the composition of this deposit. The yellow coloring of a few was the first indication. Only on the exterior, this coloring was not that of the patina of the flint. I concluded that it must be due to the ferruginous nature of the soil with which it was originally in contact. A certain stratum of the soil of the diluvium fulfilled this condition; the shade was

---

[1] These readings and the dissertation to which they refer are found in the report of the meetings and the volumes of 1836 to 1840 of Mémoires de le Société d'Émulation. See, for the dates, the extract from the report, page 428, of the volume of 1837, and following years.

surely that of my axes. They had definitely lain there; but was this location the effect of a recent occurrence and of a secondary altering, or did it date from the formation of the layer? There was the question.

In the affirmative case, that is, if the axe had been in the layer since its origin, the problem was resolved: the man who had made the instrument had existed prior to the cataclysm which formed the layer. Here there is no further possible doubt since the diluvial deposits do not present, as do the peat bogs, an elastic and permeable mass; nor like the bone caves, an inconcealable cavern, open to all who come, and which from century to century served as a sanctuary and then as a tomb to so many diverse beings. In this confusion of all eras, in this neutral ground, is a kind of caravansary of the passed generations, as though to characterize the periods.

In the diluvial formations, on the contrary, each period is clearly divided. The horizontally superimposed layers, these strata of different shades and materials, show us in capital letters the history of the past: the great convulsions of nature seem to be delineated there by the finger of God.

Though united in a single group today like the foundation of a wall, all these levels are not brothers; centuries may separate them, and the generations which saw the birth of one did not always see the formation of the next. But since the day when each bed was laid and solidified, it remained integrally the same; in being compressed, it neither lost nor gained anything. Nothing was introduced from above, nor was there any secondary infiltration: each stratum is exempt from the influence of that which followed it and that which preceded it; homogenous and compact, its modification required an influence no less powerful than that which created it. As one now sees it, so it was on the day of its formation. If a landslide or some type of action altered its regularity, an oblique or perpendicular line, cutting the horizontal line, would tell you so.

Here, gentlemen, the proofs start. They will be unanswerable: this human work for which we search, this work about which I tell you, *it is there* and has been there since the day that it was brought there. No less immobile than the layer itself, it came with the layer; it was held there as was the layer; and because it contributed to the layer's formation, it existed before it.

These shellfish, this elephant, this axe or the person who made it, were, therefore, witnesses to the cataclysm that gave our country its present configuration. Perhaps the shell, the elephant, and the axe were already fossilized at this time; could they be the debris surviving from an earlier deluge, the souvenirs of another age? Who can put limits on the past? Is it not infinite, as is the future? Where, then, is the man who has seen the beginning of any one thing? Where is he who will see it end? Let us not bargain over the duration of ages; let us believe that the days of the creation, those days that began before our sun, were the days of God, the interminable days of the world. Let us remember, finally, that for this eternal God a thousand centuries are no more than one second, and that He put on earth causes and effects which these thousands of centuries have not made any less young than they were at the time that His hand created them.

But all these foundations of the earth, all these shistose, chalky, clayey, and sandy layers which cover its core, are not the result of a sudden cause —of a convulsion or of a deluge. If the power of one torrent could have lifted in a day these beds torn away from other beds, there are also forces that are the consequence of slow action and of successive deposits from still water which, accomplishing their work, made hills and built mountains, not with masses thrown on masses but with grains of sand scattered on grains of sand. Now, if we agree that the layers at Menchecourt and others were raised by an imperceptible accumulation, by a succession of deposits and sediments, the antiquity of these bones and these axes which lie under several meters of slowly accumulated sand, covered by a layer of lime or of clay, then covered again by a bed of varied chalk and of broken stones, and the whole covered by a thick layer of vegetal soil—this antiquity, I say, will be much greater than that which the rapid formation of diluvial beds appears to be.

After having reminded you of the configuration of the terrain and the nature of the elements of which it was composed, I will repeat to you on which principles, in 1836 and 1837, I established the probability of the presence of man and his works, and the type of certitude that I had of finding them there. I based this certitude:

1st, upon the tradition of a race of men destroyed by the flood;

2nd, upon the geological proofs of this flood;

3rd, upon the existence in this era of mammals closely related to man and unable to live except within the same atmospheric conditions;

4th, on the proof, thereby acquired, that the earth was habitable for man;

5th, on the basis, in all the regions, islands, or continents where one found these large mammals, man lived or had lived, from which one might conclude that if the animals appeared on earth before the human species, man followed closely, and at the era of the flood was already sufficiently numerous to leave signs of his presence.

6th, and finally, that these human remains had been able to escape the notice of geologists and naturalists because the difference of structure which exists between the fossil types and their living analogues could have existed between antediluvial man and those of today so that one might have confused them with other mammals; that physical probabilities, present and past experience, geology as well as history, and finally universal belief come to the support of tradition; that evidently a race of men, prior to the last cataclysm that had changed the surface of the earth, had lived there at the same time and probably in the same area as the quadrupeds whose bones have been discovered.

You recognize the truth of this reasoning, but you ask of me, why were these terrains rather than others the burial place of primitive man or the repository of his artifacts?

I answer that the diluvial torrent, while sweeping the terrestrial surface, had done that which, daily, on a lesser scale, our rainstorms do when, collecting objects in the ground which are not solidly enough fixed by their weight or their appendages, they carry the articles along and throw them in some sewer; or, when the rains do not find anything but flatlands, spreads them there in more or less thick layers. Then, if you examine these layers, their analysis will indicate with certainty the areas which the flood had crossed; you will know if it had crossed a populated or desert country, a town or fields, a prairie or forest, a cultivated field or stony or arid ground; you will see also whether the area had been populated by men or by animals. In brief, in this residue of a storm you cannot only follow its course, but can describe occurrences along the way.

Without doubt, as the days pass, this analysis will become less easy; all the soluble bodies will have changed shape or will dissolve in the earthy mass, but the solid objects will still be there.

So does the torrent proceed, upsetting things, carrying off and piling up all that it seizes, forming enormous masses composed of objects belonging to every kingdom and works produced by every intelligence. There also the soft or perishable parts have disappeared; there is nothing left but that which survived the trial of time.

It is, therefore, within these ruins of the ancient world, in these deposits which have become their archives, that one must look for these traditions and, for want of medallions and inscriptions, to defend these rough stones which, in their imperfection, prove no less surely the existence of man than if he had made an entire Louvre.

Thus, strongly convinced of your approbation, I carried on my work. Circumstances favored me: immense works undertaken for the fortifications at Abbeville, the digging of a canal, the railroad tracks that were being built, revealed from 1830 to 1840 numerous strata of diluvium on top of which rests a part of our valley; the chalk which forms its base rises 33 meters above the sea level, an immense bench which, from the basin of the Somme goes to rejoin that of Paris, and thus advances towards the center of France.

A vast field was therefore open to my studies. The number of days I passed bending over these terraces which had become for me the arena of science and my promised land! The thousands of flint chips, let us say the millions, that had not been revealed to my eyes. I did my work conscientiously; all that by color or by a special cleft were distinguished from others I collected; I examined all the facets, the least broken edge did not escape me; several times I believed I had found this painfully

sought evidence: it may have been, but so meager! I found there an indication, but it was not proof.

Finally, this proof came: it was at the end of 1838 that I submitted to
you my first diluvial axes. It was also about this time, or in the course of
the year 1839, that I brought them to Paris and showed them to several
members of the Institute, notably to my respected friend, M. A. Brongniart, who was perhaps more interested in the fact that my discovery was
only illusory since, with Cuvier, he had established as a principle that
man, new on the earth, was not contemporary with the great antediluvian
pachyderms. However, Al. Brongniart, far from discouraging me, strongly
encouraged me to continue.[2]

Meanwhile, I swear to you that he could not, sirs, see the hand of man
in these rude efforts. I saw axes, and I saw correctly, but the working was
vague and the angles blunt; their flattened forms differed from those of
the polished axes, the only axes which were then known; finally, if the
traces of working were revealed there, it was necessary to see them with
eyes that believed. I had them, but I alone had them; my belief had little
influence; I had not one disciple.

I needed other proofs, as well as more research, and to attain them I
took some associates. I did not choose them from among the geologists. I
would not have found any; at the least mention of axes and of diluvium
I saw them smile. It was, therefore, among the [quarry] workers that I
looked for my helpers. I showed them my stones, and also drawings which
represented that which they were supposed to have been before the
diluvial abrasion.

In spite of this care, it took me several months to organize my students,
but with patience, with rewards distributed opportunely, and above all
with the discovery of several well-shaped bits that I found under their
eyes in some layers, I tried to mold them as skillful as myself, and before
the end of 1840 I was able to offer you, and to submit to the examination
of the Institute, twenty flints in which the human hand was detectable.

M. Brongniart no longer doubted me; M. Dumas, his son-in-law
adopted his opinion. From this moment on I had proselytes. Their number was small in comparison with the opposition. My collection, which
grew rapidly and which, from the start, I left open to the curious, attracted a few, but practical men disdained to come and see. Let us say,
they were afraid; they feared to make themselves accomplices to that
which they called a heresy, almost humbug; they did not question my
good faith, but they doubted my good sense.

I hoped that the publication of my book on the antediluvian antiquities,
which appeared first under the title of *De l'Industrie primitive* would

---

[2] This is also what MM. Flourens, Elie de Beaumont, L. Cordier, Valanciennes, de
Blainville, and Jomard did. The latter, sometime later, came to Abbeville with M.
Constant Prevost and visited the exposures and my collection. M. de Blainville came
here later, but he was interested especially in the peat bogs.

disperse these doubts; but on the contrary. Except yourselves, sirs, with whom I found constant support,[3] nobody believed me. In 1837 the theory was accepted without too many difficulties; when, realizing this theory had become a fact that everyone could verify, no one wished to believe it any more, and they confronted me with an obstacle larger than objection, than criticism, than satire, than persecution: *disdain*. They no longer discussed the theory; they did not even bother to deny it; they forgot it.

Thus my theory slept peacefully until 1854. Then Doctor Rigollot who, according to hear-say, had been for ten years my constant adversary, deciding to judge the question for himself, visited the exposures of Abbeville, and subsequently those of Saint-Acheul and of Saint Rocheles Amiens. His conversion was prompt; he saw that I was correct. Honest man that he was, he declared it loudly in a brochure that you all know.[4]

This clear, very conscientious work, which brought the author his nomination to the Institute, recalled attention to my book. Unfortunately, it was not benevolent. A purely geological question was made the subject of religious controversy. Those who did not doubt my religion,[5] accused me of temerity: an unknown archaeologist, a geologist without a degree, who would like to upset a theory confirmed by long experience and adopted by many eminent men. There, they said, was a strange pretention.

Strange, perhaps. But this pretention, Sirs, I did not have, nor have I ever had it. I found a fact: it brought forth new consequences, perhaps, but I did not make them. The truth is not the work of any one, it was created before us, and is as old as the world; often looked for, but more often denied; one finds it, but one does not invent it. Sometimes we look

[3] Among the members of the Société to whom I owe, above all, my thanks, I name Doctor Ravin, who helped me to draw the profiles; MM. Ed. Pannier and Os. Macqueron, who, with great generosity and incontestable talent, drew and lithographed all my plates; M. H. Tronnet, who reviewed all my proofs with care and knowledge that have been most helpful; MM. Louandre, father and son, Dusevel, de Marsy, Florentin Lefils, who had published more than one article to defend my book; MM. Hecquet d'Orval, Feret, Baron de Clermont-Tonnerre, Baillon, Buteux, Vion, Count d'Hinnisdal, Baron de Girardot, Di-Pietro, Abbé Cochet, Abbé Decorde, Abbé Corblet, Marcotte, Pinsard, Ch. Gomart, Count de Mailly, Doctor L. Douchet, Garnier, Goze, etc.

[4] *Mémoire sur les instruments en silex trouvés à Saint-Acheul.* Brochure in-8°, Amiens, 1854.

[5] In *Science pour tous* and in his work *L'Homme fossile*, dedicated to the learned Bishop of Tulle, M. Léopold Giraud and Doctor Halleguen, in *Annales de la philosophie chrétienne*, prove clearly that the geological discoveries of M. Boucher de Perthes can fit very well into our religious beliefs. Even *l'Univers* declared this in the same sense in the numbers of October 21 and November 16, 1859.

In England several members of the Biblical Society, who were more severe than our theologians, see in this new theory a tendency towards papism, and the English geologists who have adopted it had to defend themselves against this singular attack. In a meeting which took place at Newcastle, one of the members present answered it thus: "The facts, when they present themselves, ought not only to be accepted, but welcomed. The works of antediluvian man may wound geology and our chronology, but the wounds will heal and science will be all the better."

for it incorrectly, because it is not always in books that it is found: it is
everywhere, in the water, in the air, on the earth; we cannot take one
step without finding it, and when we do not perceive it, it is because we
close our eyes or turn our heads. Yes, it is our prejudices or our ignorance
which hinders us from perceiving it, or touching it. If we do not see it
today, we will see it tomorrow, for no matter what effort one may use
to hide it, truth will appear when its hour is come: happy then is the
one who can find it and say to the passersby: *here it is.*[6]

You will understand, Sirs, that this has connection only with moral
truths, and that I do not pretend to apply them to my modest find and to
the small corner of the veil which it may help lift.

After these objections to the organization of my book, which one could
call its morality, one came to the details: some questioned the nature of
the exposures. Here M. Rigollot was no more cautious than I myself; an
erudite naturalist and skillful archaeologist, he was not expected to be able
to distinguish a modified land from one which was not; they denied him
the knowledge possessed by the lowest of the [quarry] workmen; and
finally, to undermine his work at the base, they claimed that the layers of
Saint-Acheul, of Saint-Roch, and consequently those of Abbeville and
Paris, their analogues, were not only of recent formation but of a creation
completely modern, and one which had not preceded by much the arrival
of the Romans in Gaul. In vain, these layers, called *diluvial* by Elie de
Beaumont and, earlier, by A. Brongniart, and by Cuvier who had discovered there some of his large fossils, these layers which were *tertiary*
ten years ago, had become *quaternary,* made younger yet, and, changing
at once the name and condition, were nothing but *altered* terrain. But
altered by whom? By man? No. All the population of Gaul would not
have been enough. By a cataclysm? Which? Would it be a recent cataclysm, subsequent to the deluge of Noah? I ask you, Sirs, when the memory of the flood of the Scriptures has remained in the memory of all the
people, how the tradition of a new catastrophe which, like the preceding
one would have upset the terrestrial surface, was not handed down to
us? How would it have been forgotten, even in the time of Caesar, as
neither he nor any other historian speaks of it? How, also, could these
layers, the residues of a current which swept the earth inhabited by men
so close to a state of civilization, not present anything which shows their
arts or monuments, cements, pottery, or metal? Why also does one not
find domestic species and races which are today indigenous? No, in the

---

[6] Here is what the author said elsewhere on the same subject: "When truth is discovered, it becomes common property. He who sees it first has no more right to it
than others, and cannot say: it is mine. The astronomer does not say it about the
planet he finds in his telescope. But even though he owe his discovery to chance, is
it any the less a benefit to everyone? No. Happy is the one who has made it! for the
acquisition of a new truth is more valuable than a gold mine, and even though it
appears sterile, sooner or later it will become fecund."

layers everything denounces the recency of the ages and a vanished nature: all the organic debris were fossils.

This recent cataclysm in which the sudden alteration of the surface [occurred], at an epoch so close to ours, is thereby contradicted, first by the silence of tradition, next by the appearance of the earth, and finally, by the composition of the beds.

If we attribute this modification of the surface and the formation of the beds to successive deposits, we have for ourselves this surface and its landmarks which happily have their dates and can, thus, in many respects, show us almost from year to year the history of the soil and the variations of its level, and I say: when the position of the monuments, of which several, namely those of Nineveh, the Pyramids of Egypt, the so-called cyclopean constructions, go back three or four thousand years, when the vertical trunks of certain trees not less ancient, and when the geographical configuration of the land described by the oldest authors prove that since these times gone by the form and even the aspect of these lands have changed virtually not at all; and in addition, when the deposits of sediment, in which one follows the progress, offer a growth so slow that centimeters represent centuries, who can believe that several thousand years could be sufficient to lift up eleven meters and more of these layers that one calls altered, and how can we reconcile this alteration which, no matter what the cause, cannot but mean a disorder or an abnormal movement, with the regularity of the beds?

The formation of the peat is also a proof of the time which is required for the deposits of sediments. In the land where one has used the peat bogs since time immemorial, nobody has seen the peat grow in any noticeable manner. One rightly concludes that it takes centuries to produce a thickness of several centimeters. One can judge, after this, how long is the period which represents the peaty masses of the valley of the Somme, masses of which the thickness is as much as eleven meters, and which rest on chalk, at twelve and thirteen meters from the surface.

But the chalk base of the peat is but the exception, as it is not found here but below the layers which border the valley. The peat there lies as usual on a thin bed of clay, under which is a layer of sand and stones. Well, Sirs, in this bed of diluvium, covered by several meters of black compact peat, I found the traces of man. I collected several beautiful axes, lightly rolled, and which are no different from those of Menchecourt except in their dark yellow patina, a difference stemming from the fact that they were found, instead of as ordinarily in a bed of grey sand called "sour," in one of ferruginous yellow sand called "greasy sand," from which they got their color as you can see by those which are still imbedded in their matrix, and which I have the honor of showing you.

Faced with these facts, and in view of the large banks of Menchecourt, where are drawn, like so many ribbons and as cleanly as the colors of a flag, these superimposed beds showing you at the glance of an eye all the changes of the earth of the diluvial period, how can one say that they are of recent formation and of a cataclysm of just yesterday?

The presence of peat at the points where it replaces the vegetal earth, and the time necessary to make firm one layer of the peat bog, no matter how thick it may be, is sufficient to show the age of the soil. But if it is difficult to be precise about the age of the diluvial beds on which our

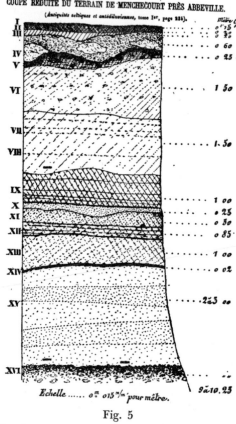

Fig. 5

Stratification at Menchecourt near Abbeville. Total thickness of section is about 19 metres. Flint axes marked by short black lines in bottom of layers VIII and XV.

valley rests at certain points and which look down on others, and to say if they are the result of several different formations separated by long periods, or the consequence of one unique and spontaneous convulsion, this difficulty is minor relative to that of the peaty deposits, and one arrives, perhaps after fairly profound study, at the knowledge of what time was necessary for the decomposition, year after year, to concentrate and to harden the vegetal masses which form a peaty bed.

I have already made several contributions on this subject by giving the measurements of the beds which cover buried pots made by the hand of man in a bed of fluvial sand, a burial which evidently started before the formation of the layer of peat. Unfortunately, the date, however approximate, of these vases which, if one judges by their imperfection and the thickness of their material, must be very ancient, remains unknown. But above, in the peat itself, I found Roman or Gallo-Roman pottery which the peat also had begun to cover. As for these, it was possible to make a calculation on the probable age.[7]

From induction to induction, one can thus learn, if not the age of the layers where our axes were found, at least the epoch when the diluvial formation was finished and could have served as the base of the peat formation.

It is these same layers of peat, subsequent to the diluvial consolidation but which perhaps followed it closely, which extend up to the Channel. This peat, which is called woody because of the ligneous parts and fruits of hazel trees of which it is in large part composed, must be older than the cataclysm which separated England from the continent. One cannot, therefore, doubt its age.

❋ ❋ ❋

Boucher de Perthes' discoveries of Paleolithic flint implements in the gravels near Abbeville and Amiens were repeatedly advertised by him in lectures and publication from 1838 on, but the time was not quite right for their acceptance. De Perthes was undaunted by those who refused to believe, and kept collecting and presenting the evidence. Sir Charles Lyell (1863:95) who knew de Perthes and had seen his sites, and who had written the first great synthesis of prehistory, wrote, "But the scientific world had no faith in the statement that works of art [i.e., artifacts], however rude, had been met with in undisturbed beds of such antiquity." In 1858 H. Falconer, an English geologist, happened to encounter de Perthes, saw the flint tools which he had found, listened to his arguments, and then urged his colleagues John Evans and Joseph Prestwich to visit France and make a study of the sites in person. This they did in 1859, and in that same year Prestwich read a paper before a meeting of the Royal Society with Lyell, Huxley, and Faraday, among others, in attendance. Prestwich's reputation was such that his firm opinion, based on facts which he had

[7] M. Cf. L. Horner, in his published work on certain potsherds of the valley of the Nile (*An Account of Some Recent Researches Near Cairo*, Philos. Trans., 1858, Vol. CXLVIII, Part 1, p. 53), gives the age of this pottery as fifteen thousand years, by calculating from a known base the time which the covering of earth needed to accumulate.

himself observed, carried great weight. His paper, if we can judge it from the abstract, is a model of careful detailing of evidence seen with his own eyes, and from it we may date the birth of modern prehistory. Fuller accounts of the famous visit of the British geologists to France may be found in Lyell (1863:93-96, 103-105), Evans (1943:100-106), and Crawford (1953:26). In the third volume of Boucher de Perthes' Antiquités Celtiques et Antédiluviennes (pp. 525-624), the reader will find a very full record of communications delivered at scientific meetings as well as full reprintings of articles which appeared between 1859-1864 in the French and British journals and newspapers accepting the theory that the Somme gravels contained man-made tools. Lyell, who visited the French Paleolithic sites at Amiens shortly after Prestwich and satisfied himself that the tools were actually lying in the deep gravels, provides us with two additional arguments on the age of the tools, one being the deep and uniform patination of the surface of the tools and the other being the occurrence of dendrites on their surfaces (Lyell, 1863:117).

The Somme finds of Boucher de Perthes posed a problem of classification. The Three Age system was well known and generally accepted by 1859 and Evans in that year hinted that the "drift" chipped implements were different from those of the "ordinary stone period" (i.e., Neolithic). French archaeologists proposed a period of polished stone and an earlier period of cut (i.e., chipped) stone for which Lubbock in 1865 coined the terms Neolithic and Paleolithic. Subsequent refinements and development of the sequence of Paleolithic cultures can be followed by consulting other sources (Daniel, 1950:85-89, 99; Breuil, 1941).

Verification of Boucher de Perthes' Claims

Joseph Prestwich

The author commences by noticing how comparatively rare are the cases even of the alleged discovery of the remains of man or of his works in the various superficial drifts, notwithstanding the extent to which these deposits are worked; and of these few cases so many have been disproved,

"On the Occurrence of Flint Implements, Associated with the Remains of Extinct Mammalia, in Undisturbed Beds of a Late Geological Period," by Joseph Prestwich. *Proceedings of the Royal Society of London*, Vol. X, [Article] IX, pp. 50-59. Abstract of Paper Read May 26, 1859. Taylor & Francis, London: 1860. (Prestwich's paper, of which one abstract was published and here reprinted, was entitled "On the Occurrence of Flint Implements, Associated with the Remains of Animals of Extinct Species in Beds of a Late Geological Period at Amiens and Abbeville and in England at Hoxne.")

that man's nonexistence on the earth until after the latest geological changes, and the extinction of the Mammoth, Tichorhine Rhinoceros, and other great mammals, had come to be considered almost in the light of an established fact. Instances, however, have from time to time occurred to throw some doubt on this view, as the well known cases of the human bones found by Dr. Schmerling in a cavern near Liege,—the remains of man, instanced by M. Marcel de Serres and others in several caverns in France,—the flint implements in Kent's Cave,—and many more. Some uncertainty, however, has always attached to cave evidence, from the circumstance that man has often inhabited such places at a comparatively late period, and may have disturbed the original cave deposit; or, after the period of his residence, the stalagmitic floor may have been broken up by natural causes, and the remains above and below it may have thus become mixed together, and afterwards sealed up by a second floor of stalagmite. Such instances of an imbedded broken stalagmitic floor are in fact known to occur; at the same time the author does not pretend to say that this will explain all cases of intermixture in caves, but that it lessens the value of the evidence from such sources.

The subject has, however, been latterly revived, and the evidence more carefully sifted by Dr. Falconer; and his preliminary reports on the Brixham Cave, presented last year to the Royal Society, announcing the carefully determined occurrence of worked flints mixed indiscriminately with the bones of the extinct Cave Bear and the Rhinoceros, attracted great and general attention amongst geologists. This remarkable discovery, and a letter written to him by Dr. Falconer on the occasion of his subsequent visit to Abbeville last autumn, instigated the author to turn his attention to other ground, which, from the interest of its later geological phenomena alone, as described by M. Buteux in his "Esquisse Géologique du Department de la Somme," he had long wished and intended to visit.

In 1849 M. Boucher de Perthes, President of the "Société d'Émulation" of Abbeville, published the first volume of a work entitled *Antiquités Celtiques et Antédiluviennes,* in which he announced the important discovery of worked flints in beds of undisturbed sand and gravel containing the remains of extinct mammalia. Although treated from an antiquarian point of view, still the statement of the geological facts by this gentleman, with good sections by M. Ravin, is perfectly clear and consistent. Nevertheless, both in France and in England, his conclusions were generally considered erroneous; nor has he since obtained such verification of the phenomena as to cause so unexpected a fact to be accepted by men of science. There have, however, been some few exceptions to the general incredulity. The late Dr. Rigollot, of Amiens, urged by M. Boucher de Perthes, not only satisfied himself of the truth of the fact, but corroborated it, in 1855, by his *Mémoire sur des instruments en silex trouvés à St. Acheul.* Some few geologists suggested further inquiry; whilst Dr. Falconer, himself convinced by M. de Perthes' explanations and specimens, warmly engaged Mr. Prestwich to examine the sections.

The author, who confesses that he undertook the inquiry full of doubt, went last Easter, first to Amiens, where he found, as described by Dr. Rigollot, the gravel beds of St. Acheul capping a low, chalk hill a mile south east of the city, about 100 feet above the level of the Somme, and not commanded by any higher ground. The following is the succession of the beds in descending order:

Average thickness

1. Brown brick-earth (*many old tombs and some coins*). With an irregular bed of flint gravel. No organic remains. *Divisional plane between 1 and 2a very uneven and indented* .... 10 to 15 ft.

2a. Whitish marl and sand with small chalk debris. Land/and freshwater shells (*Lymnea, Succinea, Helix, Bithynia, Planorbis, Pupa, Pisidium,* and *Ancylus,* all of recent species) are common, and mammalian bones and teeth are occasionally found .... 2 to 8 ft.

2b. Coarse subangular flint gravel,—white with irregular ochreous and ferruginous seams,—with tertiary flint pebbles and small sandstone blocks. Remains of shells as above, in patches of sand. Teeth and bones of the elephant, and of a species of horse, ox, and deer,—generally near base. This bed is further remarkable for containing worked flints *"Haches"* of M. de Perthes, and *"Langues de Chat"* of the workmen .... 6 to 12 ft.

Uneven surface of chalk.

The flint implements are found in considerable number in [stratum] 2b. On his first visit, the author obtained several specimens from the workmen, but he was not successful in finding any himself. On his arrival, however, at Abbeville, he received a message from M. Pinsard of Amiens, to whose cooperation he expresses himself much indebted, to inform him that one had been discovered the following day, and was left *in situ* for his inspection. On returning to the spot, this time with his friend Mr. Evans, he satisfied himself that it was truly *in situ,* 17 feet from the surface, in undisturbed ground, and he had a photographic sketch of the section taken.

Dr. Rigollot also mentions the occurrence in the gravel of round pieces of hard chalk, pierced through with a hole, which he considers were used as beads. The author found several, and recognized in them a small fossil sponge, the *Coscinopora globularis,* D'Orb., from the chalk, but does not feel quite satisfied about their artificial dressing. Some specimens do certainly appear as though the hole had been enlarged and completed.

The only mammalian remains the author here obtained, were some specimens of the teeth of a horse, but whether recent or extinct, the specimens were too imperfect to determine; and part of the tooth of an elephant (*Elephas primigenius?*). In the gravel pit of St. Roch, 1½ mile distant, and on a lower level, mammalian remains are far more abundant, and include *Elephas primigenius, Rhinoceros tichorhinus, Cervus somonensis, Bos priscus* and *Equus* (to this list the author has to add the *Hippopotamus,* of which creature four fine tusks were obtained on this last visit) but the workmen said that no worked flints were found there, although they are mentioned by Dr. Rigollot.

At Abbeville the author was much struck with the extent and beauty of M. Boucher de Perthes' collection. There were many forms of flints, in which he, however, failed to see traces of design or work, and which he should only consider as accidental; but with regard to those flint-instruments termed "axes" ("*haches*") by M. de Perthes, he entertains not the slightest doubt of their artificial make. They are of two forms, generally from 4 to 10 inches long; the outlines of two specimens are represented in the following diagram. They are very rudely made, without any

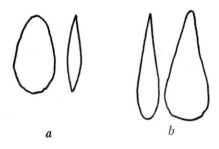

a   *b*

ground surface, and were the work of a people probably unacquainted with the use of metals. These implements are much rarer at Abbeville than at Amiens, fig. 6*a* being the common form of the former, and fig. 6*b* at the latter place. The author was not fortunate enough to find any specimens himself; but from the experience of M. de Perthes, and the evidence of the workmen, as well as from the condition of the specimens themselves, he is fully satisfied of the correctness of that gentleman's opinion, that they there also occur in beds of undisturbed sand and gravel.

At Moulin Quignon, and at St. Gilles, to the southeast of Abbeville, the deposit occurs, as at St. Acheul, on the top of a low hill, and consists of a subangular, ochreous and ferruginous flint gravel, with a few irregular seams of sand, 12 to 15 feet thick, reposing upon an uneven surface of chalk. It contains no shells, and very few bones. M. de Perthes states that he has found fragments of the teeth of the elephant here. The worked flints and the bones occur generally in the lower part of the gravel.

In the bed of gravel also on which Abbeville stands, a number of flint implements have been found, together with several teeth of the *Elephas primigenius,* and, at places, fragments of freshwater shells.

The section, however, of greatest interest is that at Menchecourt, a suburb to the northwest of Abbeville. The deposit there is very distinct in its character; it occurs pitched on the side of a chalk hill, which commands it to the northward; and it slopes down under the peat beds of the valley of the Somme to the southward. The deposit consists, in descending order, of—

Average thickness

1. A mass of brown sandy clay, with angular fragments of flints and chalk rubble. No organic remains. Base very irregular and indented into bed No. 2. .... 2 to 12 ft.

2. A light colored sandy clay ("*sable gras*" of the workmen), analogous to the loess, containing land shells, *Pupa, Helix, Clausilia* of recent species. Flint axes and mammalian remains are said to occur occasionally in this bed .... 8 to 25 ft.

3. White sand ("*sable aigre*"), with 1 to 2 feet of subangular flint gravel at base. This bed abounds in land and freshwater shells of recent species of the genera *Helix, Succinea, Cyclas, Pisidium, Valvata, Bithynia,* and *Planorbis,* together with the marine *Buccinum undatum, Cardium edule, Tellina solidula,* and *Purpura lapillus.* The author has also found the *Cyrena consobrina* and *Littorina rudis.* With them are associated numerous mammalian remains, and, it is said, flint implements .... 2 to 6 ft.

4. Light colored sandy marl, in places very hard, with *Helix, Zonites, Succinea, and Pupa.* Not traversed .... 3 +

The Mammalian remains enumerated by M. Buteux from this pit are —*Elephas primigenius, Rhinoceros tichorhinus, Cervus somonensis?, Cervus tarandus priscus, Ursus spelaeus, Hyaena spelaea, Bos primigenius, Equus adamaticus,* and a *Felis.* It would be essential to determine how these fossils are distributed—which occur in bed No. 2, and which in bed No. 3. This has not hitherto been done. The few marine shells occur mixed indiscriminately with the freshwater species, chiefly amongst the flints at the base of No. 3. They are very friable and somewhat scarce. It is on the top of this bed of flints that the greater number of bones are found, and also, it is said, the greater number of flint implements. The author, however, only saw some long flint flakes (considered by M. de Perthes as flint knives) turned out of this bed in his presence, but the workmanship was not very clear or apparent; still it was as much so as in some of the so-called flint knives from the peat beds and barrows. There are specimens, however, of true implements ("*haches*") in M. de Perthes' collection from Menchecourt; one noticed by the author was from a depth of 5, and another of 7 meters. This would take them out from bed No. 1, but would leave it uncertain whether they came from No. 2 or No. 3.

From their general appearance, and traces of the matrix, the author would be disposed to place them in bed No. 2, but M. de Perthes believes them to be from No. 3; if so, it must have been in some of the subordinate clay seams occasionally intercalated in the white sand.

Besides the concurrent testimony of all the workmen at the different pits, which the author after careful examination saw no reason to doubt, the flint implements ("*haches*") bear upon themselves internal evidence of the truth of M. de Perthes' opinion. It is a peculiarity of fractured chalk flints to become deeply and permanently stained and colored, or to be left unchanged, according to the nature of the matrix in which they are embedded. In most clay beds they become outside of a bright opaque white or porcelainic; in white calcareous or siliceous sand their fractured black surfaces remain almost unchanged; whilst in beds of ochreous and ferruginous sands, the flints are stained of the light yellow and deep brown colors so well exhibited in the common ochreous gravel of the neighborhood of London. This change is the work of very long time, and of moisture before the opening out of the beds. Now in looking over the large series of flint implements in M. de Perthes' collection, it cannot fail to strike the most casual observer that those from Menchecourt are almost always white and bright, whilst those from Moulin Quignon have a dull yellow and brown surface; and it may be noticed that whenever (as is often the case) any of the matrix adheres to the flint, it is invariably of the same nature, texture, and color as that of the respective beds themselves. In the same way at St. Acheul, where there are beds of white and others of ochreous gravel, the flint implements exhibit corresponding variations in color and adhering matrix; added to which, as the white gravel contains chalk debris, there are portions of the gravel in which the flints are more or less coated with a film of deposited carbonate of lime; and so it is with the flint implements which occur in those portions of the gravel. Further, the surface of many specimens is covered with fine dendritic markings. Some few implements also show, like the fractured flints, traces of wear, their sharp edges being blunted. In fact, the flint implements form just as much a constituent part of the gravel,—exhibiting the action of the same later influences and in the same force and degree,—as the rough mass of flint fragments with which they are associated.

With regard to the geological age of these beds, the author refers them to those usually designated as postpliocene, and notices their agreement with many beds of that age in England. The Menchecourt deposit much resembles that of Fisherton near Salisbury; the gravel of St. Acheul is like some on the Sussex coast; and that of Moulin Quignon resembles the gravel at East Croydon, Wandsworth Common, and many places near London. The author even sees reason, from the general physical phenomena, to question whether the beds of St. Acheul and Moulin Quignon may not possibly be of an age one stage older than those of Menchecourt and St. Roch; but before that point can be determined a more extended knowledge of all the organic remains of the several deposits is indispensable.

The author next proceeds to inquire into the causes which led to the rejection of this and the cases before mentioned, and shows that in the case of M. de Perthes' discovery, it was in a great degree the small size and indifferent execution of the figures and the introduction of many forms about which there might reasonably be a difference of opinion—in the case of the arrowheads in Kent's Cave a hidden error was merely suspected—and in the case of the Liege cavern he considers that the question was discussed on a false issue. He therefore is of [the] opinion that these and many similar cases require reconsideration; and that not only may some of these prove true, but that many others, kept back by doubt or supposed error, will be forthcoming.

One very remarkable instance has already been brought under the author's notice by Mr. Evans since their return from France. In the 13th volume of the *Archaeologia,* published in 1800, is a paper by Mr. John Frere, F.R.S. and F.S.A., entitled "An Account of Flint-Weapons discovered at Hoxne in Suffolk," wherein that gentleman gives a section of a brick pit in which numerous flint implements had been found, at a depth of 11 feet, in a bed of gravel containing bones of some unknown animal; and concludes from the ground being disturbed and above the valley, that the specimens must be of very great antiquity, and anterior to the last changes of the surface of the county—a very remarkable announcement, hitherto overlooked.

The author at once proceeded in search of this interesting locality, and found a section now exposed to consist of—

                                                       feet

1. Earth and a few flints 2

2. Brown brick-earth, a carbonaceous seam in middle and one of gravel at base; no organic remains. The workmen stated that two flint implements (one of which they shortly picked up in the author's presence) had been found about 10 feet from the surface during the last winter 12

3. Grey clay, in places carbonaceous and in others sandy, with recent land and freshwater shells (*Planorbis, Valvata, Succinea, Pisidium, Helix,* and *Cyclas*) and bones of Mammalia 4

4. Small subangular flint gravel and chalk pebbles 2½

5. Carbonaceous clay (stopped by water) .... ½ +

The weapons referred to by Mr. Frere are described by him as being found abundantly in bed No. 4; but at the spot where the work has now arrived, this bed is much thinner, and is not worked. In the small trench which the author caused to be dug, he found no remains either of weapons or of bones. He saw, however, in the collection of Mr. T. E. Amyot, of Diss, specimens of the weapons, also an astragalus of the elephant from, it was supposed, this bed, and, from bed No. 3, the teeth of a horse, closely resembling those from the elephant bed of Brighton.

The specimens of the weapons figured by Mr. Frere, and those now in the British Museum and elsewhere, present a singular similarity in work and shape to the more pointed forms from St. Acheul.

One very important fact connected with this section, is that it shows the relative age of the bone and implement-bearing beds. They form a thin lacustrine deposit, which seems to be superimposed on the Boulder Clay, and to pass under a bed of the ochreous sand and flint gravel belonging to the great and latest drift beds of the district.

The author purposely abstains for the present from all theoretical considerations, confining himself to the corroboration of the facts:—

1. That the flint implements are the work of man.
2. That they were found in undisturbed ground.
3. That they are associated with the remains of extinct Mammalia.
4. That the period was a late geological one, and anterior to the surface assuming its present outline, so far as some of its minor features are concerned.

He does not, however, consider that the facts, as they at present stand, of necessity carry back Man in past time more than they bring forward the great extinct Mammals towards our own time, the evidence having reference only to relative and not to absolute time; and he is of [the] opinion that many of the later geological changes may have been sudden or of shorter duration than generally considered. In fact, from the evidence here exhibited, and from all that he knows regarding drift phenomena generally, the author sees no reason against the conclusion that this period of Man and the extinct Mammals—supposing their contemporaneity to be proved—was brought to a sudden end by a temporary inundation of the land; on the contrary, he sees much to support such a view on purely geological considerations.

The paper concludes with a letter from Mr. John Evans, F.S.A. and F.G.S., regarding these implements from an antiquarian rather than a geological point of view, and dividing them into three classes:

1. Flint flakes—arrowheads or knives.

2. Pointed weapons truncated at one end, and probably lance or spear heads (fig. 6*b*).

3. Oval or almond shaped implements with a cutting edge all round, possibly used as sling stones or as axes (fig. 6*a*).

Mr. Ivans points out, that in form and workmanship those of the two last classes differed essentially from the implements of the so-called Celtic period, which are usually more or less ground and polished, and cut at the wide and not the narrow end; and that had they been found under any other circumstances, they must have been regarded as the work of some other race than the Celts, or known aboriginal tribes. He fully concurs with Mr. Prestwich, that the beds of drift in which they were found were entirely undisturbed.

※ ※ ※

Flower's paper, which describes the occurrence of Acheulian handaxes in the deep gravels at St. Acheul, constituted strong supporting evidence for Prestwich's conclusion that the handaxes (named by the workmen "cats' tongues") occurred in situ *in the gravels in association with the bones of extinct animal forms. At the time, within a year of the publication of Darwin's* Origin of Species, *this was an exciting and new vista which promised an objective means of demonstrating that man in his ascent from a prehuman ancestral form had risen by gradual improvement to his present estate. In short, the idea of man whose culture was limited to the production and use of rough stone tools fitted precisely with the concept that Darwin had implied of the rise of man from lower forms.*

A Paleolithic Handaxe from Amiens

J. W. Flower

The implement or weapon which I desire to bring under the notice of this Society . . . was found by me about a month since, when, in company with Mr. Prestwich and other Fellows of this Society, I visited some gravel pits near Amiens. When discovered, it was imbedded in a compact mass of gravel, composed of large chalk flints much water-worn and rolled, and small chalk pebbles. It was found lying at the depth of sixteen feet from the upper surface, and about eighteen inches from the face or outer surface of the quarry, to which extent the gravel had been removed by me before I found it. The bed of gravel in question forms the capping or summit of a slight elevation of the chalk. A section of this pit, which Mr. Prestwich lately exhibited to the Royal Society (Proc. Roy. Soc. vol. X, no. 35, p. 51), showed that the gravel presents here a thickness of about ten feet. Above this occurs a thin bed of coarse, white siliceous sand, interspersed with small rounded chalk pebbles; and above the sand is a layer of

"On a Flint Implement Recently Discovered at the Base of Some Beds of Drift-gravel and Brick-earth at St. Acheul, near Amiens," by J. W. Flower. *The Quarterly Journal of the Geological Society of London,* Vol. XVI, Part I, [Article] 3 (London: Longmans, Green, Longmans, and Roberts, 1860), pp. 190-192.

strong loam, of a red color, which is now extensively worked for the purpose of making bricks. The remains of the Elephant, Horse, and Deer have been occasionally found in the gravel; and we found in the sand which rests upon it an abundance of land and freshwater shells, all of recent species. No fossils of any kind were discovered by us in the brick earth lying on the surface. At the distance of a few hundred yards from the convent of St. Acheul are the remains of an ancient Roman cemetery. A large stone tomb is here left standing on the surface, the brick earth having been cleared away from it; and here many Roman coins and bronze ornaments are found.

At St. Roch (about half a mile distant from St. Acheul), we also examined a quarry of flint gravel, of precisely the same character, and, apparently, of the same period as that of St. Acheul. We procured from it two very fine tusks of the *Hippopotamus,* which had been found twenty feet from the surface. These were but little rolled or broken; and it seems probable, therefore, that the same forces that transported these flint implements to their present position may also have deposited these remains of the *Hippopotamus.*

The first discovery of these flint instruments, as well in this quarry as in other localities in the Valley of the Somme, is due to M. Boucher de Perthes, of Amiens. It was with a view to verify by personal observation the result of his researches that our visit to St. Acheul and the neighborhood was undertaken. Mr. Prestwich had, indeed, previously visited the spot, and had embodied the result of his researches in a paper which was read before the Royal Society in May last. He had not, however, succeeded in finding one of these implements *in situ,* although he had procured several of them from the laborers. It was only after laboring for several hours that I succeeded in disinterring the specimen in question.

The result of our examination perfectly satisfied us, as it had already satisfied Mr. Prestwich, of the frequent occurrence of these weapons or implements beneath the beds of loam, sand, and gravel which I have described. We not only found two good specimens of these implements, but we brought away upwards of thirty others, taken from the same pit; several of them are on the table. Some of these were found at about the same depth as that which I discovered, and some about four feet lower down. They were procured without difficulty from the laborers and their children. Mr. Prestwich, on the occasion of his first visit, in company with Mr. Evans, brought away about twenty specimens; and many others are to be seen in M. Boucher de Perthes's Museum. They are so common in the pit in question as to have acquired a trivial name, and are known by the workpeople as *langues de chat.*

There is one peculiarity in these implements which appears to deserve particular notice: they were evidently water-worn and rounded pebbles before they were formed into weapons or tools; and this, indeed, is just such a condition as we should expect to find. None but people destitute

of iron would have been content to use such rude and uncouth instruments as these; and a people unprovided with iron would also have been
unable to quarry the chalk for the sake of the flint imbedded in it, but
would have been forced to content themselves with those fragments
which lay scattered upon the surface, or but a little below it. If we examine the specimens closely, we find that, while the manufactured or
worked surfaces (namely the cutting edges and the point) are nearly as
sharp and clear as if worked yesterday, the portion left of the original, or,
if we may so call it, the *natural* surface (that which has not been struck off
in the course of manufacture) is often very much water-worn; and it also
presents that peculiar discoloration usually found in flints long exposed
to the influence of the atmosphere, extending to the depth of a quarter or
an eighth of an inch, and probably due to some chemical change resulting
from mechanical forces.

It would thus seem that those forces, whatever they may have been, by
means of which these implements were carried into their present position,
were in operation but for a short period, since otherwise the sharp edges
which they still retain would have been rounded and worn, if not altogether obliterated; and further, that the rolled and discolored surface of
the flint pebbles with which they are associated (and from which indeed it
seems probable that they were originally taken and fashioned) was due to
some former change—the drift or gravel having subsequently been merely
shifted from some other spot, bearing these implements with it, just as the
loose ballast in the hold of a vessel is shifted and rolled from one side to
another.

No one who attentively examines these implements can doubt that they
are the products of human skill. Rude and uncouth as they may appear,
that rudeness is probably not so much due to any deficiency of intelligence
in the manufacturers, as to the want of iron or some other metals where-
with to work. Probably no workman who found himself destitute of metal
tools would be able to produce from flint pebbles more useful or elegant
implements. Those who are familiar with the forms which are presented
in those flints which are casually fractured will agree that it is almost
impossible that even a single flint should be so fractured by accident as to
assume the shape of these implements; but here we have a great number,
all taken from a single quarry. Further, it will be seen that the original
or natural surface is never retained where it at all interferes with the
shape and symmetry of the weapon. Wherever it would have so interfered, chiefly on the sides and at the point, it has been chipped away; and
thus there has been no waste of labor, nothing having been removed but
that which was inconvenient. It will also be noticed that they are all
formed after a certain rude but uniform pattern; they are worked to a
blunt point at one end, with a rude cutting edge on each side, and a sort
of boss at the other extremity, forming a handle or hand-hold. In order

the better to form this double edge, a ridge is left running down the centre; and the edges have been formed by striking away the flint in splinters from each side, in a direction at right angles with, or a little oblique to, the axis, the base or under side being usually either flat, or but slightly convex.

The discovery of these implements under the circumstances indicated cannot fail to suggest many interesting inquiries. We should all desire to know something more concerning the persons by whom, and the purposes for which, they were fabricated,—how it happened that so many of them were brought together in so small a space,—and how it is that no remains have hitherto been found of those by whom they were made and used. These, however, are speculations which seem to belong to the province of archaeology rather than to that of geology; and they are only now alluded to by way of suggestion that topics of such importance and interest are well deserving the investigation of archaeologists.

❋ ❋ ❋

Lartet's letter to the President of the Geological Society of London, in which he provides evidence that cutting marks occur on the bones of extinct animals found in geologically ancient deposits, was written just at the time when Prestwich and Evans were authenticating Boucher de Perthes' observations. Lartet's evidence was convincing proof, if that was needed, that man had indeed lived at the same time as and had killed and butchered animals now extinct. Tournal had made a similar observation based on similar evidence some thirty years earlier, but like many discoveries made before the world is prepared to accept them, it seems to have been ignored.

Lartet's experimental method of sawing bones in order to reproduce the cutting marks on the ancient specimens is one of the first of its kind. A recent article by Ascher (1961) affirms once more how significant such experimental techniques can be in providing an understanding of prehistoric technology.

The discussion of tests for determining the percentage of organic matter in bones shows how interested mid-eighteenth century archaeologists were in developing techniques. For general surveys of this subject see Cook (1960) and Heizer (1950).

Proofs That Man Coexisted with Extinct Animals
Edward Lartet

You have been good enough to offer to communicate to the Geological Society of London the observations which I have for some time past made upon fossil bones exhibiting evident impressions of human agency. The specimens of them which I showed to you yesterday were those only whose origin is authentic, and which were obtained from deposits well defined in regard to geological relations. Thus the fragments of the Aurochs exhibiting very deep incisions, apparently made by an instrument having a waved edge, and the portion of the skull of the *Megaceros Hibernicus,* in which I thought I recognized significant marks of the mutilation and flaying of a recently slain animal, were obtained from the lowest layer in the cutting of the Canal de l'Ourcq, near Paris. These very specimens are figured or mentioned by Cuvier (Oss. Fossiles, 1823, tom. iv. pl. 6, fig. 9, *M. Hibernicus*); and Alex. Brongniart (Descr. des Environs de Paris, 4 to. 1822, p. 562, pl. 1a. fig. 10) has given a detailed description of the deposit, consisting of distinct layers, which he considers to be of higher antiquity than those of the valleys. The bones of the Aurochs and the *Megaceros* were found in the same layer as the remains of the Elephant (*Elephas primigenius*) of which Cuvier has given figures of two molars, which, according to that author, had not been rolled, and were found under circumstances which showed that they were in an original and not in a *remanié* deposit. I have said that the deep incisions on the bone of an Aurochs from the cutting of the Canal de l'Ourcq (which you may remember I showed you in the Gallery of the Jardin des Plantes) appear to have been made by an instrument with a waved edge. By this I meant an instrument having an edge with slight transverse inflections, so as to produce, by cutting obliquely through the bone, a plane of section somewhat undulated. The cut seems to have been made by a hatchet not entirely finished—a state in which the greatest part of the flint implements from St. Acheul, near Amiens, seem to be; but in the marked bones of Abbeville and other ancient localities the incisions must have been made by rectilinear edges. These considerations would lead us to think that, independently of the case of the hatchets simply chipped and

"On the Coexistence of Man with certain Extinct Quadrupeds, Proved by Fossil Bones, from Various Pleistocene Deposits, Bearing Incisions Made by Sharp Instruments," by E. Lartet. With additional Notes by L. Horner, Pres. G. S., and Mons. A. Delesse, for *M. G. S. Quarterly Journal of the Geological Society of London,* Vol. 16, Part 1 (May 16, 1860) (London: Longmans, Green, Longmans and Roberts) pp. 471-479.

roughed out, the place for the manufacture of which might be near that where they are now found, those primitive people must have been provided with more perfect instruments, such as would be more suited to their ordinary wants. I should therefore hesitate to adopt the system (too absolute, in my opinion) of Mr. Worsaae, who distinguishes the first subdivision of the "Stone Period" by hatchets that are merely chipped, to the exclusion of those that are polished, which he assigns to the second subdivision. It is to be presumed that the want of instruments with polished surfaces and having a fine cutting edge must have been felt from the earliest time, when the people had learned to fix, by a much more difficult process, to flints and other rocks intentional forms so well defined.

Among the bones with incisions obtained from the sands of Abbeville, there is a large antler of an extinct Stag, referred to the *Cervus Somonensis,* or the *grand Daim de la Somme* of Cuvier, together with several horns of our common Deer, which I was not able to show you. The bones of the *Rhinoceros* (*Rh. tichorhinus*) which I laid before you were found at Menchecourt, a suburb of Abbeville, where there are gravel pits which formerly afforded many fossil bones of Elephants, &c., and where M. Boucher de Perthes, at a later period, obtained the flints worked by human hands. The incisions that may be observed on those bones are neither so deep, nor do they afford evidence so striking, as those in the bones of the Aurochs from the Canal de l'Ourcq; but the shallow cuts and the incisions of the bony surfaces which may be observed upon them, especially in the articulations, have in my eyes not less value; for I have satisfied myself, by comparative trials on homologous portions of existing animals, that incisions presenting such appearances could only be made in fresh bones still retaining their cartilage. As to the fragment of the horn of the *Megaceros Hibernicus,* which Cuvier had received from England without any indication as to where it came from, you may have observed that it bears the marks of several blows, which have made incisions of a depth that it would be impossible to produce in the present state of mineralization of that fragment; further, the blow which detached the piece from the rest of the horn must have been given before that immersion in the sea which caused its fossilized condition; for in the internal cavity of this fragment there was found the valve of an *Anomia* (preserved with the specimen), which could not have found its way there except at the place of fracture. I have observed very significant marks, evidently produced by a sharp tool, on the horn of a young *Megaceros* which the late M. Alcide d'Orbigny had received from Ireland some years ago.

I would call to your recollection that the Rev. John Cumming, in his geological description of the Isle of Man (Quarterly Journal of the Geological Society, vol. ii. p. 345), notices the occurrence of the remains of the *Megaceros* imbedded in blue marl "with implements of human art and industry, though of an uncouth and ancient character;" and in a note at the foot of page 344, alluding to a submarine forest, to which he is inclined to assign a more ancient date, he says, "It is singular that the trunk of an oak tree, which has been removed from the submerged forest at Strandhall, exhibits upon its surface the marks of a hatchet." With regard to the historical existence of the *Megaceros,* after referring to what is to be found in the works of Oppian, of Julius Capitolinus, and S. Münster, I have found nothing which appears to me to justify in this respect the opinion put forth by Dr. Hibbert, and since then accepted by other palaeontologists, except Professor Owen, who, speaking of the *Megaceros* of the British Isles, entirely dissents from the opinion of Dr. Hibbert. All the remains of that animal found on this side of the Channel, which I have examined, belong to deposits of greater antiquity than that of the peat bogs.

M. Delesse has shown you fragments of bone that have been sawn, which he recently obtained from a deposit in the neighborhood of Paris, where he had previously collected remains of the Beaver, the Ox, and the Horse. From an examination of these fragments, I have satisfied myself, by experiments on recent bones, that the action of a metallic saw would not produce the transversally striated plane of section which you must have observed on those ancient bones collected by M. Delesse; but I have obtained analogous results by employing as a saw those flint knives, or splinters with a sharp chisel-edge, found in the sands of Abbeville.

If, therefore, the presence of worked flints in the diluvial banks of the Somme, long since brought to light by M. Boucher de Perthes, and more recently confirmed by the rigorous verifications of several of your learned fellow-countrymen, have established the certainty of the existence of Man at the time when those ancient erratic deposits were formed, the traces of an *intentional operation* on the bones of the *Rhinoceros,* the *Aurochs,* the *Megaceros,* the *Cervus Somonensis,* &c., supply equally the inductive demonstration of the contemporaneity of those species with the human race.

It is true that certain of those species, the *Cervus elaphus* of Linnaeus (the same as your Red-deer or Stag) and the Aurochs, are still represented in existing nature; but although it be exactly the bones of the Aurochs which exhibit the most evident proof of human action, the fact is not of less value as regards the relative antiquity; for the remains of the Aurochs have been found associated in the same beds with those of *Elephas* and *Megaceros,* not, as I have already said, by the effect of a *remaniement,* but in an original inhumation. Moreover, fossil remains of the same Aurochs have been found in England, in France, and in Italy, in preglacial deposits (that is, in deposits anterior to the most ancient pleistocene formations imbedding bones of *Elephas primigenius* and *Rhinoceros tichorhinus*). I would add, that the more rigorous observation of facts tends clearly to demonstrate that a great proportion of our living Mammifers have been contemporaneous with those two great extinct species, the first appearance of which in Western Europe must have been preceded by that of several of our still existing quadrupeds.

In endeavoring to connect those proofs of the antiquity of the human race with the geological and geographical changes which have since taken place, I have not met with any more precise induction than that offered by M. d'Archiac, viz., the relative epoch of the separation of England from the Continent. The former connection of the two is a fact generally admitted; it is proved by the similarity in structure of the opposite sides of the Channel, by the identity of species of terrestrial animals, the original intermigration of which could only have been effected by the existence of *terra firma*. M. d'Archiac (Bull. de la Soc. Geol. de France, 1ère série, t. x. p. 220, and Histoire des Progrès, &c., t. ii. pp. 127 & 170) has been led, by a series of well-weighed inductions from stratigraphical considerations, to consider the epoch of the separation of the British Islands as occurring after the deposition of the diluvial rolled pebbles, and before that of the ancient alluvium, the Loess of the North of France, of Belgium, the Valley of the Rhine, &c. The inference to be drawn from that hypothesis is self-evident; it is this, that the primitive people to whom we attribute the hatchets and other worked flints of Amiens and Abbeville might have communicated with the existing land of England by dry land, inasmuch as the separation did not take place until after the deposit of the rolled diluvial pebbles, from among which the hatchets and worked flints have been collected. On the other hand, M. Elie de Beaumont having assigned the production of the erratic phenomena existing in our valleys to the last dislocation of the Alps, we should be authorized to conclude from this second hypothesis, that the worked flints carried along with the pebbles in that erratic deposit in the bottom of the valleys afford a proof of the existence of Man at an epoch when Central Europe had not yet reached the completion of its present great orographic relief.

While it has been held that no change has taken place in the great lines of level since the formation of the erratic deposits in the lower parts of our valleys, and although such changes cannot be distinctly traced in the central parts of the continents, from the absence of standards of comparison, they are not the less easy to be recognized as having occurred, even since the existence of Man, throughout the whole extent of the European coasts, from the Gulf of Bothnia to the very eastern extremity of the Mediterranean. They have been observed by different authors on a considerable number of points of the coast, where they have verified the existence of objects of human industry in deposits of marine origin, raised up at different elevations above the sea level. Such changes, be they the result of action more or less violent, of movements more or less sudden, have not amounted to catastrophes so general as to affect to a sensible degree the regular succession of organized beings.

We find incontestable proof of this in the British Islands, whither the most considerable number of terrestrial species must necessarily have migrated prior to the separation of those islands from the Continent, and where they have established themselves and have continued by successive generations to the present day. The same thing has occurred on the Continent, where the same terrestrial fauna has continued without any other modifications than the geographical displacement of certain species and the final disappearance of some others—disappearances that have resulted, not from a simultaneous destruction, but rather from a series of successive extinctions which appear to have been equally gradual as regards space and time.

I may add to what I have stated above, that the findings of worked flints in the diluvium of Amiens and Abbeville is by no means an isolated fact. M. Gosse of Geneva, a young medical student in Paris, has recently discovered in the sands of the Parisian suburb of Grenelle, of the same age as those of Abbeville and of other parts of Europe, a flint hatchet of a most distinct form, together with knives or thin plates split in a longitudinal direction. I myself have had an opportunity of verifying these facts in the collection formed by that skillful explorer. He has shown me an Elephant's tooth, a canine tooth of a large Feline animal, and bones of the Aurochs, Horse, &c., all obtained from the same sands and from the same bed in which the flint hatchet was found.

I may add that, among the bones obtained in Switzerland under the lacustrine habitations of the Stone Period (in the lakes of Moosdorf, Bienne, and others), there never have been found any remains of the *Megaceros,* although the remains of the Elk, the Aurochs, and the *Bos primigenius* are by no means rare. In Denmark, where still more ancient stations have been carefully examined with the same object, Prof. Steenstrup has assured me that he has never discovered the smallest fragment of the *Megaceros* in the midst of the most abundant remains of the Reindeer, Elk, Aurochs, and other species of animals which from time immemorial have not existed in that region. Nevertheless these primitive stations in Denmark are referred back to a period when no other domestic animal existed in that country except the Dog. No remains have been found either of the Horse, Sheep, or Goat,—not even any kind of dwarf Ox.

If, Sir, you are of opinion that the above notes, drawn up in haste, are likely to prove interesting to the Geological Society of London, I should be happy if you would submit them to the enlightened judgment of your learned associates, and if they will receive them at the same time as a mark of my deference, and as a feeble expression of the profound gratitude I feel for the honor conferred upon me by my name having been inscribed among the Foreign Members of that Society.

ADDITION BY THE PRESIDENT

In the foregoing communication, M. Lartet has referred to my friend M. Delesse having shown me some fragments of bone bearing incisions made by a sharp instrument, which he had recently discovered in the neighborhood of Paris. He presented me with one of those which he had submitted to the examination of M. Lartet, and which I now lay before the Society, together with the following copy of a note I received from M. Delesse describing this specimen:

"I send you a fragment of a rib which I recently found at Ver, in the department of the Seine at Oise, about nine leagues from Paris, at the depth of three meters (nearly ten feet), in a kind of cleft filled by the diluvial soil (*le terrain diluvien*), occurring with the sandstone and sands belonging to the *étage* denominated *les sables de Beauchamp*. It was associated with divers bones of the Stag and Horse, and also of an animal no longer existing in the country, namely, the Beaver. I have submitted this fragment to M. Lartet, with whose profound scientific attainments you are well acquainted; but he has not been able to decide whether it belongs to a species of quadruped still living, or to one now extinct. But he considers this small fragment of a rib very interesting, from its having at one extremity traces of a rude operation of sawing, and presenting an appearance very different from that which would be produced by a metallic blade, or by a saw. M. Lartet did not rest satisfied with a mere conjecture, but ascertained by experiments on a fresh rib of an Ox that a metallic blade produced a uniform and almost a smooth cut. Hence he concludes that the rib in question had been sawn by a flint with a jagged edge. Taking a splinter of flint with a chisel-edge from the sands of Abbeville, he easily sawed a fresh rib, but always obtained an uneven, irregular cut (*des surfaces de resection avec reprises nombreuses*), such as may be observed on the specimen I send you. There is therefore every reason to believe that this rib had been sawn by a flint, and it affords proof of Man having lived in France at the same time as the Beaver, an animal no longer existing with us; and M. Lartet has thus supplied a new and elegant demonstration of the contemporaneity of Man and quadrupeds during the period of the *Terrains diluviens*."

L. Horner

SUBSEQUENT ADDITION BY THE PRESIDENT

The day after the above communication was read, on showing the fragment of bone given me by M. Delesse above referred to, it was observed that it had a remarkably fresh appearance, that it did not adhere (*happer*) to the tongue as fossil bones usually do, and that thus a doubt might exist as to its assumed antiquity. After hearing this remark, I exposed a minute fragment to the flame of a candle, when it gave out the odor of burnt animal matter; and on immersing another fragment in hydrochloric acid, after effervescence, a soft gelatinous substance, nearly the size of the original fragment, was left. Knowing full well that M. Delesse and M. Lartet would cordially agree on the importance of the most scrupulous investigation of every fact produced in evidence on this recently agitated question of the antiquity of Man, I communicated to both of them what I have stated above respecting this bone. I received immediately answers from them; and these, with their leave, I now give, not only because of their confirmation of the opinions they formerly expressed, but as containing some additional remarks of much interest.

M. Delesse, in his letter dated the 19th instant, says:—

"The specimen of the rib which I gave you was incontestably found in a sandpit (*sablonière*), where it was associated with the bones of animals no longer existing in the country—as, for example, the Beaver. I would observe that the presence of gelatine can in no way be opposed to the antiquity of that rib. I have only just now brought to a conclusion a long series of researches by which I have shown that bones even of a high antiquity still retain a notable proportion of organic matter. If you take the bones of an *Ichthyosaurus* from the Lias, or of reptiles from the Muschelkalk, you will easily satisfy yourself that, in spite of their great antiquity, they still contain a very notable proportion of organic matter. Coprolites from the oldest formations contain it. On the other hand, bones comparatively recent, such, for instance, as those found in caverns or in travelled materials, have no great amount of organic matter. In brief, the preservation of organic matter in bones is very irregular; it depends on the nature of the rock in which they are found at least quite as much as on their antiquity.

"I pronounce no opinion as to the nature of the instrument that had been employing in sawing that rib, for I made no experiments on the subject; but M. Lartet, whose caution and sagacity are known to you, made a special examination of the question along with eminent physiologists; and they had no doubt that the rib had been cut by a sharp flint."

A. Delesse

M. Lartet, in his letter dated the 22nd instant, states as follows:

"I am sorry to learn that a somewhat hasty objection has been made to the palaeontological value of the fragment of bone which you exhibited. I have no right to give any opinion regarding the locality where it was found, because I have not visited it; but the opinion of M. Delesse, who had an opportunity of examining all its geological features, is deserving of all confidence. Among the other fossil remains which he found in that locality, there is a fragment of bone of a Horse, having also traces of human agency, and which is in a much more altered condition than that of the bone he gave you; but there is another fragment, also bearing the mark of a saw, the appearance of which is quite as fresh as the specimen in your possession; nevertheless, when we endeavoured to authenticate this fragment specifically, we were unable to do so by comparing it with the homologous part in the skeleton of our living animals.

"It is moreover important to remark that, in any given locality, all the bones collected do not present the same degree of organic change. That depends, first, on their anatomical structure being more or less compact according to the species, and again, chiefly on the composition and physical condition of the mineral matter in which they have been in immediate and prolonged contact. Mr. Hart, in his description of the *Megaceros Hibernicus* (Dublin, 1830), states that a fragment of a rib analyzed by Dr. Stokes yielded 42.87 per cent. of animal matter; and Dr. Apjohn, who analyzed another portion of a rib, states as follows: 'The bone was subjected for two days to the action of dilute muriatic acid; and when examined at the end of this period, it had become as flexible as a recent bone submitted to the action of the same solvent. The cartilage and gelatine had not been perceptibly altered by time.' It is long since the observation was made by many other persons, and especially by Schmerling (*Recherches sur les ossements des cavernes de la province de Liége*, 4to. 1833, 1ère par. pp. 18-52); and the remarkable researches on this subject recently made by M. Delesse, and which he is about to publish, have demonstrated that the organic change in bones by no means bears a relation to their palaeontological antiquity. For example, he has found that the teeth of the bone bed in the Upper Keuper at Oberbronn contain more azotized organic matter than most of the tusks of the Mastodon in the Miocene limestone of Sansan or in the Miocene deposits of the Upper Garonne. Thus it is evident that, if the amount of organic matter generally diminishes in proportion as the age increases, there are, nevertheless, exceptions to that general rule.

"As to external appearance, that depends also on the circumstances of the locality. It is not long since a large number of bones of the *Hyaena spelaea* were sent to me, which had been obtained from an ancient alluvial deposit in the center of France. They were in no degree changed in weight or color, and in external appearance they were quite as fresh, if not more so than the fragment given to you by M. Delesse. I have some of them now in my possession; and they are still so much impregnated with animal matter, that I was able with the utmost ease to saw and cut them with a flint knife. On the other hand, I have now before me a statuette made of stag's horn, obtained from a grave at the external base of a barrow, certainly not older than the 12th century, the substance of which is so much altered that it might be said to be fossilized, in a certain sense of the term, as much as the greater part of those found in caverns or diluvium.

Hence we perceive that the greater or less amount of alteration in bones is not a character from which we can absolutely determine their palaeontological antiquity.

"With regard to the mode by which the fossil bones of M. Delesse have been sawn, I must confess that at first sight I thought, as M. Desnoyers did, that the operation must have been performed with a metallic plate; but upon a more attentive examination of recent bones, I became convinced that the peculiar appearance presented by the section of one of the bones in the possession of M. Delesse must have been produced by the employment of a sharp tool of *flint,* rather than by a metallic plate, which has always given me a section with a very different surface. I send you the extremity of a tooth of *Hyaena spelaea,* which has been sawn by a flint. If you examine with a magnifying glass the plane of the section, you will find the same system of *striae* as are observed in the bones collected by M. Delesse, sawn with the same kind of tool. You may further satisfy yourself that in this fragment nearly all the organic matter remains, although the tooth comes from ancient deposit."

In my letter to M. Lartet I had said that when his communication was read, Dr. Falconer observed that, a considerable time ago, M. Marcel de Serres had given an account of a fossil Stag's horn that had evidently been cut. On this M. Lartet observes—"It is very true, as Dr. Falconer remarked, that M. Marcel de Serres gave a figure in 1839 of a Stag's horn cut and fashioned by human hands. I had occasion to remark that, a long time before, M. Tournal in 1829 (Ann. des Sc. Nat. 1829, t. xviii, pp. 242 *et seq.*) and Schmerling in 1833 (*loc. cit.*) had made similar observations. I might myself have stated that among the bones of caverns I had seen those of the Rhinoceros and the Reindeer bearing marks that must have been made by man; but I was on my guard against bringing forward those facts, because they would only have afforded opponents an opportunity of bringing forward anew their favorite objection, viz., 'that nothing that had been observed in caverns was deserving of any confidence, and that the traces left by man on fossil bones might have been made a long time after the introduction of the bones into the caverns.'

"What constitutes the whole value of my observations on the impressions or marks of human agency on the fossil bones found in the diluvial deposits of Abbeville, and the cutting of the Canal de l'Ourcq, is this, that, once admitting the reality of those marks, their relative antiquity becomes rigorously demonstrated by the geological circumstances of their locality being clearly defined. At Abbeville the marked bones, as well as the flint hatchets, were found in the diluvial gravel, which is itself covered by the Loess deposit. In the cutting of the Canal de l'Ourcq, the bones of the *Aurochs* and those of the *Megaceros Hibernicus* were found at a depth of 7 meters (23 feet), in a bed of earth (*limon*) and under other beds in normal stratification. They were not rolled (as Cuvier has said) and were mixed with the remains of an Elephant, and evidently under the conditions of an original deposit.

"At the meeting of the Geological Society of France yesterday evening, M. de Verneuil exhibited a worked flint hatchet and an Elephant's tusk found in the gravel pit of Précy, near Creil, in the valley of the Oise. Thus these worked flints have been found in the diluvium of three of our valleys—of the Somme, the Seine, and the Oise."—E. Lartet

(L. Horner, May 31, 1860.)

✳ 3 ✳

THE BONES OF MAN

Fossilized bones of ancient man provide evidence objectively revealing the development of human skeletal morphology. While most biology and anthropology textbooks describe these ancient bone fragments of men, they usually concentrate on facts and fail to tell the story of the discovery in the words of the discoverer. Aleš Hrdlička's *Skeletal Remains of Early Man* (Hrdlička, 1930) is still the fullest and most detailed descriptive and historical account that has been written on the subject. This chapter includes three original accounts, each selected for its particular interest, to illustrate the discovery of man's early ancestors. The fourth item is the story of one of the earliest efforts to perpetrate a hoax of fossil man.

✳ ✳ ✳

The famous skull and bones of Neanderthal man came to light in August, 1857. While several fossil skulls had actually been found before that date,[1] they were not recognized as such at the time of their discovery. The Neanderthal skeleton found in 1857 burst upon the scientific world as the first undoubted example of geologically ancient man. The impact of this discovery on archaeological theory has been admirably treated by Eiseley (1954; 1957). For details of the Neanderthal locality and the discovery see Hrdlička (1930:148-161). Following the discovery, and before

[1] The Neanderthal skull discovered at Gibraltar in 1848 was not presented to the scientific world until 1959 when G. Busk described it in a paper read before the British Association for the Advancement of Science.

other examples of the Neanderthal type of man were found or recognized, a great controversy arose about its real significance. Schaaffhausen and Broca saw the Neanderthal, accurately as it turned out, as a normal example of primitive humanity, but Virchow (1872), Davis (1864), and Blake (1864) thought that the skull was either pathological or that of an idiot. The continuing doubts that the Neanderthal skull might be abnormal or represent a form of man different from the modern were finally settled by Eugene Dubois' discovery of the first Pithecanthropus skull in 1891 in Java.

Discovery of the Neanderthal Skull

D. Schaaffhausen

In the early part of the year 1857, a human skeleton was discovered in a limestone cave in the Neanderthal, near Hochdal, between Düsseldorf and Elberfeld. Of this, however, I was unable to procure more than a plaster cast of the cranium taken at Elberfeld, from which I drew up an account of its remarkable conformation, which was, in the first instance, read on the 4th of February, 1857, at the meeting of the Lower Rhine Medical and Natural History Society, at Bonn (Verhandl. d. Naturhist. Vereins der preuss. Rheinlande und Westphalens, xiv. Bonn, 1857). Subsequently Dr. Fuhlrott, himself gave a full account of the locality, and of the circumstances under which the discovery was made. He was of the opinion that the bones might be regarded as fossil; and in coming to this conclusion, he laid especial stress upon the existence of dendritic deposits with which their surface was covered, and which were first noticed upon them by Professor Mayer. To this communication I appended a brief report on the results of my anatomical examination of the bones. The conclusions at which I arrived: (1) that the extraordinary form of the skull was due to a natural conformation hitherto not known to exist, even in the most barbarous races; (2) that these remarkable human remains belonged to a period antecedent to the time of the Celts and Germans, and were in all probability derived from one of the wild races of northwestern Europe, spoken of by Latin writers; and which were encountered as autochthones by the German immigrants; and (3) that it was beyond doubt that these human relics were traceable to a period at which the latest

"On the Crania of the most Ancient Races of Man," by Professor D. Schaaffhausen, of Bonn. (From Müller's Archiv., 1858, pp. 453.) With remarks and original figures, taken from a cast of the neanderthal cranium, by George Busk. *The Natural History Review*, Vol. I, No. II (April, 1861), Article XVII. (London and Edinburgh: Williams and Norgate, 1861) pp. 155-174.

animals of the diluvium still existed; but that no proof in support of this assumption, nor consequently of their so-termed *fossil* condition, was afforded by the circumstances under which the bones were discovered.

As Dr. Fuhlrott has not yet published his description of these circumstances, I borrow the following account of them from one of his letters. "A small cave or grotto, high enough to admit a man, and about 15 feet deep from the entrance, which is 7 or 8 feet wide, exists in the southern wall of the gorge of the Neanderthal, as it is termed, at a distance of about 100 feet from the Düssel, and about 60 feet above the bottom of the valley. In its earlier and uninjured condition this cavern opened upon a narrow plateau lying in front of it, and from which the rocky wall descended almost perpendicularly into the river. It could be reached, though with difficulty, from above. The uneven floor was covered to a thickness of 4 or 5 feet with a deposit of mud, sparingly intermixed with rounded fragments of chert. In the removing of this deposit, the bones were discovered. The skull was the first noticed, placed nearest to the entrance of the cavern; and further in, the other bones, lying in the same horizontal plane. Of this I was assured in the most positive terms by two laborers who were employed to clear out the grotto, and who were questioned by me on the spot. At first no idea was entertained of the bones being human; and it was not till several weeks after their discovery that they were recognized as such by me, and placed in security. But, as the importance of the discovery was not at the time perceived, the laborers were very careless in the collecting, and secured chiefly only the larger bones; and to this circumstance it may be attributed that fragments merely of the probably perfect skeleton came into my possession."

My anatomical examination of these bones afforded the following results:

The cranium is of unusual size, and of a long, elliptical form. A most remarkable peculiarity is at once obvious in the extraordinary development of the frontal sinuses, owing to which the superciliary ridges, which coalesce completely in the middle, are rendered so prominent, that the frontal bone exhibits a considerable hollow or depression above, or rather behind them, whilst a deep depression is also formed in the situation of the root of the nose. The forehead is narrow and low, though the middle and hinder portions of the cranial arch are well developed. Unfortunately, the fragment of the skull that has been preserved consists only of the portion situated above the roof of the orbits and the superior occipital ridges, which are greatly developed, and almost conjoined so as to form a horizontal eminence. It includes almost the whole of the frontal bone, both parietals, a small part of the squamous and the upper third of the occipital. The recently fractured surfaces show that the skull was broken at the time of its disinterment. The cavity holds 16,876 grains of water, whence its cubical contents may be estimated at 57.64 inches, or 1033.24 cubic centimeters. In making this estimation, the water is supposed to stand on a level with the orbital plate of the frontal, with the deepest notch in the squamous margin of the parietal, and with the superior semicircular ridges of the occipital. Estimated in dried millet seed, the contents equalled 31 ounces, Prussian Apothecaries' weight. The semicircular line indicating the upper boundary of the attachment of the temporal muscle, though not very strongly marked, ascends nevertheless to more than half the height of the parietal bone. On the right superciliary ridge is observable an oblique furrow or depression, indicative of an injury received during life. The coronal and sagittal sutures are on the exterior nearly closed, and on the inside so completely ossified as to have left no traces whatever, whilst the lambdoidal remains quite open. The depressions for the Pacchionian glands are deep and numerous; and there is an unusually deep vascular groove immediately behind the coronal suture, which, as it terminates in a foramen, no doubt transmitted a *vena emissaria*. The course of the frontal suture is indicated externally by a slight ridge; and where it joins the coronal, this ridge rises into a small protuberance. The course of the sagittal suture is grooved, and above the angle of the occipital bone the parietals are depressed.

	mm.*
The length of the skull from the nasal process to the frontal over the vertex to the superior semicircular lines of the occipital measures	303 (300) = 12.0″
Circumference over the orbital ridges and the superior semicircular lines of the occipital	590 (580) = 23.37″ or 23″
Width of the frontal from the middle of the temporal line on one side to the same point on the opposite	104 (114) = 4.1″-4.5″
Length of the frontal from the nasal process to the coronal suture	133 (125) = 5.25″-5″
Extreme width of the frontal sinuses	25 (23) = 1.0″-0.9″
Vertical height above a line joining the deepest notches in the squamous border of the parietals	70 = 2.75″
Width of hinder part of skull from one parietal protuberance to the other	138 (150) = 5.4″-5.9″
Distance from the upper angle of the occipital to the superior semicircular lines	51 (60) = 1.9″-2.4″
Thickness of the bone at the parietal protuberance	8
——— at the angle of the occipital	9
——— at the superior semicircular line of the occipital	10 = 0.3″

* The numbers in brackets are those which I should assign to the different measures, as taken from the plaster cast.—G. B.

Besides the cranium, the following bones have been secured:—

1. Both thighbones, perfect. These, like the skull, and all other bones, are characterized by their unusual thickness, and the great development of all the elevations and depressions for the attachment of muscles. In the Anatomical Museum at Bonn, under the designation of "Giant's bones,"

are some recent thighbones, with which in thickness the foregoing pretty nearly correspond, although they are shorter.

	Giant's bones mm.		Fossil bones mm.
Length	542 = 21.4″	.	438 = 17.4″
Diameter of head of femur	54 = 2.14″	.	53 = 2.0″
" of lower articular end, from one condyle to the other	89 = 3.5″	.	87 = 3.4″
" of femur in the middle	33 = 1.2″	.	30 = 1.1″

2. A perfect right humerus, whose size shows that it belongs to the thigh bones.

	mm.
Length	312 = 12.3″
Thickness in the middle	26 = 1.0″
Diameter of head	49 = 1.9″

Also a perfect right radius of corresponding dimensions, and the upper third of a right ulna corresponding to the humerus and radius.

3. A left humerus, of which the upper third is wanting, and which is so much slenderer than the right as apparently to belong to a distinct individual; a left *ulna,* which, though complete, is pathologically deformed, the coronoid process being so much enlarged by bony growth, that flexure of the elbow beyond a right angle must have been impossible; the anterior fossa of the humerus for the reception of the coronoid process being also filled up with a similar bony growth. At the same time, the olecranon is curved strongly downwards. As the bone presents no sign of rachitic degeneration, it may be supposed that an injury sustained during life was the cause of the anchylosis. When the left ulna is compared with the right radius, it might at first sight be concluded that the bones respectively belonged to different individuals, the ulna being more than half an inch too short for articulation with a corresponding radius. But it is clear that this shortening, as well as the attenuation of the left humerus, are both consequent upon the pathological condition above described.

4. A left *ilium,* almost perfect, and belonging to the femur; a fragment of the right *scapula;* the anterior extremity of a rib of the right side; and the same part of a rib of the left side; the hinder part of a rib of the right side; and, lastly, two short hinder portions and one middle portion of ribs, which, from their unusually rounded shape, and abrupt curvature, more resemble the ribs of a carnivorous animal than those of a man. Dr. H. v. Meyer, however, to whose judgment I defer, will not venture to declare them to be ribs of any animal; and it only remains to suppose that this abnormal condition has arisen from an unusually powerful development of the thoracic muscles.

The bones adhere strongly to the tongue, although, as proved by the use of hydrochloric acid, the greater part of the cartilage is still retained in them, which appears, however, to have undergone that transformation into gelatine which has been observed by v. Bibra in fossil bones. The surface of all the bones is in many spots covered with minute black specks, which more especially under a lens, are seen to be formed of very delicate *dendrites*. These deposits, which were first observed on the bones by Dr. Mayer, are most distinct on the inner surface of the cranial bones. They consist of a ferruginous compound, and, from their black color, may be supposed to contain manganese. Similar dendritic formations also occur, not infrequently, on laminated rocks, and are usually found in minute fissures and cracks. At the meeting of the Lower Rhine Society at Bonn, on the 1st of April, 1857, Prof. Mayer stated that he had noticed in the museum of Poppelsdorf similar dendritic crystallizations on several fossil bones of animals, and particularly on those of *Ursus spealaeus,* but still more abundantly and beautifully displayed on the fossil bones and teeth of *Equus adamiticus, Elephas primigenius,* &c., from the caves of Bolve and Sundwig. Faint indications of similar *dendrites* were visible in a Roman skull from Siegburg; whilst other ancient skulls which had lain for centuries in the earth presented no trace of them . . .

As we cannot now look upon the primitive world as representing a wholly different condition of things, from which no transition exists to the organic life of the present time, the designation of *fossil,* as applied to *a bone,* has no longer the sense it conveyed in the time of Cuvier. Sufficient grounds exist for the assumption that man coexisted with the animals found in the diluvium; and many a barbarous race may, before all historical time, have disappeared, together with the animals of the ancient world, whilst the races whose organization is improved have continued the genus. The bones which form the subject of this Paper present characters which, although not decisive as regards a geological epoch, are, nevertheless, such as indicate a very high antiquity. It may also be remarked that, common as is the occurrence of diluvial animal bones in the muddy deposits of caverns, such remains have not hitherto been met with in the caves of the Neanderthal; and that the bones, which were covered by a deposit of mud not more than four or five feet thick, and without any protective covering of stalagmite, have retained the greatest part of their organic substance.

These circumstances might be adduced against the probability of a geological antiquity. Nor should we be justified in regarding the cranial conformation as perhaps representing the most savage primitive type of the human race, since crania exist among living savages, which, though not exhibiting such a remarkable conformation of the forehead, which gives the skull somewhat the aspect of that of the large apes, still in other respects, as for instance in the greater depth of the temporal fossae, the crest-like, prominent temporal ridges, and a generally less capacious cranial cavity, exhibit an equally low stage of development. There is no reason for supposing that the deep frontal hollow is due to any artificial flattening, such as is practiced in various modes by barbarous nations in the Old and New World. The skull is quite symmetrical, and shows no indication of counter-pressure at the occiput, whilst, according to Morton, in the Flat-heads of the Columbia, the frontal and parietal bones are always unsymmetrical. Its conformation exhibits the sparing development of the anterior part of the head which has been so often observed in very ancient crania, and affords one of the most striking proofs of the influence of culture and civilization on the form of the human skull. The Abbé Frère, whose collection of crania belonging to the different centuries of our epoch is now placed in the Anthropological Museum of the Jardin des Plantes in Paris, came to the conclusion that, in the most ancient crania, the occipital was the most, and the frontal region the least developed; and that the increase in the elevation of the latter marked the transition from barbarous to civilized man . . .

There is no reason whatever for regarding the unusual development of the frontal sinuses in the remarkable skull from the Neanderthal as an individual or pathological deformity; it is unquestionably a typical race character, and is physiologically connected with the uncommon thickness of the other bones of the skeleton, which exceeds by about one half the usual proportions. This expansion of the frontal sinuses, which are appendages of the air passages, also indicates an unusual force and power of endurance in the movements of the body, as may be concluded from the size of all the ridges and processes for the attachment of the muscles or bones. That this conclusion may be drawn from the existence of large frontal sinuses, and a prominence of the lower frontal region, is confirmed in many ways by other observations . . . The cranial capacity, compared with the uncommon strength of the corporeal frame, would seem to indicate a small cerebral development. The skull as it is holds about 31 ounces of millet seed; and as, from the proportionate size of the wanting bones, the whole cranial cavity should have about 6 ounces more added, the contents, were it perfect, may be taken at 37 ounces . . .

It is, of course, a matter of the greatest interest to inquire whether a similar conformation has been before noticed; whether it is probable that it exists only in skulls to which a high antiquity must be assigned; and whether in any instance of the kind observations may not have been made tending to supply what is wanting in the results of the investigation above detailed, and to confirm or to contradict the conclusions drawn therefrom. Large frontal sinuses, it is admitted, are occasionally noticed in skulls; but these instances afford only faint indications of the remarkable conformation which gives the cranium we are considering its brutal expression . . .

The difference as regards the cranium is most marked in the greater or less development of the anterior part of the head, and in the position of the muzzle, which is occasionally rather prominent, as is the case even at the present time in some of the German races, as for instance, in Hesse and the Westerwald . . .

Now, when it is found from these numerous examples, that a marked prominence of the supraorbital region, traces of which can be perceived even at the present time, occurs most frequently in the crania of barbarous, and especially of northern races, to some of which a high antiquity must be assigned, it may fairly be supposed that a conformation of this kind represents the faint vestiges of a primitive type, which is manifested in the most remarkable manner in the Neanderthal cranium, and which must have given the human visage an unusually savage aspect. This aspect might be termed brutal, inasmuch as the prominent supraorbital border is also characteristic of the facial conformation of the large apes, although in these animals the prominence in question is not caused by any expansion of the frontal sinuses. These sinuses have been found by Owen to be wholly wanting, as well in the Gorilla, as in two Tasmanian and an Australian skull, a circumstance which is in accordance with the weak bodily constitutions of these savages . . .

In conclusion, the following propositions may be regarded as the result of the foregoing researches:—

The fragments of crania from Schwaan and Plau, on account both of their anatomical conformation and of the circumstances under which they were found, may probably be assigned to a barbarous, aboriginal people, which inhabited the North of Europe before the *Germani;* and, as is proved by the discovery of similar remains at Minsk in Russia, and in the Neanderthal near Elberfeld, must have been extensively spread— being allied, as may be presumed from the form of the skull, with the aboriginal populations of Britain, Ireland, and Scandinavia. Whilst at Schwaan the bones were deposited in a Germanic grave of stone, and consequently are brought into relation with the historical period, the bones from Plau, on the contrary, were merely laid in the sand, together with implements of bone of the rudest kind. The Minsk skull, in like manner, was found in the sand of an ancient river bed. But the human bones and cranium from the Neanderthal exceed all the rest in those peculiarities of conformation which lead to the conclusion of their belonging to a barbarous and savage race. Whether the cavern in which they were found, unaccompanied with any trace of human art, were the place of their interment, or whether, like the bones of extinct animals elsewhere, they had been washed into it, they may still be regarded as the most ancient memorial of the early inhabitants of Europe.

REMARKS BY GEORGE BUSK

The fact of the geological antiquity of Man, or, to use other words, of his having been contemporary with extinct animals whose remains are universally regarded by geologists as "fossil," has apparently been fully established, though rather, perhaps, from the discovery of his work than of his actual remains, under certain geological conditions. It has become a matter, therefore, among others, of extreme interest to determine how far it may be possible, from the scanty remains of his bones as yet discovered, to ascertain whether, and in what respects, the priscan race or races have differed from those which at present inhabit the earth.

Although the materials as yet in our possession are far too scanty to allow of any satisfactory solution of this difficult question, they are sufficient, perhaps, to allow of its being entered upon. It is with this view that we reproduce the interesting paper by Professor Schaaffhausen, which incidentally treats upon the question at large, and contains a considerable amount of information respecting it.

The human remains there described were discovered under circumstances which, though not altogether demonstrative of their real geological position, leave no doubt of their enormous antiquity, and of the probability of their having belonged to what has been termed the quaternary period. The conformation of the cranium, moreover, in this instance is so remarkable, as to justly excite the utmost interest, approaching as it does in one respect that of some of the higher apes. It remains, consequently, a subject of the deepest importance for future discoveries to determine whether the conformation in question be merely an individual peculiarity, or a typical character. The peculiarity consists in a remarkable prominence or projection of the superciliary region of the forehead; for the enlargement in this part is so great, that it can hardly be described as limited to the superciliary ridges. Dr. Schaaffhausen appears to regard this extraordinary conformation as due to an expansion of the frontal sinuses. In this we are not disposed altogether to agree with him; but as we have had an opportunity, through the kindness of Sir Charles Lyell, of examining only a plaster cast of the cranium, in which the interior is not shown, we, of course, are able to speak but doubtfully on the subject. A main reason for our disagreement with Professor Schaaffhausen arises from the circumstance that a considerable elevation of the same part is often observed in recent crania, more especially, as he states, in those belonging to savage and barbarous races, in which no extraordinary expansion of the sinuses is found to exist; and, secondly, because the frontal sinuses rarely, we believe, extend beyond half the length of the supraorbital border; whilst in many cases—and this is particularly evident in the Neanderthal cranium—the elevation is continued to the outer angular process of the frontal bone, which, in that cranium, is very remarkably thickened.

The lateral extent of the frontal sinus, in cases where the superciliary borders are much elevated, is usually imperfectly indicated by an opening or depression, through which the frontal nerve passes; and this depression is very manifest, especially on the right side, in the fossil cranium, in which it is regarded by Professor Schaaffhausen, we believe erroneously, as indicative of an injury received during life. In the mature Chimpanzee and Gorilla, the supraorbital ridges are, as is well known, remarkably developed: in the former case, we are not aware that the enlargement is accompanied with any expansion of the frontal sinuses, which in fact do not exist in the ape, but it is due simply to a projection of the margin of the orbit, which cavity is larger in proportion to the skull behind it, than it is in the human subject, and is thus in accordance with the greater development of the face generally. In the old Gorilla, on the other hand, although the bone itself is enormously thickened in the monstrous projection above the orbit, there are very large frontal sinuses. However this may be, the protuberance in question must be regarded as showing a very savage type; and, in the extent to which it exists in the Neanderthal cranium, it affords a character in which that skull approaches that of the Gorilla and Chimpanzee.

Dr. Schaaffhausen appears to have taken considerable pains to inquire whether a similar conformation, or one approaching it, has been observed in other instances of ancient or modern skulls, but without success . . .

❋ ❋ ❋

In 1887, Eugene Dubois began serving as "Health Officer of the Second Class" in the Dutch Colonial military forces in southeast Asia. Trained in anatomy and paleontology, he was sent to Java in 1889 by the Netherlands Indian Government to look for human fossils. In 1891 he discovered the skull of a fossilized human which he named Pithecanthropus erectus *("erect ape-man"). One of his earliest papers on this find was published in Dublin, and the following extract is a summary of that paper with added remarks from experts who were asked for their opinions. The story of Dubois' search is told by Hrdlička (1930:28-65) and Von Koenigswald (1956). Not only did the discovery of* Pithecanthropus *fully support Schaaffhausen's view that the Neanderthal skull was a primitive form of ancient humanity, but in addition the Java skull was clearly even more primitive, as well as geologically older, than the Neanderthal. It will thus be seen that not only was the* Pithecanthropus *skull important by itself, but it proved conclusively the widely held belief proposed by Darwin that human evolution had proceeded from very primitive types through less primitive ones to the type of humanity exhibited by modern man. Charles Darwin in 1871 in* The Descent of Man *had complained about the scarcity of human fossils and expressed the conviction that such finds would accumulate only as a result of much time spent in hard work—it was Dubois who verified this conviction.*

Pithecanthropus in Java

Eugene Dubois

Many years ago, Dr. Dubois said Junghuhn and others had discovered fossil remains in Java. With the object of continuing the work of exploration, he (Dr. Dubois) had been employed by the Dutch Indian Government to make further investigations. During the years 1890-95 he had been successful in obtaining a large quantity of remains of mammals and reptiles, belonging mainly to extinct species, closely allied as one might expect to the later Tertiary and Pleistocene faunae of India.

The chief localities in which these discoveries were made are in the southern slope of a low range of hills, called the Keudengs, which extends for about 60 miles between the residences Kediri, Madiun, and Surakarta on the one side, and Rembang and Samarang on the other.

The area in which these vertebrate remains are abundantly found has, in many places, a breadth averaging from one to three miles. The specimens discovered were lying in beds of cemented volcanic tuff, consisting of clay, sand, and lapilli stone. The very general occurrence of the remains of freshwater animals in these beds and their arrangement in what English geologists call current bedding or false bedding prove conclusively their fluviatile origin. The strata throughout the whole area have undergone considerable disturbance by folding, the result of which has been to give them a general southerly dip of 3° to 15°. The whole formation reaches a maximum thickness of more than 350 meters.

The strata rest unconformably upon beds of marine marl, sand, and limestone, which are according to Professor Martin, of Leiden, of Pliocene age.

The fossil vertebrate fauna met with in these strata is the same throughout the Keudeng and other localities in Java. Its age can only be decided after the description of Dr. Dubois' collection has been published, but there are already sufficient grounds for saying that the stratigraphical position of the fauna and its relation to the Post-Tertiary and Pleistocene vertebrate faunae of India points to the conclusion that it is most probably younger Pliocene. In no case, however, can it be later than the

"On Pithecanthropus Erectus: a Transitional Form between Man and the Apes," by Dr. Eugene Dubois. *The Journal of the Anthropological Institute of Great Britain and Ireland*, Vol. XXV (1896), [Art.] XVI (London: Kegan Paul, Trench, Trübner & Co.), pp. 240-255 (Abstract of paper published in *Transactions of the Royal Dublin Society* 6:1-18, 1896).

oldest Pleistocene, for the species found belong exclusively to living genera, except the extinct *subgenera* Stegodon and Hexaprotodon, and must therefore be younger than the principal part of the Upper Miocene or Lower Pliocene Siwalik fauna, which includes a good many extinct genera; further the number of the extinct species seems to be somewhat greater than that of the Narbadá fauna, which belongs to the early Pleistocene.

In the neighborhood of Trinil (in the regency of Ngawi, of the Residency Madiun) Dr. Dubois discovered a spot at the foot of the Keudeng very rich in fossil remains. Here in August, 1891, and during the following year he unearthed a large quantity of fossil bones, amongst which he discovered the calvaria, thighbone, and teeth of a great man-like mammal, which he considered an intermediate form between man and the apes, and named accordingly *Pithecanthropus erectus*. So much impressed was Dr. Dubois with the importance of his find, that he determined at once to publish a provisional description of the remains.

This monograph, which was necessarily incomplete, owing to the author's isolation from various sources of comparison and reference, has given rise to much discussion amongst anatomists and zoologists in Europe and America, and it was with the view of providing further information that Dr. Dubois had returned to Europe, bringing with him the specimens in question.

The lecturer then proceeded to furnish a more detailed account of the locality from which the remains were obtained.

In the neighborhood of Trinil the Bengawan or Solo River runs as far as Ngawi, a distance of 7½ miles, between steep banks, composed almost exclusively of the above-mentioned volcanic sand and lapilli, cemented together and hardened into soft rock, similar to those in the Siwalik hills. In this area the strata have a general dip south of about 5°, and are only concealed by a thin covering of vegetable mold; through these, in the immediate vicinity of Trinil, the river has cut its channel to a depth of 12 to 15 meters.

At points above and below Trinil, the Pliocene marl and limestone appear under these strata.

The first fossil bones here discovered were cut out of the rock by means of hammer and chisel, and consisted of the horn of a species of small deer, which is among the commonest of the fauna, a molar tooth of Stegodon, and a few other bones, all belonging to the same homogeneous fauna met with in other parts of the Keudeng Hills.

In making the excavations care was taken that the layers were removed one by one. They consisted from above downwards of alternately colored sandrock which became coarser owing to a greater admixture of lapilli especially in the deepest layer, which measured about one meter in thickness, and which merged below with a conglomerate layer. Under this there is a sharply defined layer of hardened blackish clay. In the sandrock the bones were found in increasing numbers from above down-wards, so that the lapilli layer contained the most; in the conglomerate layer but few were met with; whilst in the clay none were discovered.

It was in the lapilli layer on the left bank of the river, amidst hundreds of other skeletal remains, that the third molar tooth was found. This was in September, 1891; here also, a month later, on exactly the same

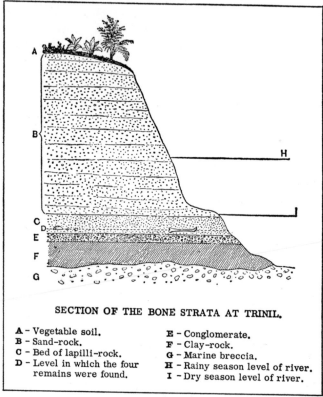

SECTION OF THE BONE STRATA AT TRINIL.

A – Vegetable soil.   E – Conglomerate.
B – Sand-rock.   F – Clay-rock.
C – Bed of lapilli-rock.   G – Marine breccia.
D – Level in which the four   H – Rainy season level of river.
    remains were found.   I – Dry season level of river.

Fig. 6

level in that layer the cranium was discovered at a point one meter distant from the spot where the tooth was picked up. The mammalian remains found in the same layer are for the most part those of extinct species, for it is almost certain that some of them are now living in Java.

These comprised the bones of a species of Cervus which still survives in the Malayan Isles. Many remains of Stegodon, besides some of a species of Bubalus apparently identical with the Siwalik species. At the same time a *Bos elephas* differing from the known species, living or fossil, was discovered. In addition the genera *Rhinoceros, Sus, Felis, Hyaena,* and others were represented, whilst a gavial and crocodile were found which differ somewhat from the existing species in India, were unearthed.

The setting in of the rainy season prevented the continuance of the excavations until next May, when work was resumed, with the result that in August, 1892, the left femur was discovered in precisely the same layer at a distance of 15 meters from the spot where the skullcap and molar tooth were found in the previous year.

In the October following a second molar tooth was discovered. This lay 3 meters from the place where the skullcap was picked up, in a direction towards the spot where the femur was found. This tooth was not described in Dr. Dubois' first monograph, as it was only subsequently met with among a number of teeth taken from the same place.

Of the remains of animals found in the same strata in other places, the most interesting are a gigantic pangolin (*Mauis*), three times as large as the existing Javanese species, a hippopotamus belonging to an extinct Siwalik sub-genus, a tapir, an elephas, and the extinct sub-genus leptobos.

These details as to the geological conditions under which the four bones were discovered were advanced to prove that they not only came from the same bed, most probably late Pliocene, but that they were all found at precisely the same level in it, hence most probably they must be of equal age. The fact that their contours are sharp is opposed to the view that they have been washed out of an older (later?) bed. Dr. Dubois therefore thought that there was little reason to doubt their origin from the rocky strata.

All the bones were in the same state of fossilization, harder than marble, very heavy, and of a chocolate-brown color. The femur was twice the weight of a recent human femur of the same dimensions. The erosion on the surface of the skullcap was not the result of disease as some critics have suggested, but was due to the corroding influence of the water, which had similarly affected all the bones found in this locality.

In discussing the question as to whether the bones belonged to the same individual or not, Dr. Dubois stated that in his opinion the distances apart at which they were found was no argument against their common origin. In his experience he had frequently found portions of the same skeleton as widely separated and, in some instances, fragments of the same bone were met with as far apart. Nor had he ever found anything like a complete skeleton which seemed to prove that the bones must have been widely scattered. Dr. Dubois advanced the theory that in all probability the remains were those of animals which had perished in volcanic catastrophes, their corpses being washed down in the course of a large Pliocene river. Most probably the bones, before they were deposited and buried in the old alluvia, were separated from one another by the rotting of the flesh or it may be together with the flesh were torn apart by crocodiles. In support of the latter view Dr. Dubois noted the fact that many remains of crocodiles were found as well as the marks of their teeth in the spongy parts of many fossil bones.

Considering the few examples there are of the fossil remains of anthropoid apes, and the absence of human remains from strata older than the middle Pleistocene, the lecturer urged that it was almost impossible to conceive that the thighbone now discovered, which most certainly belonged to the Tertiary Period, could be human, whilst the skull found alongside of it should be regarded as that of a great anthropoid ape, a supposition which would necessarily involve their separate origin; much more reasonable to him appeared the view that they belonged to one and the same intermediate form.

Dr. Dubois, in referring to his critics, divided them into two groups, the first, which included Professors Sir W. Turner, Cunningham, A. Keith, Lydekker, Paul Matschie, Rudolph Martin, and A. Pettit, held that the thighbone and the calvaria were human. The second group consisted of those who thought that the skull was simian and the femur human, and who further denied that there was any organic connection between them.

Only Professor Manouvrier of Paris, and Professor Marsh in America admitted the *possibility* of the remains belonging to a transition form between man and the apes.

In discussing the bones in detail, Dr. Dubois said most were agreed that the femur was human and not simian in character. Virchow alone was singular in maintaining the view that it belonged to the ape, most probably a Hylobates, and advanced in support of his opinion the fact that the bone had a straight candle-like shaft such as never occurs in man.

The lecturer however declined to agree with this conclusion, as he pointed out that the shaft of the bone was distinctly curved, though not to the same extent as is ordinarily met with in human femora. Further there could be little doubt that the fossil bone belonged to a form having an erect posture, and in this respect the condyles are quite human in their characters, contrasting markedly with those of Hylobates, which are distinctly simian.

Dr. Dubois, however, drew attention to three minor points of difference between the fossil bone and the typical human femur, and stated that after having examined a very large number of human femora of different races, he had been led to consider these three characters as marks of differentiation from the human femur. The points of difference referred to by the lecturer were—

1. The more rounded form of the shaft on its inner side.
2. A less extensive popliteal area which, moreover, is convex in its middle, thus imparting a rounded, instead of a flattened, form to the shaft in this situation.
3. A less raised and more simian-like trochanteric line.

Dr. Dubois laid particular stress on the small development of the popliteal space, the like of which he had never seen in a human femur, and pointed out that Dr. Hepburn had shown that in Hylobates the *vastus internus* muscle and the *femoral head* of the *biceps flexor cruris* came into close proximity to each other on the lower part of the posterior surface of the femur *below* the level of the insertion of the adductor magnus muscle. They are only separated from each other by a strong intermuscular septum, which extends to within an inch of the inner joint. By this means the superior part of the popliteal suface of the femur is rendered *convex,* and presents a median longitudinal elevation. An extension of these muscular attachments would exactly produce the appearances found in *Pithecanthropus erectus.*

Dr. Manouvrier too admitted that he had never seen a similar form of popliteal surface, though he had examined many thousands of specimens. Dr. Dubois, therefore, held that though the femur might be human, yet considering the circumstances under which it was found associated with an ape-like skull and simian teeth, he was justified in assuming that it was not human but belonged to an intermediate form. A form possibly like that of a gigantic gibbon, for it was only necessary to double the linear dimensions of the thigh bone and skull of an existing Hylobates to have dimensions exactly corresponding to the Java form.

In referring to the exostosis which is connected with the fossil bone behind the shaft just below the small trochanter, the lecturer stated that most were agreed that this pathological growth could have effected little if any change in the normal general form of the bone.

In regard to the skullcap there was much greater divergence of opinion. Cunningham, Turner, A. Keith, R. Martin, and Topinard regarded it as human. Lydekker thinks it that of a microcephalic idiot, whilst Krause, Waldeyer, Virchow, Hamy, Manouvrier, Flower, and Marsh denied the possibility of it being human, and regarded it as more probably that of an ape. The calvaria measures 185 mm. in length and 130 mm. in breadth; its cranial capacity has been estimated at 1,000 cc.

This is in marked contrast with the highest cranial capacities of the anthropoid apes, which never exceed 600 cc., and more usually measure about 500 cc. On the other hand many instances are met with among Australian Veddahs and Andamanese of a cranial capacity as low as 1,000 cc.

As the cranial capacity is doubtless correlated with the size of the body, Dr. Dubois pointed out that assuming the femur to belong to the skull, the height of the individual estimated from it according to human proportions would be 165 to 170 cm. Contrasting this with the height of Veddah women, which averages about 143 cm., we are justified in declining to admit the possibility of a skull with such a small capacity being human. The other alternative is that the skull is that of a microcephalic idiot; all things considered this is most improbable. It is far more likely, therefore, assuming the skull and femur to belong to the same individual that we have *not* to deal with a human cranium.

The Trinil skull in form and size very closely resembles the type of the anthropoid apes. The smallness of the arch of the vertex, the low receding forehead, the *torus occipitalis,* and the especially strong projection of the orbital parts of the frontal bones, are all simian characters. Further, the superior occipital ridge seems to unite with the posterior part of the temporal ridge, and forms a well marked swelling, common as a rule in the skulls of full grown apes, but never seen in human crania, not excepting those of microcephalic idiots.

Whilst admitting the close resemblance between the Trinil skull of the Neanderthal and Spy crania, Dr. Dubois drew attention to the difference in size and capacity between his specimen and those mentioned. The Neanderthal skull has an estimated capacity of 1230 cc., whilst its length and breadth exceeds the Trinil skull by about 15 mm., the same hold good with regard to the Spy crania. The most important points of difference between the Spy skulls and Dr. Dubois' specimen were the more marked flattening of the parietal region and the relatively greater dimensions of the orbital parts of the Java skull. The Trinil skull differed in similar respects from the microcephalic skull described by Professor Cunningham.

As Virchow has pointed out the orbital part of the Trinil skull is quite different from that of man, and on comparing the fossil calvaria with crania of the anthropoid apes, the proportion between the lengths of its orbital and cerebral parts is found to be exactly the same as in the skulls of gibbons. In Hylobates alone is the arch of the cranium as high as in Pithecanthropus. A further point of importance in the Trinil skull is the pronounced forward slope of the infra-inial part of the occiput; in this respect it differs little from the human form, and is much more marked than in the anthropoid apes, as the following figures show.

In the anthropoids the angle formed by the median line of the nuchal plane and the median line from the glabella to the hinder border of the foramen magnum varied from 83° to 86°, in *Semnopithecus maurus* it was 90°, in *Macacus cynomolgus* 106°. In man the angle is about 50°, in the No. 2 Spy skull 56°, in the microcephalic skull described by Cunningham it is 68°, whilst in Pithecanthropus it equals 65°.

In discussing the question of the teeth, one of which had been discovered since the publication of his memoir, Dr. Dubois stated there was much difference of opinion regarding their origin—Krause, Ten Kate, and Turner considered them simian, whilst R. Martin, Lyddeker, Cunningham, and Manouvrier inclined to the view that they were human. Both the teeth are modelled after exactly the same type, so that there is little ground for disputing the connection between them, the crenalion of the crowns is the same, and the dimensions are not dissimilar. The more recently discovered tooth was much more worn on the crown than the third molar previously found, but Dr. Dubois pointed out that it was not uncommon to find the second molars more worn than the third molars, so that this circumstance did not disprove the assumption that the two teeth belonged to the same individual.

Dr. Dubois considered that the teeth were not human, first on account of their great size and the divergent nature and length of their fangs, and secondly, because the *buccal* posterior cusp is in a state of retrogression, exactly as is seen in the case of the molars of anthropoid apes.

Summing up his arguments the lecturer said that on geological and anatomical grounds we were justified in assuming that we had in these four specimens evidence of a form intermediate between man and the anthropoid apes, and further, that it is exceedingly probable that the several bones all belonged to one and the same individual.

The concluding words of the lecture may be given *in extenso:*—

"I attempted to give here a diagrammatic representation of my views with reference to the phylogenetic evolution of man and the apes.

"In the Eocene, when the Old World and American mammal fauna were more nearly related, we have a hypothetical genus, Archipithecus, from which diversed a branch giving rise to the platyrrhine apes, the families Cebidae and Hapalidae. In the early Miocene, or perhaps, in the Upper Eocene, from a common hypothetical Palaeoceropithecus, the ancestor of the Old World apes, there branched off all the lower Old World apes, the Cercopithecidae. Afterwards in the Miocene, when the main stem had become more anthropoid, there branched off the Upper Miocene or Lower Pliocene from Dryopithecus, which in its characters is intermediate between the lower catarrhine apes and the man-like apes. Still later in the Miocene originated the hypothetical form Prothylobates, a very generalized form, which I regard as the ancestor of all the anthropoid apes and man. During the Middle and Upper Miocene, there originated from this stem-form first a branch giving rise to Pliopithecus, and the form from which we have the femur of Eppelsheim ('Dryopithecus' sec. Pohlig), which I call Pliohylobates; further, the existing genus Hylobates; secondly, branches giving rise to Simia and to Troglodytes and gorilla.

"Lastly, we have in the main stem, originating from Prothylobates, during the Lower Pliocene (or Upper Miocene) the Siwalik Palaeopithecus, which after a careful examination of the specimen in the Indian museum at Calcutta, on which the genus is founded, I regard as a decidedly Hylobatoid form, but approaching towards man. Between this form and man comes in the Upper Pliocene, Pithecanthropus, which, while still retaining many Hylobatoid characters, approaches, as I have tried to show, nearest of all to man, but cannot be placed in the genus *Homo*."

The following discussion took place on exhibition of the remains of *Pithecanthropus erectus* to a meeting of the Institute.

Sir WILLIAM FLOWER congratulated Dr. Dubois upon the results of his successful exploration in Java, resulting in the discovery of a large and interesting Mammalian fauna, and said that all present must feel particularly indebted to him for giving them an opportunity of inspecting the specimens he had exhibited that evening, and for the full and lucid explanation he had given of them. It was unfortunate that the fragmentary condition of the remains of *Pithecanthropus* was such as to leave much of its real nature open to conjecture. A comparison of the cranium with that of the Neanderthal man, showed a decidedly lower form, especially in the narrower frontal region. On the whole it presented, except in size, a remarkable resemblance to that of *Hylobates*.

Sir JOHN LUBBOCK also congratulated Dr. Dubois on his interesting discovery. He asked for some further details as to the position of the bones with reference to the remains of the Pliocene Mammalia, for in Dr. Dubois' original memoir this was not explained in detail. He also inquired whether the great amount of abnormal growth on the femur would not have considerably interfered with the movement of the animal. If so that would point to its being human. A man might well have been engaged in some sedentary occupation, or perhaps supported by his family. A monkey, however, was more dependent on retaining its activity unimpaired.

Mr. BLAND SUTTON was of opinion that the three specimens—calvaria, teeth, and femur—should be separately discussed. It was pure assumption to believe that they belonged to the same individuals. In regard to the teeth and calvaria he would not offer an opinion. The femur was undoubtedly human, and exhibited the muscular markings characteristic of a typical thighbone of a thoroughly adult man. The irregular bony mass connected with the shaft was such as is met with in that very rare disease known as *myositis ossificans,* which is characterized by extensive ossification of the tendons and tissues of muscles at their attachments. Thus it was curious that two sets of human remains, the Neanderthal and the Javan, which had given rise to much discussion, belonged to diseased skeletons; the Neanderthal fragments exhibited clear and undoubted evidence of rickets.

Mr. Sutton was of opinion that the attempt to form a new genus for these remains was at least premature, and the generalization as to the probable phylogeny of anthropoids and man based upon it, was one calculated to bring ridicule upon Anthropological Science.

Mr. E. T. NEWTON called attention to the fact that the bones of *Pithecanthropus* being, apparently, in a similarly mineralized condition to those of the extinct animals found in the same stratum, was strong evidence of their being of the same age. It was a noteworthy fact that so many observers were agreed as to the great similarity to *Hylobates* presented by the calvaria and femur of *Pithecanthropus*, and from the occurrence of the latter in beds where several of the forms were gigantic representations of living genera, nothing was more likely than that *Pithecanthropus* was a gigantic *Hylobates*. And still further, it was in *Hylobates*, rather than in the larger anthropoid apes, that many anatomists traced the greatest resemblance to Man.

Sir WILLIAM TURNER said: The opportunity which Dr. Dubois has given us of seeing his very interesting specimens and the fuller description of the conditions under which they were found, have enabled us to realize their characters and antiquity much more clearly than was possible from a perusal of his memoir published last year. The association of these specimens with bones and teeth of mammals, many of which are now extinct, and their correspondence with them in mineralization, shows them to be of undoubted antiquity, and if their human character is accepted, makes them rank as the most ancient human remains which have yet been discovered. As regards the thighbone, the opportunity of carefully examining it, both last week in Edinburgh, and now at this meeting, does not lead me to alter the opinion which I expressed in my published criticism of the original memoir, that there is nothing in its form and appearance which would lead one to say that it possessed characters specifically or generically distinct from those of a human thighbone, and in this respect my conclusion is in harmony with the opinions of many anatomists who have seen it. The bone is in various parts undoubtedly modified from disease; for in addition to the remarkable branched and pointed exostosis, there is evidence of a pathological growth of bone for some distance down the linea aspera, and of new bone growth around the posterior border of the articular area of the condyles. Clearly therefore increased periosteal bone formation had been taking place for some time before death, and it is not unlikely that the convexity of the popliteal surface of the bone, to which Dr. Dubois attaches so much importance as differentiating it from the human femur, may have been produced by increased periosteal activity in that region. Further it may be stated that there seems to be no prolongation of articular area on the back of the femur immediately above the inner condyle, such as Havelock Charles has associated with the squatting posture.

As regards the skullcap, now that one has seen it, there is more difficulty in coming to a conclusion. If, however, the thighbone and calvaria belong to the same skeleton, and Dr. Dubois, from his personal examination of the locality, has no doubt on this point, the establishment of the human character of the femur would require us to regard the calvaria as also human. Without question they were found in the same geological horizon and belong to the same epoch. The calvaria is less distinctively human than the Neanderthal skullcap which everyone now admits to be human. In the latter there is a forehead with rounded frontal eminences, but in the Java specimen the frontal bone is flattened and slopes abruptly backwards in a manner such as approximates it much more to the shape in the ape than to a human skull, even as low as the

Neanderthal; though I should state that in the Edinburgh University Museum is the cast of a microcephalic woman with a frontal flattening very like that of the Java calvaria. In the parietal region the Neanderthal and Java specimens have a great resemblance to each other, and both differ from the corresponding region in the ape by their considerable breadth and less rounded sides. In the occipital region, as Dr. Dubois testifies, the form is more human than ape-like. The internal capacity of 1,000 cc. is more like that of man than of the ape. No existing species of ape has a greater internal capacity than from 500 to 600 cc., whilst I and other anatomists have measured many human crania with a capacity of less than 1,100. As the capacity indicates the mass of the brain and its possibilities to exercise function both as a sensori-motor center and as the seat of intelligence, it will rest with those who regard this calvaria as belonging to a *Hylobates,* much larger than any existing species, to give a satisfactory explanation of the presence of so large a brain in an animal, which, if the thighbone belonged to the skull, had not the bulk of body of a large gorilla; in which animal the brain cavity does not reach 600 cc. The thighbone certainly cannot be regarded as that of *Hylobates.* In conclusion, may I express the thanks of anthropologists in this country to Dr. Dubois for his courtesy in bringing the specimens for our inspection, and further hope that the government of the Netherlands may continue the search for additional remains in the same locality.

Dr. GARSON said that he had studied Dr. Dubois' memoir on *Pithecanthropus erectus* very carefully and also the various criticisms of it which had been published. He was therefore extremely glad to see the specimens themselves, as they showed many morphological details of which the plates and diagrams gave but an imperfect idea; the paper also which Dr. Dubois had read that evening threw further light on the specimens. In the first instance he had been very uncertain as to the geological epoch to which they should be referred, but from the additional information Dr. Dubois had just given regarding the mammalian fauna found in the same formation with them, he was satisfied as to their being Pliocene. As regards the specimens themselves, although there was no absolute proof that they all belonged to the same skeleton, he did not think there was any positive proof to the contrary. Some authorities had urged, from a study of the plates, that the femur was less worn than the calvaria, but examination of the specimens themselves does not support this view. Again it had been said that the last molar tooth was little worn and therefore probably came from a younger cranium than that found. He had seen several instances, however, where the last molar was almost unworn while the other teeth of the series were considerably worn and the skull was thoroughly adult with the sutures obliterated, precisely as was shown by the calvaria and the other molar tooth recently added to the specimens now under consideration. The local conditions under which the specimens were found must have considerable weight in determining the question as to whether or not the several fragments belonged to the same individual; of these Dr. Dubois was in the most favorable position to judge.

The femur is extremely human-like, and if taken alone would undoubtedly be said to be that of *Homo*. The last molar tooth, also, might perhaps be ascribed to the same genus, as in a skull of an Australian native in the Royal College of Surgeons Museum he had found a last upper molar tooth measuring 16 mm. transversely and 11.4 mm. in the anteroposterior direction, which is even slightly larger than in the Javan specimen. The calvaria, on the other hand, is very different, and much more gibbon-like than one would imagine from the drawings of it. The large bony formation on the femur is very similar in size and character to what occurs in the femur of a skeleton of a man in the Pathological Collection of the College of Surgeons, except that in the latter specimen it is situated lower down on the shaft of the bone, and the ossification extends from the femur to the ischium; there are also several other ossifications of the muscular attachments and aponeuroses. The modification of the surfaces for the attachments of the muscles of the back of the thigh near the popliteal region of the femur from Java are interesting, but even if the bone be taken by itself, he was not certain as to their significance. The fact that a pathological condition of great rarity to the extent to which it obtains, is present in the femur, is apt to make one think it possible that an aberrant condition may also be present in the calvaria, and that it might have belonged to a microcephalic *Homo sapiens*. The probability of chances is, however, very much against such a combination of abnormalities occurring in the same individual. The characters of the calvaria also did not, to his mind, support such a conclusion. By these the specimen, if taken alone, might be ascribed to a large extinct *Hylobates,* although it should be remembered that in these large extinct forms the brain is proportionately smaller than in the recent, whereas in this specimen the capacity of the calvaria indicates as far as he could judge a proportionally larger brain. This then brings us to the hypothesis of Dr. Dubois, that the position which should be assigned to it is somewhere on a phylogenetic line between *Hylobates* and *Homo*. The characters of the femur and also of the molar tooth, particularly as regards its fangs, being in some respects different from those of *Homo sapiens,* and considering the strong opinion Dr. Dubois has formed from examination of the strata and the other mammalian remains therein contained, it is most reasonable to conclude that the specimens are probably parts of the skeleton of one animal, and that it belonged to one of those extinct species of primates more or less related to *Homo sapiens,* which there are strong *a priori* grounds to believe existed in Pliocene times. He was of opinion that the specimens could not be ascribed to either the genus *Homo* or species *sapiens,* but must be classed as another and distinct genus and species, but he did not think it necessary to create a new family of Primates for the specimens as their characters were sufficiently close to those of *Homo* to be included in the family Hominidae.

Mr. KEITH saw no reason for dissenting from Dr. Dubois' conclusion that these fossil remains belonged to a late Tertiary period. He thought Dr. Dubois was also right in regarding the remains as of one species, but it was open to question if of one individual. The third molar was slightly worn, the second considerably so; such a condition indicated an animal in an early stage of maturity. But the sutures of the calvaria were ossified; such a condition occurred only in the later stages of human life, very seldom in the earlier. It was true that ossification of the sutures began in the early stages of maturity of the apes' skull, but ossification was directly due to the great development of the temporal and occipital long ridges—a development absent in this calvaria. The sutures would therefore follow the course of ossification usually taken in the human skull, so that the teeth and calvaria evidently belonged to different individuals.

The chief question that had to be settled was, whether the skull was human or not. What was the criterion of a human skull? What was the criterion of an ape's skull? How were they to be distinguished? To his mind there were only two differences between the skulls of men and apes, and they were differences, not in kind, but in degree. The first difference was in the large excess of cranial capacity of the human skull; in the extent of its cranial capacity the skull before them merited to be called human. The second difference between the skulls of apes and men lay in the large development of muscular ridges and processes for the fixation of the masticatory apparatus; the development was extensive in apes; it was slight in men. In the extent of this development, also, the calvaria in question was distinctly human.

Dr. Dubois had placed *Pithecanthropus* directly in the stem of the human race, and regarded it as representing the human race during the late Tertiary period. *Pithecanthropus* was, in short, Pliocene man. He thoroughly agreed with Dr. Dubois as to the genealogical position of *Pithecanthropus,* but entirely differed from him as to his method of nomenclature. In fact, the question arose, where in the ancestry of the human race was one to draw a line to mark where pithecoid forms cease and men commence. Dr. Dubois had drawn that line between the Tertiary and Quaternary periods; but it seemed to him, that in the nomenclature of a race, the same principle should be followed as in the nomenclature of a human individual. The same name serves in infancy as in old age. Hence he thought it better to call Dr. Dubois' *Pithecanthropus erectus*—Pliocene Man.

Professor THOMSON said what struck him most was the very different complexion put upon the case, now that they had an opportunity of examining the actual specimens. This only went to prove how difficult it was to form any correct opinion on such a matter by the mere perusal of a monograph, however good. For his part all he felt justified in saying was that the calvaria was undoubtedly ape-like in all its characters, except in regard to its capacity: on the other hand the femur displayed all the features of a well-developed human thighbone.

He could not agree with Dr. Dubois in the arguments he advanced regarding the causation of this peculiar modelling of the popliteal surface, for it seemed to the speaker that the same arguments would apply equally well against Dr. Dubois' conclusions; for, according to his own showing, there was little difference between the popliteal surface in man and the chimpanzee, though in the latter the adductor magnus muscle was extensively attached to that surface.

Regarding the teeth Professor Thomson was not inclined to admit the impossibility of their being human, for an examination of Australian crania had led him to conclude that the size of the teeth was not sufficient to preclude the possibility that they were human molars.

As to whether or no the calvaria and thighbone belonged to the same individual was a matter of vital importance. Unfortunately the evidence advanced was not conclusive, and the only course left open at present was to reserve one's judgment. This, however, did not detract from the remarkable value of the discovery of this skull, which he regarded as by far the most important contribution to our knowledge of an intermediate form between man and the known apes.

Prof. G. D. THANE said the difficulty of forming an opinion upon the remains before the meeting is rendered very great by the circumstance that the indications afforded by the femur and by the calvaria are directly opposed to one another. The femur in its conformation is human, and of a high type. It is a question whether the peculiar features of the lower part of this bone referred to by Dr. Dubois may not be related to the pathological processes by which it has been affected. The individual to whom this femur belonged undoubtedly stood on the lower limbs only with the knee joint fully extended, as indicated by the designation *"erectus"* given by Dr. Dubois, possessed a great toe, and not an opposable hallux, and was therefore zoologically "man." The teeth are human in their characters, but peculiar in their large size and their spreading fangs. The calvaria, however, apart from its size, appears to resemble more nearly that of one of the higher apes than the corresponding part of a European skull, and approaches more closely to the former than the Neanderthal specimen. Probably its most pronounced simian feature is the form of the occiput. Assuming provisionally that the remains are from the same individual, judgment must be reserved in view of the isolated character of the find, since there is always the possibility of the calvaria belonging to an exception, or microcephalic individual of a well developed human variety. But, just as the racial character of the Neanderthal skull was established by the discoveries at Spy, so it may be hoped that in the future other specimens will be forthcoming which will establish the value of these as bringing before us a distant stage in the phylogeny of Man.

❋ ❋ ❋

The discovery in 1924 of a fossilized primate skull which was assigned the taxonomic name of Australopithecus africanus *("southern ape of Africa") offered something really new in the way of fossils. Since 1925 a number of new finds of the* Australopithecus *genus, as well as others, have been made. It is impossible to summarize here either the variety of types or the various views which authorities have held or now hold on them. Thus, the significance of these finds to the evolution of primate stock to man's relationship with the* Australopithecinae, *to their geological dating, or to the possibility that they were tool-makers and tool-users, is far from determined. It is enough to say that a whole new vista of human evolution was opened by the discovery of the* Australopithecus *skull. It has led to directed search for additional evidence both in South and East Africa, and within the last few years two new finds made by L. S. B. Leakey in Olduvai Gorge have produced the most ancient remains of man thus far discovered (see* National Geographic Magazine *for September, 1960 and October, 1961). For a general survey of the significance of the* Australopithecinae *for human evolution the reader is referred to W. E. Le Gros Clark, 1960, and Mayr, 1950.*

The First South African Manlike Ape

R. A. Dart

Towards the close of 1924, Miss Josephine Salmons, student demonstrator of anatomy in the University of the Witwatersrand, brought to me the fossilized skull of a cercopithecid monkey which, through her instrumentality, was very generously loaned to the Department for description by its owner, Mr. E. G. Izod, of the Rand Mines Limited. I learned that this valuable fossil had been blasted out of the limestone cliff formation—at a vertical depth of 50 feet and a horizontal depth of

"*Australopithecus africanus:* The Man-Ape of South Africa," by Raymond A. Dart. *Nature,* Vol. CXV (February 7, 1925), (London: Macmillan and Co., Ltd.), pp. 195-199. Reprinted by permission of Professor Raymond A. Dart and the editor of *Nature.*

200 feet—at Taungs, which lies 80 miles north of Kimberley on the main line to Rhodesia, in Bechuanaland, by operatives of the Northern Lime Company. Important stratigraphical evidence has been forthcoming recently from this district concerning the succession of stone ages in South Africa (Neville Jones, Jour. Roy. Anthrop. Inst., 1920), and the feeling was entertained that this lime deposit, like that of Broken Hill in Rhodesia, might contain fossil remains of primitive man.

I immediately consulted Dr. R. B. Young, professor of geology in the University of Witwatersrand, about the discovery, and he, by a fortunate coincidence, was called down to Taungs almost synchronously to investigate geologically the lime deposits of an adjacent farm. During his visit to Taungs, Prof. Young was enabled, through the courtesy of Mr. A. F. Campbell, general manager of the Northern Lime Company, to inspect the site of the discovery and to select further samples of fossil material for me from the same formation. These included a natural cercopithecid endocranial cast, a second and larger cast, and some rock fragments disclosing portions of bone. Finally, Dr. Gordon D. Laing, senior lecturer in anatomy, obtained news, through his friend Mr. Ridley Hendry, of another primate skull from the same cliff. This cercopithecid skull, the possession of Mr. De Wet, of the Langlaagte Deej Mine, has also been liberally entrusted by him to the Department for scientific investigation.

The cercopithecid remains placed at our disposal certainly represent more than one species of catarrhine ape. The discovery of Cercopithecidae in this area is not novel, for I have been informed that Mr. S. Haughton has in the press a paper discussing at least one species of baboon from this same spot. It is of importance that, outside of the famous Fayüm area, primate deposits have been found on the African mainland at Oldoway (Hans Reck, *Sitzungsbericht der Gesellsch. Naturforsch. Freunde*, 1914), on the shores of Victoria Nyanza (C. W. Andrews, *Ann. Mag. Nat. Hist.*, 1916), and in Bechuanaland, for these discoveries lend promise to the expectation that a tolerably complete story of higher primate evolution in Africa will yet be wrested from our rocks.

In manipulating the pieces of rock brought back by Prof. Young, I found that the larger natural endocranial cast articulated exactly by its fractured frontal extremity with another piece of rock in which the broken mandible was visible. After cleaning the rock mass, the outline of the hinder and lower part of the facial skeleton came into view. Careful development of the solid limestone in which it was embedded finally revealed the almost entire face . . .

It was apparent when the larger endocranial cast was first observed that it was specially important, for its size and sulcal pattern revealed sufficient similarity with those of the chimpanzee and gorilla to demonstrate that one was handling in this instance an anthropoid and not a cercopithecid ape. Fossil anthropoids have not hitherto been recorded south of the Fayüm in Egypt, and living anthropoids have not been discovered in recent times south of Lake Kivu region in the Belgian Congo, nearly 2000 miles to the north, as the crow flies.

All fossil anthropoids found hitherto have been known only from mandibular or maxillary fragments, so far as crania are concerned, and so the general appearance of the types they represented has been unknown; consequently, a condition of affairs where virtually the whole face and lower jaw, replete with teeth, together with the major portion of the brain pattern, have been preserved, constitutes a specimen of unusual value in fossil anthropoid discovery. Here, as in *Homo rhodesiensis*, Southern Africa has provided documents of higher primate evolution that are amongst the most complete extant.

Apart from this evidential completeness, the specimen is of importance because it exhibits an extinct race of apes *intermediate between living anthropoids and man.*

In the first place, the whole cranium displays *humanoid* rather than anthropoid lineaments. It is markedly dolichocephalic and leptoprosopic, and manifests in a striking degree the *harmonious relation* of calvaria to face emphasized by Pruner-Bey. As Topinard says, "A cranium elongated from before backwards, and at the same time elevated, is already in harmony by itself; but if the face, on the other hand, is elongated from above downwards, and narrows, the harmony is complete." I have assessed roughly the difference in the relationship of the glabella-gnathion facial length to the glabella-inion calvarial length in recent African anthropoids of an age comparable with that of this specimen (depicted in Duckworth's "Anthropology and Morphology," second edition, vol. i.), and find that, if the glabella-inion length be regarded in all three as 100, then the glabella-gnathion length in the young chimpanzee is approximately 88, in the young gorilla 80, and in this fossil 70, which proportion suitably demonstrates the enhanced relationship of cerebral length to facial length in the fossil.

The glabella is tolerably pronounced, but any traces of the salient supra-orbital ridges, which are present even in immature living anthropoids, are here entirely absent. Thus the relatively increased glabella-inion measurement is due to brain and not to bone. Allowing 4 mm. for the bone thickness in the inion region, that measurement in the fossil is 127 mm.; i.e., 4 mm. less than the same measurement in an adult chimpanzee in the Anatomy Museum at the University of the Witwatersrand. The orbits are not in any sense detached from the forehead, which rises steadily from their margins in a fashion amazingly human. The interorbital width is very small (13 mm.) and the ethmoids are not blown out laterally as in modern African anthropoids. This lack of ethmoidal expansion causes the lacrimal fossae to face posteriorly and to lie relatively far back in the orbits, as in man. The orbits, instead of being subquadrate as in anthropoids, are almost circular, furnishing an orbital index of 100, which is well within the range of human variation (Topinard, "Anthropology"). The malars, zygomatic arches, maxillae, and mandible all betray a delicate and humanoid character. The facial prognathism is relatively slight, the gnathic index of Flower giving a value of 109, which is scarcely greater than that of certain Bushmen (Strandloopers) examined by Shrubsall. The nasal bones are not prolonged below the level of the lower orbital margins, as in anthropoids, but end above these, as in man, and are incompletely fused together in their lower half. Their maximum length (17 mm.) is not so great as that of the nasals in *Eoanthropus dawsoni.* They are depressed in the median line, as in the chimpanzee, in their lower half, but it seems probable that this depression has occurred post-mortem, for the upper half of each bone is arched forwards. The nasal aperture is small and is just wider than it is high (17 mm. x 16 mm.). There is no nasal spine, the floor of the nasal cavity being continuous with the anterior aspects of the alveolar portions of the maxillae, after the fashion of the chimpanzee and of certain New Caledonians and negroes.

In the second place, the dentition is *humanoid* rather than anthropoid. The specimen is juvenile, for the first permanent molar tooth only has erupted in both jaws on both sides of the face; i.e., it corresponds anatomically with a human child of six years of age. Observations upon the milk dentition of living primates are few, and only one molar tooth of the deciduous dentition in one fossil anthropoid is known (Gregory, "The Origin and Evolution of the Human Dentition," 1920). Hence the data for the necessary comparisons are meager, but certain striking features of the milk dentition of this creature may be mentioned. The tips of the canine teeth transgress very slightly (0.5-0.75 mm.) the general margin of the teeth in each jaw, i.e., very little more than does the human milk canine. There is no diastema whatever between the premolars and canines on either side of the lower jaw, such as is present in the deciduous dentition of living anthropoids; but the canines in this jaw come, as in the human jaw, into alignment with the incisors (Gregory, *loc. cit.*). There is a diastema (2 mm. on the right side, and 3 mm. on the left side) between the canines and lateral incisors of the upper jaw; but seeing, first, that the incisors are narrow, and, secondly, that diastemata (1 mm.-1.5 mm.) occur between the central incisors of the upper jaw and between the medial and lateral incisors of both sides in the lower jaw, and, thirdly, that some separation of the milk teeth takes place even in mankind (Tomes, "Dental Anatomy," seventh edition) during the establishment of the permanent dentition, it is evident that the diastemata which occur in the upper jaw are small. The lower canines, nevertheless, show wearing facets, both for the upper canines and for the upper lateral incisors.

The incisors as a group are irregular in size, tend to overlap one another, and are almost vertical, as in man; they are not symmetrical and well spaced, and do not project forwards markedly, as in anthropoids. The upper lateral incisors do project forwards to some extent and perhaps also do the upper central incisors very slightly, but the lateral lower incisors betray no evidence of forward projection, and the central lower incisors are not even vertical as in most races of mankind, but are directed slightly backwards, as *sometimes* occurs in man. Owing to these remarkably human characters displayed by the deciduous dentition, when contour tracings of the upper jaw are made, it is found that the jaw and the teeth, as a whole, take up a parabolic arrangement comparable only with that presented by mankind amongst the higher primates. These facts, together with the more minute anatomy of the teeth, will be illustrated and discussed in the memoir which is in the process of elaboration concerning the fossil remains.

In the third place, the mandible itself is *humanoid* rather than anthropoid. Its ramus is, on the whole, short and slender as compared with that of anthropoids, but the bone itself is more massive than that of a human being of the same age. Its symphyseal region is virtually complete and reveals anteriorly a more vertical outline than is found in anthropoids or even in the jaw of Piltdown man. The anterior symphyseal surface is scarcely less vertical than that of Heidelberg man. The posterior symphyseal surface in living anthropoids differs from that of modern man in possessing a pronounced posterior prolongation of the lower border, which joins together the two halves of the mandible, and so forms the well-known *simian shelf* and above it a deep genial impression for the attachment of the tongue musculature. In this character, *Eoanthropus dawsoni* scarcely differs from the anthropoids, especially the chimpanzee; but this new fossil betrays no evidence of such a shelf, the lower border of the mandible having been massive and rounded after the fashion of the mandible of *Homo heidelbergensis*.

That hominid characters were not restricted to the face in this extinct primate group is borne out by the relatively forward situation of the foramen magnum. The position of the basion can be assessed within a few millimeters of error, because a portion of the right exoccipital is present alongside the cast of the basal aspect of the cerebellum. Its position is such that the basi-prosthion measurement is 89 mm., while the basi-inion measurement is at least 54 mm. This relationship may be expressed in the form of a "head-balancing" index of 60.7. The same index in a baboon provides a value of 41.3, in an adult chimpanzee 50.7, in Rhodesian man 83.7, in a dolichocephalic European 90.9, and in a brachycephalic European 105.8. It is significant that this index, which indicates in a measure the poise of the skull upon the vertebral column, points to the assumption by this fossil group of an attitude appreciably more erect than that of modern anthropoids. The improved poise of the head, and the better posture of the whole body framework which accompanied this alteration in the angle at which its dominant member was supported, is of great significance. It means that a greater reliance was being placed by this group upon the feet as organs of progression, and that the hands were being freed from their more primitive function of accessory organs of locomotion. Bipedal animals, their hands were assuming a higher evolutionary role not only as delicate tactual, examining organs which were adding copiously to the animal's knowledge of its physical environment, but also as instruments of the growing intelligence in carrying out more elaborate, purposeful, and skilled movements, and as organs of offence and defence. The latter is rendered the more probable, in view, first, of their failure to develop massive canines and hideous features, and secondly, of the fact that even living baboons and anthropoid apes can and do use sticks and stones as implements and as weapons of offence ("Descent of Man," p. 81 *et seq.*).

Lastly, there remains a consideration of the endocranial cast which was responsible for the discovery of the face. The cast comprises the right cerebral and cerebrellar hemispheres (both of which fortunately meet the median line throughout their entire dorsal length) and the anterior portion of the left cerebral hemisphere. The remainder of the cranial cavity seems to have been empty, for the left face of the cast is clothed with a picturesque lime crystal deposit; the vacuity in the left half of the cranial cavity was probably responsible for the fragmentation of the specimen during blasting. The cranial capacity of the specimen may best be appreciated by the statement that the length of the cavity could not have been less than 114 mm., which is 3 mm. greater than that of an adult chimpanzee in the Museum of the Anatomy Department in the University of the Witwatersrand, and only 14 mm. less than the greatest length of the cast of the endocranium of a gorilla chosen for casting on account of its great size. Few data are available concerning the expansion of brain matter which takes place in the living anthropoid brain between the time of eruption of the first permanent molars and the time of their becoming adult. So far as man is concerned, Owen ("Anatomy of Vertebrates," vol. iii) tells us that "The brain has advanced to near its term of size at about ten years, but it does not usually obtain its full development till between twenty and thirty years of age." R. Boyd (1960) discovered an increase in weight of nearly 250 grams in the brains of male human beings after they had reached the age of seven years. It is therefore reasonable to believe that the adult forms typified by our present specimen possessed brains which were larger than that of this juvenile specimen, and equalled, if they did not actually supersede, that of the gorilla in absolute size.

Whatever the total dimensions of the adult brain may have been, there are not lacking evidences that the brain in this group of fossil forms was distinctive in type and was an instrument of greater intelligence than that of living anthropoids. The face of the endocranial cast is scarred unfortunately in several places. It is evident that the relative proportion of cerebral to cerebellar matter in this brain was greater than in the gorilla's. The brain does not show that general pre- and post-Rolandic flattening characteristic of the living anthropoids, but presents a rounded and well-filled-out contour, which points to a symmetrical and balanced development of the faculties of associative memory and intelligent activity. The pithecoid type of parallel sulcus is preserved, but the sulcus lunatus has been thrust backwards towards the occipital pole by a pronounced general bulging of the parieto-temporo-occipital association areas.

To emphasize this matter, I have reproduced superimposed coronal contour tracings taken at the widest part of the parietal region in the gorilla endocranial cast and in this fossil. Nothing could illustrate better the mental gap that exists between living anthropoid apes and the group of creatures which the fossil represents than the flattened atrophic appearance of the parietal region of the brain (which lies between the visual field on one hand, and the tactile and auditory fields on the other) in the former and its surgent vertical and dorso-lateral expansion in the latter. The expansion in this area of the brain is significant in that it explains the posterior *humanoid* situation of the sulcus lunatus. It indicates (together with the narrow interorbital interval and human characters of the orbit) the fact that this group of beings, having acquired the faculty of stereoscopic vision, had profited beyond living anthropoids by setting aside a relatively much larger area of the cerebral cortex to serve as a storehouse of information concerning their objective environment as its details were simultaneously revealed to the senses of vision and touch, and also of hearing. They possessed to a degree unappreciated by living anthropoids the use of their hands and ears and the consequent faculty of associating with the color, form, and general appearance of objects, their weight, texture, resilience, and flexibility, as well as the significance of sounds emitted by them. In other words, their eyes saw, their ears heard, and their hands handled objects with greater meaning and to fuller purpose than the corresponding organs in recent apes. They had laid down the foundations of that discriminative knowledge of the appearance, feeling, and sound of things that was a necessary milestone in the acquisition of articulate speech.

There is, therefore, an ultrasimian quality of the brain depicted in this immature endocranial cast which harmonizes with the ultrasimian features revealed by the entire cranial topography and corroborates the various inferences drawn therefrom. The two thousand miles of territory which separate this creature from its nearest living anthropoid cousins is indirect testimony to its increased intelligence and mastery of its environment. It is manifest that we are in the presence here of a prehuman stock, neither chimpanzee nor gorilla, which possesses a series of differential characters not encountered hitherto in any anthropoid stock. This complex of characters exhibited is such that it cannot be interpreted as belonging to a form ancestral to any living anthropoid. For this reason, we may be equally confident that there can be no question here of a primitive anthropoid stock such as has been recovered from the Egyptian Fayüm. Fossil anthropoids, varieties of Dryopithecus, have been retrieved in many parts of Europe, Northern Africa, and Northern India, but the present specimen, despite its youth, cannot be confused with anthropoids having the dryopithecid dentition. Other fossil anthropoids from the Siwalik hills in India (Miocene and Pliocene) are known which, according to certain observers, may be ancestral to modern anthropoids and even to man.

Whether our present fossil is to be correlated with the discoveries made in India is not yet apparent; that question can only be solved by a careful comparison of the permanent molar teeth from both localities. It is obvious, meanwhile, that it represents a fossil group distinctly advanced beyond living anthropoids in those two dominantly human characters of facial and dental recession on one hand, and improved quality of the brain on the other. Unlike Pithecanthropus, it does not represent an ape-like man, a caricature of precocious hominid failure, but a creature well advanced beyond modern anthropoids in just those characters, facial and cerebral, which are to be anticipated in an extinct link between man and his simian ancestor. At the same time, it is equally evident that a creature with anthropoid brain capacity and lacking the distinctive, localized temporal expansions which appear to be concomitant with and necessary to articulate man, is no true man. It is therefore logically regarded as a man-like ape. I propose tentatively, then, that a new family of *Homo-simiadae* be created for the reception of the group of individuals which it represents, and that the first known species of the group be designated *Australopithecus africanus,* in commemoration, first, of the extreme southern and unexpected horizon of its discovery, and, secondly, of the continent in which so many new and important discoveries connected with the early history of man have recently been made, thus vindicating the Darwinian claim that Africa would prove to be the cradle of mankind.

It will appear to many a remarkable fact that an ultrasimian and prehuman stock should be discovered, in the first place, at this extreme southern point in Africa, and, secondly, in Bechuanaland, for one does not associate with the present climatic conditions obtaining on the eastern fringe of the Kalahari desert an environment favorable to higher primate life. It is generally believed by geologists (*vide* A. W. Rogers, "Post-Cretaceous Climates of South Africa," *South African Journal of Science,* vol. xix, 1922) that the climate has fluctuated within exceedingly narrow limits in this country since Cretaceous times. We must therefore conclude that it was only the enhanced cerebral powers possessed by this group which made their existence possible in this untoward environment.

In anticipating the discovery of the true links between the apes and man in tropical countries, there has been a tendency to overlook the fact that, in the luxuriant forests of the tropical belts, Nature was supplying with profligate and lavish hand an easy and sluggish solution, by adaptive specialization, of the problem of existence in creatures so well equipped mentally as living anthropoids are. For the production of man a different apprenticeship was needed to sharpen the wits and quicken the higher manifestations of intellect—a more open veldt country where competition was keener between swiftness and stealth, and where adroitness of thinking and movement played a preponderating role in the preservation of the species. Darwin has said, "no country in the world abounds in a greater degree with dangerous beasts than Southern Africa," and, in my opinion, Southern Africa, by providing a vast open country with occasional wooded belts and a relative scarcity of water, together with a fierce and bitter mammalian competition, furnished a laboratory such as was essential to this penultimate phase of human evolution.

In Southern Africa, where climatic conditions appear to have fluctuated little since Cretaceous times, and where ample dolomitic formations have provided innumerable refuges during life, and burial-places after death, for our troglodytic forefathers, we may confidently anticipate many complementary discoveries concerning this period in our evolution.

In conclusion, I desire to place on record my indebtedness to Miss Salmons, Prof. Young, and Mr. Campbell, without whose aid the discovery would not have been made; to Mr. Len Richardson for providing the photographs; to Dr. Laing and my laboratory staff for their willing assistance; and particularly to Mr. H. Le Helloco, student demonstrator in the Anatomy Department, who has prepared the illustrations for this preliminary statement.

✳ ✳ ✳

The Calaveras skull, discovered in 1886, was one of the most notorious archaeological hoaxes perpetrated in the nineteenth century. J. D. Whitney, an eminent American geologist, had been appointed to carry out a geological survey of California. He believed the skull was authentic and considered it a reliable example of Tertiary man. Later inquiry (summarized by Holmes, 1901, and Hrdlička, 1907) produced evidence that the skull was a recent one, first found in a nearby Indian burial ground and then secretly taken into the mine by one of the workers and left there as a joke. The skull was taken by many to be evidence of a fully developed human type dating from the Pliocene. The reader who has followed the contents of this volume thus far will understand that in the absence of any geologically dated human fossils discovered by 1886 there seemed nothing impossible about the claim of a human skull from late Tertiary (Pliocene) deposits. While we do not know precisely why the skull was "planted" in the bottom of the mine, the idea may have been suggested by the wide attention and interest that the Neanderthal skull received in the popular press and among scientists. It may also have been suggested by the Natchez remains, discovered in 1844, which became widely known through the writings of Sir Charles Lyell (1863:200-205; see also Hrdlička, 1907:15-19). A bibliography of works written about the Calaveras skull can be found in Heizer (1948), and a history of archaeological hoaxes is presented by Munro (1905) and Vayson de Pradenne (1932).

The Calaveras Hoax

J. D. Whitney

This skull was taken from a shaft sunk on a mining claim at Altaville, near Angel's [Camp], in Calaveras County, by Mr. James Matson. By him it was given to Mr. Scribner, of Angel's, and by Mr. Scribner to Dr. [Thomas] Jones. Mr. Matson states that the skull was found at a depth of about one hundred and thirty feet, in a bed of gravel five feet in thickness, above which are four beds of consolidated volcanic ash, locally known as "lava"; these volcanic beds are separated from each other by layers of gravel, and Mr. Matson gives the following as the section of the various deposits passed through in sinking the shaft, which is one hundred and fifty-three feet deep, to the bed rock:

1.	Black lava	40	feet
2.	Gravel	3	"
3.	Light lava	30	"
4.	Gravel	5	"
5.	Light lava	15	"
6.	Gravel	25	"
7.	Dark brown lava	9	"
8.	Gravel	5	"
9.	Red lava	4	"
10.	Red gravel	17	"

153 feet

The skull was found, according to Mr. Matson, in bed number 8, just above the lowest stratum of lava. With the skull were found fragments of silicified wood, the whole being covered and partly incrusted with stony matter, so that the fact of its being a skull was not recognized until

"Notice of a Human Skull, Recently Taken from a Shaft near Angel's, Calaveras County," by J. D. Whitney. Proceedings of the California Academy of Natural Sciences, Vol. III (1863-1867), pp. 277-278, paper read at regular meeting, July 18, 1866.

after it had passed into Mr. Scribner's hands, by whom it was cleaned and presented to Dr. Jones.

The skull is said by Mr. Matson to have been taken from the shaft February 25th, 1866, and it came into my hands in the July following, when I immediately proceeded to the locality; but found the shaft temporarily abandoned and partly filled with water, so that it was impossible at that time to make any further search in the bed from which the skull was procured. A careful inquiry into all the circumstances of the alleged discovery, and an interview with all the persons who had been in any way connected with it, impressed upon my mind the conviction that the facts were as stated above, and that there was every reason to believe that the skull really came from the position assigned to it by Mr. Matson. Still, as it is evidently highly desirable that as large an amount of evidence as possible should be accumulated in regard to a discovery of so much importance, I made arrangements that I should be notified whenever the shaft was reopened and the water taken out, and hope at a future meeting to be able to lay before the Academy the results of a personal examination of this interesting locality, and of further excavations in the bed from which the skull was taken.

Assuming the correctness of Mr. Matson's statements, this relic of human antiquity is easily seen to be an object of the greatest interest to the ethnologist as well as the geologist. The previous investigations of the Geological Survey have clearly demonstrated the fact that man was contemporaneous with the mastodon and elephant, since the works of his hands have been repeatedly found in such connection with the bones of these animals that it would be impossible to account for the facts observed in any other theory. (See Geology of California, Vol. I, p. 252.) But in the case of the skull now laid before the Academy, the geological position to which it must be assigned is, apparently, still lower than that of the mastodon, since the remains of this animal, as well as the elephant, which are so abundantly scattered over the State, are always (so far as our observations yet extend) limited in their position to the superficial deposits, and have never been found at any considerable depth below the surface. There is every reason to believe that these great proboscidians lived at a very recent date, (geologically speaking) and posterior to the epoch of the existence of glaciers in the Sierra Nevada, and also after the close of the period of activity of the now extinct volcanoes of that great chain. In fact, they belong to the present epoch. The bed, on the other hand, in which this skull was found, must have been deposited at a time when the volcanoes of the Sierra were still in vigorous action, and, as seems to us highly probable from a careful consideration of the geological structure of the region, previous to the glacial epoch of the Sierra, and also previous to the erosion of the cañons of the present rivers. No pains will be spared, however, to investigate all the conditions of the occurrence of this skull, and they will be fully reported on at a future time.

The portions of the skull which are preserved are, the frontal bone, the nasal bone, the superior maxillary bone of the right side, the malar bones, a part of the temporal bone of the left side, with the mastoid process and the zygomatic process, and the whole of the orbits of both eyes. The base of the skull is embedded in a mass of bone breccia and small pebbles of volcanic rock, incrusted with a thin layer of carbonate of lime, which appears once to have extended over the whole surface of the skull and of which a considerable portion still remains, the rest having been removed apparently in the process of cleaning. Under the malar bone of the left side, a snail shell is lodged, and partly concealed by the breccia of bone wedged in the cavity. This shell is the *Helix Mormonum*, according to Dr. Cooper, a species now living in the region where the skull was obtained. Although not competent to express a decided opinion on the subject of the ethnological relations of this skull, I should suppose that it belonged to the type of Indians now inhabiting the foothills of the Sierra. It is certain that the facial angle is not one indicating a low order of intellect. The skull, however, seems to have been very thick and solid. It will be placed in the hands of competent craniologists for examination and description, as soon as reliable information has been obtained with regard to its occurrence, or whenever all has been ascertained that can be.

❊ 4 ❊

SOME EARLY COLLECTORS

Greek and Roman interest in the past as evidenced by antiquities was limited largely to collecting items which referred either to actual heroes or mythological personages. There was, therefore, no intellectual interest in archaeology as a means of studying the past. The Greek and Roman past was adequately explained by their mythology.

❊ ❊ ❊

The Greeks and Romans as Archaeologists

A. J. B. Wace

Among all the records of Greece and Rome that have come down to us we do not find many instances of what we might term archaeology. Certainly there is no systematic archaeology or anything in the nature of a scientific approach to archaeological problems. Art criticism there was. Sculptors of note like Polyclitus and Lysippus wrote on the canons of proportion. Authors such as Antigonus of Carystus and Xenocrates of Athens were art historians and art critics. Lucian, who was a sculptor, also

"The Greeks and Romans as Archaeologists," by Alan J. B. Wace. Société Royale d'Archéologie d'Alexandrie, *Bulletin No. 38*, (Alexandria, 1949) pp. 21-35. Reprinted by permission of the Société Royale d'Archéologie d'Alexandrie and Mrs. Helen Wace.

wrote on art at a later date. In their interest in days gone by the Greeks and Romans were principally attracted by what are generally termed antiquities. Such antiquities, however, were rather those of language, of religious practice, and of civil institutions. These were the questions which most interested the authors whose works survive, at least in part, Plutarch, Varro, and Aulus Gellius. Ovid in his *Fasti* is mainly concerned with religious affairs. Vitruvius made notes and observations on earlier buildings, but took a constructional rather than an antiquarian interest in them. Dionysius of Halicarnassus preferred literary or linguistic antiquities.

The Greeks and Romans knew well, of course, that there had been men on this earth long before their times and that they had left some monuments of themselves and traces of their presence. Hesiod and Ovid both detail the succession of the four ages through which man was believed to have passed. The Golden Age came first, naturally, and then followed that of Silver. To these succeeded in turn the Ages of Bronze and of Iron. This succession was more or less generally accepted. The ancients believed that mankind was not necessarily progressing in civilization, virtue, and comfort, but that each succeeding age was worse than its predecessor. Hesiod puts the age of the heroes celebrated by Homer in the period between the Age of Bronze and that of Iron. In other words, he came remarkably near the period which modern archaeologists would now assign to the Trojan War.

Both Greeks and Romans were well aware of the existence of ruined cities, of rifled tombs, of desecrated temples, and of great fortresses built by mighty men of old. Pausanias for instance records the belief that the great walls of Mycenae and Tiryns were built by the Cyclopes, and in Athens and elsewhere early walls of great rough blocks of stone were known as Pelasgian. The identification of the Pelasgians, that mysterious race which the Greeks credited with so many antiquities of all kinds, still eludes modern scholars. The Greeks realized that there had been other men and other races on earth and in their own lands before them, but they never seem to have advanced further than the recording of legends and traditions. Little or no effort seems ever to have been made to verify traditions by actual research on the ancient monuments, or to subject legends to a critical or comparative study. Thucydides, it is true, in the beginning of his first book, does give one of the few instances where archaeological evidence is employed to test the truth of a story. In speaking of the purification of Delos, when the Athenians removed all the burials from the sacred island to Rheneia opposite, he says that they recognized certain tombs as those of Carians by their armor and weapons, since these were like those of the Carians of his own time. This confirmed for Thucydides and the Athenians the tradition that the islands had once been occupied by Carians, a tradition which we now know is archaeologically possible.

A case such as this is exceptional. Pausanias expresses the opinion that the heroes used bronze weapons and confirms this by an appeal to Homer who says that the axe of Peisander and the arrow of Meriones were of bronze. He then quotes what is practically archaeological evidence and remarks that the spear of Achilles in the temple of Athena at Phaselis was of bronze and of bronze also was the knife of Memnon in the temple of Asclepius at Nicomedia. With this we cannot quarrel and modern research agrees that the age depicted by Homer was essentially an age of bronze.

The reference to objects preserved in temples is interesting. The treasure chambers of Greek temples, in addition to the actual treasures of coin and precious metal that they contained, were also full of miscellaneous objects of all kinds which had been dedicated from time to time to the god or goddess. They were in a sense museums of curiosities and antiquities. When we also take into consideration the sculptures and paintings that adorned Greek sanctuaries we realize that these collections of antiquities and works of art might perhaps in other circumstances have developed into something resembling modern museums and art galleries.

In the Parthenon was Xerxes' throne. In the temple of Athena at Lindus and in that of Hera at Samos were linen tunics or corslets decorated with tapestry woven ornament, apparently, which had been dedicated by Amasis, King of Egypt. Pliny records that Mucianus a Roman commander who wrote a book on *mirabilia* and travelled in the Aegean said that the corslet at Lindus had been almost worn to pieces by visitors touching it. In the temple of Hera at Sybaris was kept the tunic of Alkisthenes which seems to have been an exceptionally fine example of Near Eastern tapestry weaving. Another famous textile was the cloak said to have been woven by Helikon, the weaver of legendary fame, which Plutarch says the Rhodians presented to Alexander the Great.

Some of the temple dedications were works of art like the textiles just mentioned, and some were intrinsically valuable owing to their material, but many of the dedications in temples were of comparatively small value and importance and would be regarded by us more as curios. We have many inscriptions from several famous sanctuaries giving long lists of the sacred treasures. The inventories of the Parthenon at Athens mentioned Persian swords plated with gold, presumably dedications of spoils taken in the Persian War. Those of the sanctuary of Asclepius at Athens include many golden eyes, presumably offerings from grateful worshippers whom the god had cured of diseases of the eyes. The inventories of the temple of Artemis Brauronia at Athens give long lists of clothes dedicated to the goddess and many of the items are noted as being tattered. The inventories of the great sanctuary of Apollo at Delos are most interesting and give a most vivid idea of what a temple treasury contained. Precious metals predominate of course, but there are many curious offerings as well. The dedications were kept on shelves or stands which were numbered so that the objects could be easily located. Some things were kept in boxes or chests. The exact position in the temple is given and objects hanging on the wall for instance are often mentioned. The offerings themselves were vessels of gold, silver, and bronze of all shapes and sizes and the gold and silver objects are nearly always recorded by their weight. There are pictures, lamps, jewellery, censers, braziers. Minute descriptions are given: the golden statuette with no legs or arms; a bronze jug with one handle, but no bottom; footbaths, two of which are not sound; a cow without its left horn. In a list of wooden beds so many are listed as new, so many as old, and others as needing repair. We come across the works of Alcaeus in a three cornered case, or Cretan bows with their quivers. Everything was listed and catalogued down to small scraps of gold and silver. In fact on reading one of these lists we are reminded of museum storerooms with their shelves and labels and stands and objects hanging on the wall. Yet though they had these ready made museums, so to speak, at hand, the Greeks and the Romans seem to have made little or no attempt to study the older offerings. In our eyes the archaeological value of such collections would be immense and we can only regret that the ancient Greeks and Romans did not themselves study these treasures scientifically and critically.

The Romans in their temples and public buildings had antiques of great value and interest. In the temple of Semo Sanctus was a wooden shield covered with oxhide on which was written in old characters a treaty concluded by Tarquinius Superbus with Gabii. In the Regia were the *ancilia,* the shields of the Salii the dancing priests of Mars. In the Capitol were the Sibylline books and the list could be much prolonged. The Romans, however, have left us nothing even approaching a scientific account of these objects which would be of extraordinary value to us. In Latin literature there are many references to the sacred stone of Cybele, the Great Mother, which was brought to Rome in 204 B.C. when her worship was established in the city. No Latin author, however, has left us any good description of the stone which seems to have been a meteorite venerated as a fetish. Livy records a tradition about the tomb of Aeneas, but no investigation of it ever seems to have been attempted. Similarly the *Casa Romuli* on the Palatine and the *Niger Lapis* on the Comitum were taken at their face value, so to speak, and no efforts, so far as we know, were ever made to verify the truth of the legends about them by excavation or other archaeological methods.

As just remarked, practical archaeological research by excavation and kindred methods to solve a problem or to investigate something not understood was rarely employed by the ancients. The most usual form of such research was an attempt to find buried treasure, real or imaginary, and the discovery of the bones of heroes which somewhat like the relics of saints in medieval Europe would be conveyed to some city where they would be venerated and regarded as a kind of palladium.

A well known instance of this is connected with the bones of Theseus. He was naturally worshipped in Athens as one of the great Athenian national heroes, but his grave was reputed to be in the island of Skyros where he had been treacherously killed by King Lycomedes. The Athenians were told by an oracle that they must bring his bones back home. They had not long conquered and colonized Lemnos and were anxious to occupy Skyros too. They asked permission of the islanders to look for Theseus' tomb. The islanders made difficulties or so the Athenians asserted. This gave the Athenians an excuse for reducing the island, expelling the population, and peopling it with Athenian colonists. Cimon, the great Athenian general and statesman, conducted a long and patient search for the tomb. At last he noticed one day an eagle pecking at the ground and tearing at it with its talons. He dug there and found the grave of a tall warrior buried with a bronze spear and sword beside him. This was obviously the grave of Theseus. So he brought these relics with great ceremony to Athens where they were deposited in one of the shrines dedicated to the national hero.

In Greece today when an ancient grave is found the bones always seem to the modern people to be of great size and they are often described as those of giants. . . .

Another case is connected with Sparta and her long struggle with Tegea. The Spartans in the course of their seemingly endless and inconclusive war against the Tegeans had great difficulty in getting the advantage. So they sought the advice of the Delphic oracle and were told to bring home the tomb of Orestes to Sparta. They sought everywhere, but could not find the tomb and appealed to the oracle again. The oracle replied with some mysterious verses rather like the clues in a treasure hunt. They indicated that the tomb was in Tegea, but the meaning was by no means clear. The tomb was said to be where twin winds are always blowing, where shock answers shock, and anguish is piled on anguish. Sparta was then at peace with Tegea and so a Spartan named Lichas was sent to see what he could discover. On arrival at Tegea he happened to go into a smithy and watched the blacksmith at work and was much struck with his operations, and said so. The blacksmith said that his work was nothing to cause wonder, but what he had recently found in digging a well in his courtyard was something to cause wonder. He had found a coffin seven cubits long and in it a skeleton of the same length. Lichas reported to Sparta and interpreted these bones as being those of Orestes according to the oracle. The bellows of the smithy were the twin winds always blowing. The shock answering shock was the hammer on the anvil. Anguish piled on anguish was the welding of iron to iron, for iron has always brought woe to mankind. Lichas was instructed to go to Tegea and secure the bones. To cover his purpose the Spartans made a pretence of banishing him. On reaching Tegea he went to the smithy and tried to buy the site, but for a long time the owner would not yield. At last Lichas succeeded in persuading the blacksmith to sell his smithy and then he excavated the tomb and took the bones home to Sparta.

Tegea seems to have been a favorite site for excavations. About the time when Vespasian was proclaimed emperor in Alexandria excavations were carried out at Tegea according to the indications of some soothsayers. These resulted in the discovery of some vases of ancient workmanship. On one of them was a representation very like Vespasian which was of course a good omen for the newly proclaimed emperor.

Yet another case of excavation is connected with Sparta. Plutarch says that when Agesilaus, king of Sparta, was campaigning in Boeotia he heard that at Haliartus was the tomb of Alcmena the mother of Heracles from whom the Spartan kings claimed descent. He therefore excavated the tomb to secure the relics of Alcmena and take them to Sparta. In it he found a bronze tablet of great age which was inscribed with strange characters. They were quite legible and were thought to be Egyptian. Agesilaus accordingly wrote to the King of Egypt, sent him the tablet, and asked for a translation. The tablet was entrusted to the priest Chonouphis, who stated that the characters were of the age of Proteus, King of Egypt at the time of the Trojan War. The meaning, he said, was that the Greeks should lay aside their arms and institute competitions in honor of the Muses and indulge only in literary and philosophical contests. It would seem from this interpretation that the learned Chonouphis was unable to decipher the script and not wishing to acknowledge his ignorance had invented this apocryphal message to the Greeks. If as we now might suspect the tomb of Alcmena was one of the beehive or tholos tombs of the Mycenaean period the bronze tablet may well have been inscribed with characters of the Minoan-Mycenaean script.

If this suggestion is correct this would have been the first recorded discovery of the pre-Phoenician Greek alphabet. There was another probable instance later in the days of Nero. In the thirteenth year of that emperor when Rutilius Rufus was governor of Crete there was an earthquake at Knossos which caused a tomb to open. This was investigated by some shepherds who found in it a tin chest with some documents of lime bark. These they gave to their master Eupraxides who sent them to the Governor and the latter sent them on to the emperor. The documents were said by the experts whom Nero consulted to be written in Phoenician and to be the memoirs of Dictys of Crete who had been a companion of Idomeneus and Meriones in the Trojan War. He had written his account of the Trojan War and given instructions that it should be placed in his tomb. Nero had the documents translated into Greek and put in his library under the name of Dictys. It is quite probable that these documents were also written in the Minoan-Mycenaean script and we can forgive the experts for having claimed to be able to translate them. Who would not translate anything for an emperor such as Nero?

We possess a Latin version of Dictys by L. Septimius and this was the inspiration for most of the medieval romances of the Trojan War which are mainly based on Dictys and not on Homer. Septimius tells the story of the discovery of the documents and it was for long believed that the whole tale was a literary imposture and that no Greek version had ever existed. At Tebtunis, however, Grenfell and Hunt found a fragment of the Greek text dating from the second century A.D., but it is still not possible to be sure about Dictys. The memoirs attributed to Dictys may be the composition of one of Nero's experts who, unable to translate the documents, wrote a romance of the Trojan War which apparently satisfied the emperor. That the documents were in the Minoan-Mycenaean script is very likely, because hundreds of clay tablets in that script have been found at Knossos in Evans' excavations. Some of these tablets seem to have been kept in wooden chests. Others apparently had been stored in stone cists lined with lead. It is possible that the leaden lining of such a cist is the tin of the story. Even then if the memoirs of Dictys are a literary falsification, it is quite probable that as a result of an earthquake Minoan inscribed tablets were found at Knossos in the days of Nero.

Herodotus has some interesting remarks on the Cadmean letters and the beginnings of the Greek alphabet which he reinforces by reference to inscriptions which he saw at Thebes. He speaks of the introduction of letters by Cadmus and imagines that they were similar to the Phoenician, but that the Greeks changed the sound and forms of some of the letters. He gives the texts of the inscriptions which he saw on three bronze tripods dedicated in the temple of the Ismenian Apollo at Thebes. The inscriptions are in hexameters. One of them Herodotus dates to the time of Laius, the father of Oedipus, and another to the reign of Laodamas, the grandson of Oedipus. He apparently found no difficulty in reading or understanding the inscriptions and presumably therefore they must have been in some archaic form of the Greek alphabet. If the inscriptions had been in the Minoan-Mycenaean script it would be surprising if Herodotus had been able to read them. We can hardly imagine that a Greek alphabet intelligible to Herodotus existed as early as the time of Oedipus and it is therefore to be feared that his dating of the inscription may not be correct.

Nero strangely enough seems to have been easily imposed upon. A man called Bassus won his attention with a tale which he said had been revealed to him in a dream, that Dido's treasure was buried in a cave somewhere in Africa and only waiting to be found. As Nero was at the time short of money he jumped at this opportunity of getting rich quickly. A special expedition was sent in haste to find the treasure. A frenzied search was made and Rome was on its tiptoes for news of the treasure hunt. Great bodies of men to excavate were organized and much fruitless digging took place all about Africa, that is in the Roman province of Africa, the modern Tunisia. In the end Bassus had to confess that it was all a hoax and committed suicide.

When Dido was building Carthage the legend says that a horse's head was found in the excavations for the foundations of the city. It is not clear from the accounts we have whether this was an actual horse's head or, what is more likely, a horse's head in bronze. If the latter it may have been the accidental discovery of a buried ancient work of art. In this connection we may recall that the badge of Carthage on its coins is a horse's head.

A well known case of excavations carried out for the sake of finding antiquities is recorded by Strabo. When Julius Caesar rebuilt Corinth and established a Roman colony there the colonists accidentally discovered some of the ancient cemeteries. In these they found vases of bronze and terracotta, especially the latter which were ornamented with reliefs. These they were able to sell at high prices to Roman collectors until the supply was exhausted.

This is an indication that there were dealers in antiquities and works of art who supplied Roman collectors with antiques and kindred artistic objects. We know too that statuettes and vases of Corinthian bronze were much prized by Roman connoisseurs. Cicero often mentions them, but what the main source of supply was we do not know. Julius Caesar was a collector of gems and his collection was given to the temple of Venus Genetrix, the legendary ancestress of the Julian *gens*. Marcellus, the nephew of Augustus, also collected gems and his collection found a home in the temple of Apollo on the Palatine.

All Romans liked to acquire works of art to display their culture and to ornament their villas. We have the famous case of Verres who plundered Sicily for his collection and no doubt other Romans, Mummius for instance, either on the conquest of a country or else while ruling it as a province used their positions to collect works of art. They had in many cases little real artistic appreciation as is shown by the tale of Mummius who contracted with the shippers of the plunder of Corinth that any works of art lost should be replaced by others of equal value. Some Romans, men of Cicero's type and education, thought of themselves as connoisseurs and collected works of art seriously. To supply them there must have been dealers. Cicero records to Pompey's credit that after his campaigns in Asia he did not merely refrain from plundering Greek cities of their treasures, but did not even think it worth while to visit them.

The plundering of conquered countries by the conqueror has been usually looked upon in all periods and in all lands as a more or less normal event. Assyrians, Persians, and other conquerors in the Near East took away as a matter of course statues from the shrines of countries they subdued. So Xerxes removed from Athens the bronze statues of the tyrannicides, Harmodius and Aristogeiton, which were afterwards restored by Alexander or one of his successors. Another statue found by Alexander in Persia was the bronze statue of Apollo from Miletus which

Darius had removed on the capture of that city. It was restored to Miletus by Seleucus in 295 B.C. Herodotus tells a story about Datis who was induced by a dream to restore a gilt statue of Apollo found among the plunder in a Phoenician ship in his fleet. He himself deposited it at Delos and gave orders for its return. The French excavators at Susa found a large bronze knuckle bone which bears an inscription showing that it had been once dedicated in a Greek temple. This obviously was another piece of Persian plunder.

Alexander's successors, the rulers of the Hellenistic monarchies of the Near East, were collectors and rivalled one another in their efforts to secure works of art to adorn their capitals. The Ptolemies collected books and as book collectors competed with the Attalid kings of Pergamum. The latter again besides books collected works of art in general and were also generous patrons, like the Medici, of contemporary artists. King Nicomedes of Bithynia tried to secure for his collection the Aphrodite of Cnidus by Praxiteles. Although he offered a high price, the whole national debt of the city, the people of Cnidus refused to part with their treasure.

Under the empire Rome became full of art galleries, if we may apply that modern name to the collections of statuary and paintings formed in the porticoes and baths of the city. Well known examples are the portico of Octavia and the Baths of Titus and of Caracalla, which contained the Laocoon and the Farnese Bull and Heracles. Pliny and other ancient authors make many references to such collections. Some of the statues in these galleries were undoubtedly originals, but some must have been copies in marble of ancient works in bronze. There may even have been bronze copies of ancient bronze statues, for there is in the Cairo Museum part of a mold for casting a life size head of Polyclitan style. We know too that in the Hellenistic period copies of famous bronzes of earlier date were being made, as witnessed by the marble copy of the Polyclitan Diadumenus found in a house at Delos. If the houses of rich Hellenistic merchants at Delos were adorned with full size marble copies of famous statues it is not surprising that the Romans imitated them. We have instances such as the cargo of marble sculptures found in a wrecked ship off the island of Anti-Kythera and the marbles found in Piraeus harbour to show that there was a brisk export trade in marble copies of statues. Bronzes too were exported and these may have been originals, for the few in the Anti-Kythera cargo seem to have been wrenched from their bases. Other instances of bronzes found in the sea are the wrecked cargoes found at Artemisium and near Mahdia in Tunis and the Piombino bronze Apollo found off the northwest coast of Italy. The last seems to have been taken from a shrine according to the inscription on it.

We have this clear evidence of the existence of a trade in works of art especially statuary, but unfortunately we know nothing about the dealers or their practices. Romans, such as Cicero or Caesar for his collection of gems, must presumably have bought their new acquisitions through dealers, and the majority of collectors can hardly have acquired any original work of art of great importance either in bronze or marble except in rare cases. The busts for instance both in bronze and in marble which ornamented the villa at Herculaneum are undoubtedly copies of portraits of famous men or of the heads of well known statues and it is unfortunate from our point of view that the owner did not have them properly labelled. Many instances of the use of copies of works to adorn villas could be quoted, the Discobolus of Castel Porziano, the Marsyas of Castel Gandolfo, and the multitude of copies from Hadrian's Villa.

It is possible that in some cases copies were palmed off as originals on unsuspecting clients, *nouveaux riches* of the type of Trimalchio, and we cannot be sure that connoisseurs of the type of Cicero or Atticus were infallible. The marble Aphrodite by Phidias in the Portico of Octavia in Rome recorded by Pliny may well have been a marble copy after Phidias who is not otherwise known as a marble worker. Similarly Pliny's remarks that he found Kanachos, a famous master of bronze statues, recorded as having also made marble statues may be due to the fact that Pliny found in some Roman collections one or more marble figures copied from bronzes by Kanachos.

We have records of inscriptions found in Rome or Italy giving the signatures of the sculptors Lysippus, Kalamis, and Sthennis in Greek and of the sculptors Bryaxis, Polyclitus, and Praxiteles found in Italy on the vases of statues, but we have no means of judging whether the works that stood on these bases were of bronze or marble and were original works or copies. In the case of Latin inscriptions we suspect that the statues were copies, but those with the Greek inscriptions may have been genuine. We simply cannot tell. There is also the possibility that in some cases since the name of the artist was unknown a statue was attributed to some famous artist by the owner in all good faith, probably from ignorance just as we know that today in private collections and even in some public collections in all countries pictures have been assigned incorrectly to famous artists. This is rather different from the case of a dealer who gives a famous artist's name to a work of art in order [to] sell it well or in order to pass off a copy as an original. Phaedrus says:

> ut quidam artifices nostro faciunt saeculo
> qui pretium operis maius inueniunt, nouo
> si marmori adscripserunt Praxitelem suo . . . .

On the other hand on the bronze bust of the Polyclitan Doryphorus from Herculaneum we find not the signature of Polyclitus, but of an unknown Apollonius.

The Greeks and the Romans travelled about the world much as we do, for pleasure, for the sake of seeing famous places and famous buildings.

One Roman consul before he returned to Rome after settling up political matters at the conclusion of a victorious war against King Perseus of Macedonia made a tour of Greece. Another Roman commander visited various famous places on the coast of Asia Minor, among the islands, and in Greece itself. He wrote notes of what he saw as an account of *mirabilia*, but most unluckily it is lost and we have only a few quotations from it preserved by others. One Greek, whose name even we do not know, wrote a kind of gossiping guide to Greece describing his travels and his impressions. He does not, however, describe any of the temples or other monuments of antiquity or famous shrines, but his account of Greece is so racy and so chatty that we are sorry we do not possess more of his work and that he apparently took for granted the sights and monuments of the country. He tells us nothing about them. If only we had an account of an Olympic festival from him! Another traveller, Dion of Prusa, who found Rome in the days of the emperor Domitian uncomfortable, especially for a Stoic philosopher, spent most of his time travelling about the Greek world in the east. He travelled from city to city and country to country giving lectures more or less popular on Stoic philosophy. Unfortunately he was more interested in promoting this kind of Stoic propaganda and in keeping alive the Hellenic spirit among the other nations of the east and does not seem to have made any notes on his travels or the places he visited.

A far greater traveller is the famous Pausanias who lived in the days of Hadrian and Antoninus Pius in the middle of the second century A.D. He wrote a description of Greece which we have and it is, so to speak, the first guide book known. It is for us today the most valuable work we possess for ancient Greek topography. His descriptions of the cities and sanctuaries of Greece are the best of guides for the modern archaeologist and explorer. He is, however, not critical enough. On one occasion in a temple in Arcadia he says that a group of statues was all carved from one block of marble. The remains of the group have been found and it is composed of several pieces of marble. So Pausanias evidently wrote down what the dragoman in the temple told him without checking the statement. Though he must have read the inscriptions on statues and monuments he rarely quotes them in support of his statements. He gives us the traditions and legends, but makes no attempt to investigate them. If he had done so his work would have been not merely indispensable to the modern scholar, but really invaluable. Poets too occasionally give us descriptions of famous monuments. Euripides in the Ion describes the sculptures and appearance of the temple of the Palatine Apollo at Rome and its decoration, and Ovid in the Fasti mentions the sculpture of the temple of Mars Ultor at Rome. Poets, however, from the nature of their calling cannot be regarded as accurate describers of monuments or things. They were poets and not archaeologists or writers of guide books.

Aulus Gellius gives one instance in which an anecdote was checked by reference to an inscription, the first use of epigraphy. Tiro, Cicero's secretary, in a letter said that when Pompey was about to dedicate the temple of Victory which formed part of the great theater he had built, the first theater in stone to be constructed in Rome, he wished to inscribe on it his name and titles. He therefore began to ask whether it was correct to write 'consul tertio' or 'consul tertium.' He sought the opinion of all the learned men in Rome. Some said one, some said the other. Then Pompey asked Cicero who was thus placed in a difficulty. Cicero was afraid that the learned men whose opinion he might reject would think he did not approve of them personally. So he persuaded Pompey not to write either 'tertio' or 'tertium,' but just the letters T E R T, so that the meaning would be clear enough, although no one could guess whether T E R T, stood for 'tertio' or 'tertium.' Gellius, however, adds that that is not the way the inscription appeared in his time, for a long time after the dedication when part of the theater had collapsed the number of Pompey's consulship was found to be indicated not by T E R T, but by three vertical strokes only.

Pompey dedicated his theater in 55 B.C. If the temple of Victory is the Temple of Venus Victrix which formed part of the theater and if it was dedicated in his third consulship it would have been dedicated in 52 B.C.

Pompey's theater was damaged in 32 B.C. by a storm and repaired by Augustus who especially notes that in repairing it he nowhere recorded his own name. This would mean that the original inscription would have been preserved. The theater was burnt in the reign of Tiberius and restored by Caligula and Claudius, and again burnt in 80 A.D. and restored by Titus and Domitian. This last would have been the theater seen by Aulus Gellius who lived from 117 to 180 A.D. and wrote mostly, so it seems, between about 143 and 148 A.D. It is curious that Tiro who must have seen the actual inscription often should have made a mistake especially when his account is confirmed by Varro. Perhaps in one of the post-Augustan restorations the letters T E R T were replaced by three vertical strokes. This would reconcile the account of Tiro and Varro with the epigraphical note preserved by Gellius.

Generally speaking the ancient writers, at least those whose works have come down to us, took things too much for granted especially as regards monuments or sites familiar to them. In Alexandria itself the Tomb of Alexander was a place of Pilgrimage for all comers. We know from the lives of Augustus and Caracalla that the body of the conqueror, probably a gold wrapped mummy, could be seen by visitors, distinguished visitors at least. No ancient author, however, either Greek or Latin, not even the learned Strabo, has given us an account of the tomb, of its arrangement, and of its contents. We do not even know with any degree of certainty the position of the tomb within the city. The ancient writers took the Tomb of Alexander so much for granted and imagined that the whole [world] knew and would always know all about it and where it was that they did not take the trouble to leave for us any description of it or of its position in Alexandria. It is this habit, to which all men are liable, of taking things for granted that has been the cause of so many gaps in our knowledge of ancient things and of ancient times. Pausanias is the only ancient writer whose works we possess who made a serious attempt to describe monuments and works of art and the topography of the cities and countryside. Even he takes far too much for granted and consequently his descriptions are not always clear to us. Indeed with a modern guide book it is not always absolutely easy to find the way about a strange town or country and still less to follow a modern description of an ancient or of an excavated site. We too have the advantage of plans and illustrations whereas Pausanias and Strabo had not.

After this survey, necessarily brief, of the attitude of the Greeks and Romans towards the monuments and relics of past times we can realize, as stated at the beginning, that they had no real intellectual curiosity as regards ancient monuments or works of art. They were apt to regard them as curiosities and they practically never indulged in any learned examination or discussion of them. They took them and the traditions about them at their face value and never really tried to make any scientific or critical examination of them. Finally there was never any attempt at excavation or any other form of what we should call scientific research in art history or in archaeology. Still less no ancient scholar ever tried, as do our modern prehistorians, to reconstruct the history of the past by observation, by recording, or by excavating its remains. Thucydides in his observations of the graves on Delos is the only case that approaches this kind of research and his observations were not due to any definite or organized effort, but to an accidental discovery during a process of religious purification. Had the Greeks and Romans possessed any real feeling for antiquity they would never have reused so many monuments or architectural members in later buildings. It is perhaps lucky for us that they did not have that sense, since this custom of reusing material has resulted in the preservation of much that would otherwise have been lost. One case of this is the use by the Athenians of the debris from the Persian destruction of the shrines and monuments on the Acropolis to level the area when they began to reconstruct their sanctuaries. Another striking instance is the Arch of Constantine which is adorned with reliefs of many dates and styles. Constantine both in this and in his removal of the Serpent Column of Platea from Delphi to Constantinople had no idea of preserving them for posterity, but merely of glorifying himself and of exhibiting his own greatness to his own and later generations. Some modern founders of museums have at times acted in much the same way and they too have lacked what we should call a scientific approach towards art history and archaeology. It is the lack of the sense of acquiring knowledge from a study of the monuments for its own sake and of any method of logical or critical research as regards antiquities of all kinds that has made the task of reading the remains of ancient Greece and Rome more difficult for posterity.

We must not forget, however, that the past for the Greeks and Romans was still comparatively young and in comparing their interests with ours that a great number of the objects of our archaeological researches were part of their daily lives.

✳ ✳ ✳

Stephens' account of his plans to purchase the ruins of the great Maya cities of Quiriguá and Palenque sounds, today, not a little ludicrous. He was serious, nevertheless, and, although transporting the huge monuments from either site would probably have been impossible, we may be certain that if he had been able to purchase the sites, he would have tried to remove the better portable sculptures.

The wholesale export of antiquities was going on full blast in the Old World when Stephens made his Central American tour. Lord Elgin, who had been appointed British Ambassador to Constantinople in 1799, secured in 1801 a firman from the Porte to remove any "inscriptions and figures" which he desired. Lord Elgin's agent, Dr. Hunt, while engaged in collecting Greek sculptures in Athens, wrote to Elgin, "If your Lordship would come here in a large Man of War, that beautiful little model of ancient art [the Erechtheum] might be transported wholly to England." Elgin was unable to do this, and had to be satisfied with taking down the metopes, sculptured by Phidias, from the Parthenon, and they may be seen today in the British Museum (Clarke, 1945:191-198). Botta, Place, and Layard in Mesopotamia (Lloyd, 1955) removed great numbers of Assyrian sculptures to Paris and London in the mid-nineteenth century, though not without severe losses: in 1855 two hundred and forty cases of material were lost when the transport rafts were attacked and sunk by Arab brigands at Kurnah, where the Tigris and Euphrates join to form the Shatt-al-Arab.

Lord Elgin and Stephens justified their acts and plans with the idea that by removing such antiquities they would be preserved, whereas if they were left to their rightful owners, who did not appreciate them, they would be destroyed. The wholesale removal of antiquities has long since ceased, but such incidents provide us with an interesting aspect of one phase of archaeological collecting.

Buying a Maya City

John L. Stephens

A LOST CITY [PALENQUE]

The general character of these ruins is the same as at Copan. The monuments are much larger, but they are sculptured in lower relief, less rich in design, and more faded and worn, probably being of a much older date.

Of one thing there is no doubt: a large city once stood there; its name is lost, its history unknown; and, except for a notice taken from Mr. C.'s [Catherwood's] notes, and inserted by the Señores Payes in a Guatimala paper after the visit, which found its way to this country [i.e., the U.S.A.] and Europe, no account of its existence has ever before been published. For centuries it has lain as completely buried as if covered with the lava of Vesuvius. Every traveller from Yzabel to Guatimala has passed within three hours of it; we ourselves had done the same; and yet there it lay, like the rock-built city of Edom, unvisited, unsought, and utterly unknown.

The morning after Mr. C. returned I called upon Señor Payes, the only one of the brothers then in Guatimala, and opened a negotiation for the purchase of these ruins. Besides their entire newness and immense interest as an unexplored field of antiquarian research, the monuments were but a mile from the river, the ground was level to the bank, and the river from that place was navigable; the city might be transported bodily and set up in New York. I expressly stated (and my reason for doing so will be obvious) that I was acting in this matter on my own account, that it was entirely a personal affair; but Señor Payes would consider me as acting for my government, and said, what I am sure he meant, that if his family was as it had been once, they would be proud to present the whole to the United States; in that country they were not appreciated, and he would be happy to contribute to the cause of science in ours; but they were impoverished by the convulsions of the country; and, at all events, he could give me no answer till his brothers returned, who were expected in two or three days. Unfortunately, as I believe for both of us, Señor Payes consulted with the French consul general, who put an exaggerated value upon the ruins, referring him to the expenditure of several hundred thousand dollars by the French government in transporting one of the obelisks of Luxor from Thebes to Paris. Probably, before

Incidents of Travel in Central America, Chiapas, and Yuchtan, Vol. II, by John L. Stephens (New York: Harper and Brothers, 1842), pp. 361-365, 123-124, 469.

the speculating scheme referred to, the owners would have been glad to sell the whole tract, consisting of more than fifty thousand acres, with everything on it, known and unknown, for a few thousand dollars. I was anxious to visit them myself, and learn with more certainty the possibility of their removal, but was afraid of increasing the extravagance of his notions. His brothers did not arrive, and one of them unfortunately died on the road. I had not the government for paymaster; it might be necessary to throw up the purchase on account of the cost of removal; and I left an offer with Mr. Savage, the result of which is still uncertain; but I trust that when these pages reach the hands of the reader, two of the largest monuments will be on their way to this city . . .

But to return to things more in my line. We had another long journey before us. Our next move was for Yucatan. From Mr. Catherwood's condition I had great fear that we would not be able to accomplish what we purposed; but, at all events, it was necessary to go down to the sea-coast. There were two routes, either by Tobasco or the Laguna, to Campeachy, and war again confronted us. Both Tobasco and Campeachy were beseiged by the Liberals, or, as they were called, the Revolutionists. The former route required three days' journey by land, the latter one short day; and as Mr. C. was not able to ride, this determined us. In the meantime, while waiting for his recovery, and so as not to rust and be utterly useless when I returned home, I started another operation, viz., the purchase of the city of Palenque. I am bound to say, however, that I was not bold enough to originate this, but fell into it accidentally, in a long conversation with the prefect about the richness of the soil, the cheapness of the land, its vicinity to the seaboard and the United States, and easy communication with New York. He told me that a merchant of Tobasco, who had visited the place, had proposed to purchase a tract of land and establish a colony of emigrants, but he had gone away and never returned. He added, that for two years a government order from the State of Ciapas, to which the region belonged, had been lying in his hands for the sale of all land in the vicinity lying within certain limits; but there were no purchasers, and no sales were ever made. Upon inquiry I learned that this order, in its terms, embraced the ground occupied by the ruined city. No exception whatever was made in favor of it. He showed me the order, which was imperative; and he said that if any exception was intended, it would have been so expressed; wherefore he considered himself bound to receive an offer for any portion of the land. The sale was directed to be by appraisement, the applicant to name one man, the prefect another, and, if necessary, they two to name a third; and the application with the price fixed and the boundaries, was to be sent to Ciudad Real for the approval of the governor and a deed.

The tract containing the ruins consisted of about six thousand acres of good land, which according to the usual appraisement, would cost about fifteen hundred dollars, and the prefect said that it would not be valued a cent higher on account of the ruins. I resolved immediately to buy it. I would fit up the palace and repeople the old city of Palenque. But there was one difficulty: by the laws of Mexico no stranger can purchase lands unless married to a *hija del pais,* or daughter of the country. This, by the way, is a grand stroke of policy, holding up the most powerful attraction of the country to seduce men from their natural allegiance, and radicate them in the soil; and it is taking them where weak, and vulnerable; for, when wandering in strange countries, alone and friendless, buffeted and battered, with no one to care for him, there are moments when a lovely woman might root the stranger to any spot on earth. On principle I have always resisted such tendencies, but I never before found it to my interest to give way. The ruined city of Palenque was a most desirable piece of property.

The case was embarrassing and complicated. Society in Palenque was small; the oldest young lady was not more than fourteen, and the prettiest woman, who already had contributed most to our happiness (she made our cigars), was already married. The house containing the two [hieroglyphic] tablets belonged to a widow lady and a single sister, good looking, amiable, and both about forty. The house was one of the neatest in the place. I always liked to visit it, and had before thought that, if passing a year at the ruins, it would be delightful to have this house in the village for recreating and occasional visits. With either of these ladies would come possession of the house and the two stone tablets; but the difficulty was that there were two of them, both equally interesting and equally interested. I am particular in mentioning these little circumstances, to show the difficulties that attended every step of our enterprise in that country. There was an alternative, and that was to purchase in the name of some other person; but I did not know any one I could trust. At length, however, I hit upon Mr. Russell, the American consul at Laguna, who was married to a Spanish lady, and already had large possessions in the country; and I arranged with the prefect to make the purchase in his name. Pawling was to accompany me to the Laguna, for the purpose of procuring and carrying back evidence of Mr. Russell's cooperation and the necessary funds, and was to act as my agent in completing the purchase. The perfect was personally anxious to complete it. The buildings, he said, were fast going to decay, and in a few years more would be mounds of ruins. In that country they were not appreciated or understood, and he had the liberal wish that the tablets of hieroglyphics particularly might find their way to other countries, be inspected and studied by scientific men, and their origin and history be ascertained. Besides, he had an idea that immense discoveries were still to be made and treasures found, and he was anxious for a thorough exploration, in which he should himself cooperate. The two tablets which I had attempted to purchase were highly prized by the owners, but he thought they could be secured by purchasing the house, and I authorized him to buy it at a fixed price.

In my many conversations with the prefect I had broached the subject of making casts from the tablets. Like every other official whom I met, he supposed that I was acting under a commission from my government, which idea was sustained by having in my employ a man of such character and appearance as Pawling, though every time I put my hand in my pocket I had a feeling sense that the case was far otherwise. In the matter of casts he offered every assistance, but there was no plaster of Paris nearer than the Laguna or Campeachy, and perhaps not there. We had made an experiment at the ruins by catching in the river a large quantity of snails and burning the shells, but it did not answer. He referred us to some limestone in the neighborhood, but this would not do. Pawling knew nothing of casting. The idea had never entered his mind before, but he was willing to undertake this. Mr. Catherwood, who had been shut up in Athens during the Greek revolution, when it was beseiged by the Turks, and in pursuing his artistical studies had perforce made castings with his own hands, gave him written instructions, and it was agreed that when he returned with the credentials from Mr. Russell he should bring back plaster of Paris, and, while the proceedings for completing the purchase were pending, should occupy himself in this new branch of business. . . .

Having mentioned in the preceding pages efforts to introduce into this country [the United States] some of the antiquities therein described, the author considers it proper to say that, immediately on his return home, a few friends, whose names he would have great pleasure in making known if he were at liberty to do so, undertook to provide the sum of $20,000 for the purpose of carrying that object into effect. Under their direction, the author wrote to his agent at Guatimala, to purchase the ruins of Quirigua, or such monuments as it might be considered advisable to remove, at a price beyond what would have been accepted for them when he left Guatimala; but, unfortunately, in the meantime, a notice taken from Mr. Catherwood's memoranda, and inserted by the proprietors in a Guatimala paper, had reached this country, been translated and copied into some of our own journals, and one eulogistic paragraph, probably forgotten as soon as it was written, was sent back to Guatimala, which gave the proprietor such an exaggerated notion of their value that he refused the offer. From vague conversations with foreigners who had never seen and knew nothing of them, he conceived the idea that all the governments of Europe would vie with each other for their possession; and still entertaining the foolish belief that the author was acting on behalf of his government, said that, if the President of the United States wanted them, he must pay $20,000 for them; in the mean time he resolved to wait for offers from England and France. By the last advices he was still under the same hallucination.

References to General Surveys of the History of Archaeology

Boule, M. and H. V. Vallois
1946 *Les Hommes Fossiles* (Paris: Masson et Cie.), Chapter 1, "Historical Development of Prehistory."

Braidwood, R. J.
1959 "Archaeology and Evolutionary Theory." From *Evolution and Anthropology: a Centenary Appraisal* (Washington, D.C.: The Anthropological Society of Washington), pp. 76-89.

Casson, S.
1939 *The Discovery of Man: the Story of the Inquiry Into Human Origins* (New York: Harper and Brothers).

Ceram, C. W.
1958 *The March of Archaeology* (New York: Alfred A. Knopf, Inc.), Chronological table of important events in the development of prehistory, pp. 307-315.

Daniel, G. E.
1950 *A Hundred Years of Archaeology* (London: The Macmillan Co., Ltd.), Chronological table of persons and events, pp. 327-336.
1959 "The Idea of Man's Antiquity" *Scientific American,* 201, 167-176.

Daux, G.
1948 *Les Étapes de l'archéologie* (Paris: Presses Universitaires de France).

Hamy, E. T.
1870 *Précis de paléontologie humaine* (Paris: J.-B. Baillière et fils).

Laming, A., ed.
1952 *La Découverte du passé.* (Paris: Editions A. et J. Picard & Cie.) Brief history of the science of prehistory, pp. 15-25.

Michaelis, A.
1906 *Die archäologischen Entdeckungen des neunzehnten Jahrhunderts.* (Leipzig: Verlag von E. A. Seeman) Chronological table of growth of prehistory, pp. 293-300. Translated as *A Century of Archaeological Discoveries* (London: John Murray) by Bettina Kahnweiler.

Morlot, A.
1861 "General Views on Archaeology." *Report of the Smithsonian Institution for 1860,* pp. 284-343.
1864 "The First Steps in the Study of High Antiquity in Europe." *Report of the Smithsonian Institution for 1863,* pp. 400-403.

Peake, H. J. E.
1940 "The Study of Prehistoric Times." *Journal of The Royal Anthropological Institute,* Vol. 70, pp. 103-146.

von Oppeln-Bronikowski, F.
   1931   *Die archäologischen Entdeckungen im 20. Jahrhundert.* (Berlin: H. Keller) (This work may be considered a continuation of that of Michaelis, 1906.)

Shorr, P.
   1935   "The Genesis of Prehistorical Research." *Isis,* Vol. 23, pp. 425-443.

Wahle, E.
   1950-51   "Geschichte der prähistorischen Forschung." *Anthropos,* Vol. 45, No. 4-6, pp. 1-538; Vol. 46, No. 1-2, pp. 49-112.

Wegener, M.
   1951   *Altertumskunde.* Munich.

Wilson, T.
   1899   "The Beginnings of the Science of Prehistoric Anthropology." *Proceedings of the American Association for the Advancement of Science,* Vol. 48, pp. 309-353.

Bibliography

Aitken, M. J.
1961 *Physics and Archaeology.* (New York: Interscience Publishers, Inc.)

Albright, W. F.
1940 *From the Stone Age to Christianity.* (Baltimore: The Johns Hopkins Press)

Ascher, R.
1961 "Experimental Archeology." *American Anthropologist,* Vol. 63, pp. 793-816.

Baldry, H. C.
1956 "Hesiod's Five Ages." *Journal of the History of Ideas,* Vol. 17, pp. 553-554.

Blake, C. C.
1864 "On the Alleged Peculiar Characters and Assumed Antiquity of the Human Cranium from the Neanderthal." *Journal of the Anthropological Society of London,* Vol. 2, pp. 139-157.

Blinkenberg, C.
1911 *The Thunderweapon in Religion and Folklore: A Study in Comparative Archaeology.* (Cambridge: Cambridge University Press)

Boule, M. and H. V. Vallois
1946 *Les Hommes Fossiles* (Paris: Editions A. et J. Picard et Cie.)

Bowen, R. N. C.
1958 *The Exploration of Time.* (London: G. Newnes, Ltd.)

Breuil, H.
1941 "The Discovery of the Antiquity of Man; Some of the Evidence." Huxley Memorial Lecture, Royal Anthropological Institute. London. (Published also in *Anthropos,* Vol. 37-40, pp. 667-687. 1942-45.)

Brown, H.
1954 *The Challenge of Man's Future.* (New York: The Viking Press, Inc.)

Brunet, P.
1950 "Les Premiers Linéaments de la science géologique: Agricola, Palissy, George Owen." *Revue d'histoire des sciences et leurs applications* (January), pp. 67-79.

Carnot, A.
1893 "Recherches sur la composition générale et la teneur en fluor des os modernes et des os fossiles des différents âges." *Annales des Mines, Mémoires,* Ser. 9, Vol. 3, pp. 155-195. Paris.

Childe, V. G.
1944a "Archaeological Ages as Technological Stages." Huxley Memorial Lecture. (London: Royal Anthropological Institute)

1944b   "Historical Analysis of Archaeological Method." *Nature*, Vol. 153, pp. 206-207.

1953   *What is History?* (New York: Henry Schuman, Inc.)

Clark, G.

1957   *Archaeology and Society*. (Cambridge: Harvard University Press)

Clark, W. E. L. G.

1960   *The Antecedents of Man*. (Chicago: Quadrangle Books, Inc.)

Clarke, M. L.

1945   *Greek Studies in England, 1700-1830*. (Cambridge: Cambridge University Press)

Cook, S. F.

1960   "Dating Prehistoric Bone by Chemical Analysis." From *The Application of Quantitative Methods in Archaeology*, R. F. Heizer and S. F. Cook, eds. Viking Fund Publications in Anthropology, No. 28, pp. 223-245. Chicago.

Crawford, O. G. S.

1932   "The Dialectical Process in the History of Science." *The Sociological Review*, Vol. 24, pp. 165-173.

1953   *Archaeology in the Field*. (New York: Frederick A. Praeger, Inc.)

Daniel, G.

1943   *The Three Ages*. (Cambridge: Cambridge University Press)

1943   *A Hundred Years of Archaeology*. (London: The Macmillan Co., Ltd.)

Darwin, C. G.

1960   "Can Man Control His Numbers?" From *The Evolution of Man*, S. Tax, ed. (University of Chicago Press), pp. 463-473.

Davis, J. B.

1864   *The Neanderthal Skull*. London.

de Blasio, A.

1922   "Un nouveau document de l'homme paléolithique dans la province de Bénévent." *Bulletin Société d'Anthropologie de Paris*, Ser. 7, Vol. 3, pp. 86-89.

De Vries, H. and K. P. Oakley

1959   "Radiocarbon Dating of the Piltdown Skull and Jaw." *Nature*, Vol. 184, pp. 224-226.

Douglass, A. E.

1921   "Dating Our Prehistoric Ruins." *Natural History*, Vol. 21, pp. 27-30.

1929   "The Secret of the Southwest Solved by Talkative Tree Rings." *National Geographic Magazine*, Vol. 56, pp. 737-770.

1935   "Dating Pueblo Bonito and Other Ruins of the Southwest." *National Geographic Society, Contributed Technical Papers*, Pueblo Bonito Series No. 1.

Ehrich, R. W. and G. M. Henderson

1954   "Concerning the Piltdown Hoax and the Rise of a New Dogmatism." *American Anthropologist*, Vol. 56, pp. 433-441.

Eiseley, L. C.

1954   "The Reception of the First Missing Links." *Proceedings of the American Philosophical Society*, Vol. 98, pp. 453-465.

1957 "Neanderthal Man and the Dawn of Human Paleontology." *Quarterly Review of Biology,* Vol. 32, pp. 323-329.

1961 *Darwin's Century.* (New York: Doubleday & Company, Inc. Anchor Books—A244)

Evans, Joan
1943 *Time and Chance.* (London and New York: Longmans, Green & Co., Inc.)

Fox, A. Lane (Gen. A. H. Pitt-Rivers)
1870 Primitive Warfare, Sec. III; On the Resemblance of the Weapons of Early Races, their Variations, Continuity and Development of Form —Metal Period. *Journal of the Royal United Service Institute,* Vol. 13, pp. 509-539.

Giddings, J. L.
1962 *Development of Tree-Ring Dating as an Archaeological Aid.* From *Tree Growth,* T. T. Kozlowski, ed. (New York: The Ronald Press Co.), pp. 119-132.

Griffiths, J. G.
1961 *The Death of Adam.* (New York: Mentor Books—MT339)

Griffin, James B.
1955 "Chronology and the Dating Process." *Yearbook of Anthropology, 1955,* pp. 133-147. (University of Chicago Press)

1959 "The Pursuit of Archaeology in the United States." *American Anthropologist,* Vol. 61, pp. 379-388.

Griffiths, J. G.
1956 "Archaeology and Hesiod's Five Ages." *Journal of the History of Ideas,* Vol. 17, pp. 109-119.

Haber, F. C.
1959a "Fossils and Early Cosmology." From *Forerunners of Darwin, 1745-1859,* B. Glass *et al.,* eds. (Baltimore: The Johns Hopkins Press), pp. 3-48.

1959b "Fossils and the Idea of a Process of Time in Natural History." From *Forerunners of Darwin, 1745-1859,* B. Glass *et al.,* eds. (Baltimore: The Johns Hopkins Press), pp. 222-261.

1959c *The Age of the World: Moses to Darwin.* (Baltimore: The Johns Hopkins Press)

Hamy, E. T.
1870 *Précis de paléontologie humaine.* (Paris: J.-B. Baillière et fils)

Heizer, R. F.
1948 "A Bibliography of Ancient Man in California." *University of California Archaeological Survey, Report* No. 2. (Berkeley)

1950 "On the Methods of Chemical Analysis as an Aid to Prehistoric Cultural Chronology." *University of California Archaeological Survey, Report* No. 7 (Berkeley), pp. 5-9.

1953 "Long Range Dating in Archaeology." From *Anthropology Today,* A. L. Kroeber, ed. (University of Chicago Press), pp. 1-42.

1962 The Background of Thomsen's Three Age System. *Technology and Culture,* Vol. 3, pp. 259-266; 1962.

Heizer, R. F. (ed.)
  1959   *The Archaeologist at Work.* (New York: Harpers and Brothers)
Holmes, W. H.
  1901   "Review of the Evidence Relating to Auriferous Gravel Man in California." *Smithsonian Institution, Annual Report for 1899,* pp. 419-472.
Hrdlička, Aleš
  1907   "Skeletal Remains Suggesting or Attributed to Early Man in North America." *Bureau of American Ethnology, Bulletin 33.*
  1930   "The Skeletal Remains of Early Man." *Smithsonian Institution, Miscellaneous Collections,* Vol. 83.
Kendrick, T. D.
  1950   *British Antiquity.* (London: Methuen & Co., Ltd.)
Laming, A. (ed.)
  1952   *La Découverte du passé.* (Paris: Editions A. et J. Picard et Cie.)
Lang, A.
  1908   "Homer and Anthropology." From *Anthropology and the Classics,* R. R. Marett, ed. (Oxford: The Clarendon Press)
Lenoble, R.
  1954   "La Géologie au milieu du XVIIe siècle." *Les Conférences du Palais de la Découverte, Série D,* No. 27. (Université de Paris)
Libby, W. F.
  1955   *Radiocarbon Dating* (2d ed.). (University of Chicago Press)
Lloyd, S.
  1955   *Foundations in the Dust.* (London: Penguin Books, Ltd.—A336)
Lot, F.
  1961   *The End of the Ancient World and the Beginnings of the Middle Ages.* Harper Torchbook (TB1044) (New York: Harper and Brothers)
Lubbock, Sir John
  1865   *Prehistoric Times as Illustrated by Ancient Remains and the Manners and Customs of Modern Savages.* (London)
Lyell, C.
  1863   *The Geological Evidences of the Antiquity of Man* (2d American ed.). (Philadelphia: J. B. Lippincott)
MacCurdy, G. G.
  1916   "The Revision of Eoanthropus Dawsoni." *Science,* n.s., Vol. 43, pp. 228-231.
Mayr, E.
  1950   "Taxonomic Categories in Fossil Hominids." From *Origin and Evolution of Man.* Cold Spring Harbor Symposia on Quantitative Biology, Vol. 15, pp. 109-117.
Middleton, J.
  1844   "On Fluorine in Bones, Its Source and Its Application to the Determination of the Geological Age of Fossil Bones." *Proceedings of the Geological Society of London,* Vol. 4, pp. 431-433.
Miller, G. S., Jr.
  1915   "The Jaw of Piltdown Man." *Smithsonian Institution, Miscellaneous Collections,* Vol. 65, No. 12.

Montelius, G. O. A.
 1895 *La Civilization primitive en Italie depuis l'introduction des métaux.*
    (Stockholm: Imprimerie royale)

Morlot, A.
 1864 "The First Steps in the Study of High Antiquity in Europe." *Smithsonian Institution, Annual Report for 1863*, pp. 400-403.

Morrison, P. and E.
 1952 "The Strange Life of Charles Babbage." *Scientific American*, Vol. 186, pp. 66-73.

Munro, R.
 1905 *Archaeology and False Antiquities.* (London: Methuen and Co.)

Myres, J. L.
 1908 "Herodotus and Anthropology." From *Anthropology and the Classics*, R. R. Marett, ed. (Oxford: The Clarendon Press)

Nicholson, E. M.
 1961 "The Place of Conservation." From *The Humanist Frame*, J. Huxley, ed., pp. 387-397. (New York: Harper and Brothers)

Oakley, K. P.
 1955 "Further Contributions to the Solution of the Piltdown Problem." *Bulletin of the British Museum (Natural History), Geology*, Vol. 2, No. 6. (London)

O'Laverty, J.
 1857 "Relative Antiquity of Stone and Bronze Weapons." *Ulster Journal of Archaeology*, Vol. 5, pp. 122-127.

Page, D.
 1959 "History and the Homeric Iliad." *Sather Classical Lectures*, Vol. 32. (Berkeley: University of California Press)

Peake, H. J. E.
 1940 "The Study of Prehistoric Times." *Royal Anthropological Institute*, Vol. 70, pp. 103-146.

Petrie, W. M. F.
 1901 "Diospolis Parva." From *Egyptian Exploration Fund Memoirs*, pp. 4-8. (London: Kegan Paul, Trench, Trübner & Co.) Reprinted in part in Heizer, ed., 1959, pp. 376-383.

Piggott, S.
 1937 "Prehistory and the Romantic Movement." *Antiquity*, Vol. 11, pp. 31-38.
 1950 *William Stukely, an Eighteenth-Century Antiquary.* (Oxford: The Clarendon Press.)
 1960 "Prehistory and Evolutionary Theory." From *The Evolution of Man*, S. Tax, ed., pp. 85-97. (University of Chicago Press)

Putnam, F. W.
 1899 A Problem in American Anthropology. *Proceedings of the American Association for the Advancement of Science*, Vol. 48, pp. 1-17.

Richter, G. M. A.
 1958 *Attic Red-Figured Vases; a Survey.* (New Haven: Yale University Press)

Rowe, J. H.
   1961   "Stratigraphy and Seriation." *American Antiquity,* Vol. 26, pp. 324-330.
   n.d.   Problems in the History of Archaeology (unpublished).

Salzman, L. F.
   1951   "First Discovery of Implement Known to Date from Prehistoric Times."
          Archaeological News Letter, Vol. 4, No. 2, p. 20. (London)

Sanford, E. M.
   1944   "The Study of Ancient History in the Middle Ages." *Journal of the
          History of Ideas,* Vol. 5, pp. 21-43.

Smiley, T. L. (ed.)
   1955   "Geochronology." *University of Arizona Physical Science Bulletin,* No. 2.
          (Tucson)

Smith, G. E.
   1916   "Men of the Old Stone Age." *American Museum Journal,* Vol. 16.
          pp. 319-325.

Stallings, W. S., Jr.
   1939   "Dating Prehistoric Ruins by Tree-Rings." *Laboratory of Anthropology,
          General Series, Bulletin* No. 8. (Santa Fe)

"Trevelyan"
   1857   "Letters on Irish Antiquities by a Cornish Man." *Ulster Journal of
          Archaeology,* Vol. 5, pp. 150-152, 185-187, 336-342.

Vayson de Pradenne, A.
   1932   *Les fraudes en archéologie préhistorique avec quelques exemples de
          comparaison en archéologie générale et sciences naturelles.* (Paris:
          E. Nourry)

Viollier, D.
   1901   "Essai sur les fibules de l'âge du fer trouvées en Suisse." *Anz. Schweizer.
          Altertumsk.*

Virchow, R.
   1872   "Untersuchung des Neanderthals-Schädels." *Zeitschrift für Ethnologie,*
          Vol. 4, pp. 157-165.

Vogt, W.
   1948   *Road to Survival.* (New York: William Sloane Associates)

von Foerster, H., P. M. Mora and L. W. Amiot
   1960   Doomsday: Friday, 13 November, A.D. 2026." *Science,* Vol. 132, pp.
          1291-1295.

von Hoerner, S.
   1961   "The Search for Signals from Other Civilizations." *Science,* Vol. 134,
          pp. 1839-1843.

von Koenigswald, G. H. R.
   1956   *Meeting Prehistoric Man.* (New York: Harpers and Brothers)

Walters, H. B.
   1934   *The English Antiquaries of the Sixteenth, Seventeenth, and Eighteenth
          Centuries.* (London: E. Walters)

Washburn, S. L.
   1953   The Piltdown Hoax. *American Anthropologist,* Vol. 55, pp. 759-762.

Weidenreich, F.
    1943   "The Skull of Sinanthropus Pekinensis." *Paleo*
            No. 10, Whole Series No. 127. (Chungking: N
            of China)

Weiner, J. S.
    1955   *The Piltdown Forgery.* (London: Oxford University Pre

West, R. G.
    1956   "The Quaternary Deposits at Hoxne." *Proceedings of the*
            Society, n.s., Vol. 20, pp. 131-139.

Woodford, A. D.
    1935   "Historical Introduction to Geology." *Pan American Geologist,* Vol. 64,
            pp. 1-7. (Des Moines)

Zeuner, F. E.
    1958   *Dating the Past* (4th ed., rev.). (London: Methuen & Co., Ltd.)

TWENTIETH CENTURY VIEWS

Future Titles